Introduction to Credibility Theory

4th Edition

THOMAS N. HERZOG, PhD, ASA

ACTEX Publications, Inc.
Winsted, CT

To Tracy, Steve, and Evelyn

Manufactured in the United States of America

Cover design: Christine Phelps

10 9 8 7 6 5 4 3 2 1

Herzog, Thomas N., 1946-
  Introduction to credibility theory / Thomas N. Herzog. -- 4th ed.
      p. cm.
  Includes bibliographical references and index.
  ISBN 978-1-56698-764-6 (alk. paper)
  1. Credibility theory (Insurance) I. Title. II. Title: Crediblity theory.
  HG8782.H53 2010
  306.3--dc22
                                                          2010028230

ISBN: 978-1-56698-764-6

PREFACE

This text is intended to introduce the reader to a wide variety of credibility models and, in so doing, trace the historical development of the subject. The Bayesian approach to statistics is emphasized, revealing the author's personal preference. The reader should be able to use this work as a foundation for understanding more sophisticated treatments in other works. For example, by seeing how various formulas are derived in the Bayesian paradigm, the reader should be able to understand other works describing the Bayesian approach to credibility. Another goal is to present the key assumptions underlying the various credibility models and to discuss the advantages and disadvantages of the various approaches.

This work is intended to be largely self-contained. Although numerous references to the technical literature are provided, few are necessary for an understanding of the material discussed here. Rather, they are provided for those who would like to consult original sources and/or obtain some insight into the more advanced topics omitted from this introductory work. A large number of exercises are provided to help reinforce understanding of the material. Most of these have been taken from past examinations of the Casualty Actuarial Society. Complete solutions to all of the text exercises are available in a companion solutions manual.

The emphasis in the first ten chapters of this introductory text is on basic statistical concepts.

In Chapter 1, we (a) discuss two major statistical paradigms, (b) offer a glimpse into the nature of credibility, (c) introduce a simple practical problem later solved in Chapter 6 using credibility procedures, and (d) present a brief review of the key historical developments in credibility theory and its application to practical insurance problems.

In Chapter 2, we review the basic concepts of Bayesian analysis, and in Chapter 3 we discuss statistical loss functions. In Chapter 4, we use an example originally employed by Hewitt [1970] to illustrate the use of Bayesian concepts in the insurance ratemaking process. The key ideas are the use of the predictive distribution of aggregate claim amounts and the use of the (Bayesian) conditional mean to estimate pure premium amounts.

In Chapter 5, we describe the limited fluctuation credibility model. This is primarily of historical interest, because it is not in wide use today.

In Chapter 6, we present the development of an alternative credibility model proposed by Bühlmann [1967] as well as a special case of a more general model proposed by Bühlmann and Straub [1972]. The general Bühlmann-Straub model is presented in Chapter 7.

In Chapter 8, we discuss an important general result of Ericson [1970]. It turns out that some specific results described in Mayerson [1964] are simply special cases of Ericson's more general result. We also present an example which shows that the Bühlmann estimate does not always equal the corresponding Bayesian estimate. In Chapter 9, we use the statistical machinery developed to describe Ericson's result to construct the predictive distribution of a more realistic two-stage model. Here the number of claims is assumed to follow a Poisson distribution and the claim amounts are based on an exponential distribution.

In Chapter 10, we show that Bühlmann's model produces least squares linear approximations to the Bayesian estimate of the pure premium.

In the first ten chapters, we do not discuss important practical issues such as how to apply these procedures in dealing with issues likely to be encountered in real-life situations. Moreover, we do not attempt to discuss more sophisticated theoretical concepts such as multivariate extensions of the results presented here. These are all left for a more advanced treatment in later chapters and elsewhere.

The three prior editions of this text have been in use since 1994. Our goal over all of these years has been to make this text of practical use to the working actuary/actuarial student. To further this goal, we have added three new chapters to this fourth edition. Each of Chapters 11 through 15 now deals in depth with a practical application of the concepts developed earlier in the text. Chapter 11 discusses a Bayesian procedure for comparing two binomial proportions. Many researchers, including us, feel that this is far superior to the frequentist scheme of deciding whether or not to reject the null hypothesis that the two proportions are equal. Chapter 12 describes a procedure suggested by Fuhrer [1988] that has application to health insurance. Chapter 13 summarizes work completed by Rosenberg and Farrell [2008] that describes a scheme for predicting the frequency and severity of hospitalization cost for a group of young children suffering from cystic fibrosis. Chapters 14 and 15 continue from earlier editions. In Chapter 14, we use the concept of conjugate prior distributions to estimate probabilities arising from a data quality problem. In Chapter 15, we present an application of empirical Bayesian procedures to a problem in automobile insurance ratemaking. This is the application and solution proposed by Morris and van Slyke [1979].

The other major change in the fourth edition is in Chapter 1 where we have expanded the historical discussion surrounding the work of Bayes himself as well as Laplace.

We assume here that the reader has a working knowledge of (1) the integration techniques normally taught during the second semester of a university course in calculus, (2) basic probability and statistics as taught during a two-semester university course having a calculus prerequisite, and (3) matrix manipulation and multiplication techniques. In particular regard to integral calculus, we assume that the reader can perform integration by parts and integration by change of variable (as done in Section 9.4). We also note that in a number places we have changed either the order of integration or summation. In general such manipulation requires the verification of one or more conditions to ensure that the sums actually converge. Because we are dealing here with probabilities that sum to one, we are never in danger of diverging to infinity. Hence, we will omit the verification step in this work.

For many years, the topic of credibility theory has been included in the preliminary exams jointly sponsored by the Casualty Actuarial Society and the Society of Actuaries. All of the topics in that collection as well as the general learning objectives and the sample exam questions are thoroughly covered by this text. It has thus been an officially approved reference for this topic for most of those years.

Many people have contributed to the completion of this project. In particular I am grateful to the late Professor James C. Hickman, FSA, ACAS, University of Wisconsin, and Gary G. Venter, FCAS, ASA, CERA, MAAA for their generous assistance with an initial version of this work. Jim taught me a lot about Bayesian statistics and Gary introduced me to the Bühlmann and limited fluctuation approaches. Gary also read this and earlier versions and suggested a number of the figures that appear in Chapters 6 and 10.

I also want to thank Professor Donald B. Rubin of Harvard University for introducing me to the Bayesian paradigm. One of my other early teachers was Professor Dennis V. Lindley, at George Washington University. I would also like to express my appreciation to Professor James C. Owings, Jr., my dissertation advisor in the Department of Mathematics at the University of Maryland.

In addition to Gary Venter, I am also indebted to the other members of the initial editorial review team for their suggestions that improved the exposition and notation of this work. This group included Professor Elias Shiu, ASA, University of Iowa, Professor Samuel H. Cox, FSA, University of Manitoba, Professor Larry Santoro, College of Insurance, Professor Michael R. Powers, Temple University, and David F. Mohrman, FCAS, and Stephen W. Philbrick, FCAS, both of Towers Watson. Professor Shiu supplied me with the clever proofs presented in Sections 3.2 and 5.2.

The fourth edition was also reviewed by Steven Craighead, Margie Rosenberg, Dennis Tolley, Chuck Fuhrer, Bob Cumming, Joan Barrett, and Vincent Kane. The author is grateful for their generous and thoughtful assistance with this text.

Finally, I would like to thank the staff of ACTEX Publications, Inc, especially Marilyn Baleshiski and Gail Hall for their assistance with the publication of this text.

Reston, Virginia   Thomas N. Herzog, Ph.D., ASA
June 2010

CONTENTS

CHAPTER 10 CREDIBILITY AND LEAST SQUARES 183

CHAPTER 11 CASE STUDY: CLINICAL TRIALS – AN APPLICATION OF BAYESIAN INFERENCE ABOUT BINOMIAL PROPORTIONS 193

CHAPTER 12 CASE STUDY: APPLICATION OF CREDIBILITY TO GROUP HEALTH INSURANCE 205

CHAPTER 15 MORRIS - VAN SLYKE ESTIMATION 247

APPENDIX A: PREDICTIVE MODELING OF COSTS FOR A CHRONIC DISEASE WITH ACUTE HIGH-COST EPISODES 261

APPENDIX B: COMPARING CREDIBILITY ESTIMATES OF HEALTH INSURANCE CLAIMS COSTS   293

CHAPTER 1

INTRODUCTION AND HISTORY

1.1 INTRODUCTION

According to Rodermund [1989, page 3], "the concept of credibility has been the casualty actuaries' most important and enduring contribution to casualty actuarial science."

In order to present a brief history of credibility, it will be helpful to begin by describing two major statistical paradigms and three major approaches to credibility. This will facilitate our description of the historical development.

1.2 STATISTICAL PARADIGMS

Credibility is an example of a statistical estimate. Statistical estimates are obtained through the use of statistical formulas or models which, in turn, are based on statistical approaches or paradigms. There are two major statistical paradigms of current interest, which are (a) the **frequentist** or **classical** paradigm, and (b) the **Bayesian** paradigm.

In the frequentist paradigm, the probability of an event is based on its relative frequency. All prior and/or collateral information is ignored. Proponents of the frequentist paradigm view it as being objective, because all attention is devoted to the observations (data). Some of the key constructs of the frequentist paradigm are the Neyman-Pearson Lemma, tests of statistical hypotheses, confidence intervals, and unbiased estimates.

In the Bayesian paradigm, probability is treated as a rational measure of belief. Thus, the Bayesian paradigm is based on personal or subjective probabilities and involves the use of Bayes' theorem. Prior and/or collateral information is incorporated explicitly into the model via the prior distribu tion and the likelihood. Some of the key constructs of the Bayesian paradigm, in addition to Bayes' theorem itself, are conditional probabilities, prior distributions, predictive distributions, and (posterior) odds ratios.

1.3   WHAT IS CREDIBILITY?

Suppose we have two collections of data, as illustrated in the following figure.

Prior Observations					Current Observations			
#	#	#	#		#	#	#	#
#	#	#	#		#	#	#	#
#	#	#	#		#	#	#	#
#	#	#	#		#	#	#	#

FIGURE 1.1

One collection consists of current observations, taken from the most recent period of observation. The second collection has observations for one or more prior periods. The various approaches to credibility give us different "recipes" for combining the two collections of observations to obtain an overall estimate.

Under some approaches to credibility, a compromise estimator, C, is calculated from the relationship

$$C = ZR + (1-Z)H, \tag{1.1}$$

where R is the mean of the current observations (for example, the data), H is the prior mean (for example, an estimate based on the actuary's prior data and/or opinion), and Z is the credibility factor, satisfying the condition $0 \leq Z \leq 1$. Under these approaches, the credibility estimator of the quantity of interest is derived as a linear compromise between the current observations and the actuary's prior opinion. Graphically we see that the compromise estimator, C, is somewhere on the line segment between R and H, as shown in Figure 1.2.

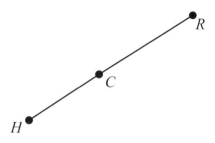

FIGURE 1.2

The symbol Z denotes the weight assigned to the (current) data and $(1–Z)$ the weight assigned to the prior data. This formulation of Equation (1.1), which includes the concept of prior data, is in the spirit of the Bayesian paradigm. As an insurance example, a new insurance rate, C, is derived as a weighted average of an old insurance rate, H, and an insurance rate, R, whose calculation is based solely on observations from a recent period. An alternative interpretation of Equation (1.1) is to let C be the insurance rate for a particular class of business, to let R be the insurance rate whose calculation is based solely on the recent experience of that class, and to let H be the insurance rate whose computation takes into account the experience of all classes combined.

To illustrate the types of practical problems that are addressed by credibility theory, we present here the statement of a problem typical of those solved in this text. Because we have not yet developed the technical machinery required to solve such a problem, we defer its solution until Section 6.6.1 (see Example 6.5).

EXAMPLE 1.1

An insurance company has two policies of group workers' compensation. The aggregate claim amounts in millions of dollars for the first three policy years are summarized in the table below. Estimate the aggregate claim amount during the fourth policy year for each of the two group policies.

Aggregate Claim Amounts			
Group Policy	Policy Year		
	1	2	3
1	5	8	11
2	11	13	12

Over the years there have been three major approaches to credibility: limited fluctuation, greatest accuracy, and Bayesian. The first two approaches fall under the frequentist paradigm, as neither entails the use of Bayes' theorem. Moreover, neither approach explicitly requires prior information (i.e., a formal prior probability distribution) in order to compute either the credibility factor, Z, or the estimate, C. The most well-developed approach to greatest accuracy credibility is least squares credibility. Because this approach was popularized by Hans Bühlmann, it is referred to in this text as Bühlmann's approach.

1.4 THREE APPROACHES TO CREDIBILITY

The limited fluctuation and Bühlmann approaches both involve the explicit calculation of the credibility factor, Z, and the use of Equation (1.1) to obtain the compromise estimator, C. On the other hand, the Bayesian approach requires neither the direct calculation of Z nor the use of Equation (1.1).

1.4.1 LIMITED FLUCTUATION APPROACH

Mowbray [1914] described a limited fluctuation approach for deriving the number of exposures required for full credibility, the case where $Z = 1$. Perryman [1932] proposed a limited fluctuation approach to partial credibility problems, those for which $Z < 1$. More modern treatments of the limited fluctuation approach to both full credibility and partial credibility are found in Longley-Cook [1962] and in Chapter 8 of Hossack, Pollard, and Zehnwirth [1983]. Outside of North America this approach is sometimes called "American credibility."

1.4.2 BÜHLMANN'S APPROACH

Bühlmann's approach, as described in this text, is based on Bühlmann [1967], which had its origins in a paper by Bailey [1942 and 1943]. Bühlmann and Straub [1972] describe an important generalization of the 1967 Bühlmann work.

1.5   BAYESIAN APPROACH TO CREDIBILITY

1.5.1   BAYESIAN STATISTICAL INFERENCE –
THE EARLY YEARS

The Bayesian approach goes all the way back to the Reverend Thomas Bayes who was born in London, England around 1702. According to Stigler [1986], "Bayes was an ordained Nonconformist minister in Turnbridge Wells (about 35 miles southeast of London)." Although Bayes was elected a fellow of the Royal Society in 1742, his major work was not published until 1764, almost three years after his death. For a long time, his membership in the Royal Society was something of a mystery. Recently-discovered letters, however, now indicate that he did indeed have private correspondence with the other leading intellectuals of his era in London. When Bayes died in 1761, he left £100 and his scientific papers to his friend, Richard Price. After adding an introduction and an appendix, Price presented Bayes' essay "Toward Solving a Problem in the Doctrine of Chance" to the Royal Society.

The famous French astronomer, probabilist and mathematician Pierre Simon Laplace, who lived from 1749-1827, both championed and extended Bayes' work. In his text entitled *Essai philosophie sur les probabilities* (*Philosophical Essay on Probabilities*), Laplace described a mathematical framework for conducting statistical inference. This extended the work of Bayes and constituted the essence of Bayesian statistical inference. Laplace took this work seriously as the following passage from the beginning of his *Essay* indicates:

> "Here I will present ... the principles and general results of the theory, applying them to the most important questions of life, which are indeed, for the most part, only questions of probability."

Inverse Probabilities and Statistical Inference

Bayes' theorem has practical application in many fields. Kanellos [2003] presents one in a recent article about the application of Bayes' theorem to data searches entitled "18th Century Theory is New Force in Computing." Bayes' Theorem is important to actuaries because it enables them to perform statistical inference by computing *inverse probabilities*.

What exactly do we mean by "inverse probabilities"? We use the term "inverse" because we are inferring backwards from results (or effects) to causes. Let's look at some simple examples to examine this further.

A typical probability problem might be stated as follows: I have a standard die with six sides numbered from "one" through "six" and throw the die three times. What is the probability that the result of each of these three tosses of the die will be a "six"?

Now, I might have a second (non-standard) die with three sides numbered "1" and three sides numbered "six." Again I can ask the same question: What is the probability that the result of each of these three tosses of the die will be a "six"?

The idea behind inverse probabilities is to turn the question around. Here, we might observe that the results of three throws of a die were all "sixes." We then ask the question: What is the probability that we threw the standard die (as opposed to the non-standard die), given these results?

1.5.2 WHITNEY'S VIEW OF CREDIBILITY

Whitney [1918] stated that the credibility factor, Z, needed to be of the form

$$Z = \frac{n}{n+k}$$

where n represents "earned premiums" and k is a constant to be determined. The problem was how to determine k. Whitney noted that, "In practice k must be determined by judgment."[1] Whitney also noted that, "The detailed solution to this problem depends upon the use of inverse probabilities" via Bayes' Theorem.[2]

Predictive Distributions

In insurance work, we typically experience a number of claims or an aggregate amount of losses in one or more prior observation periods. The questions we want to answer are:

---

[1] See Whitney [1918, page 289].
[2] See Whitney [1918, page 277].

(1) Given such results, how many claims will we experience during the next observation period?

(2) Given such results, what will be the aggregate loss amount during the next observation period?

Using Bayes' Theorem, we can construct an entire probability distribution for such future claim frequencies or loss amounts. Probability distributions of this type are usually called **predictive distributions**. Predictive distributions give the actuary much more information than would an average or other summary statistic. A predictive distribution provides the actuary with much more information than just the expected aggregate amount of losses in the next period. It provides the actuary with a complete profile of the tail of the probability distribution of aggregate losses for use in a "value-at-risk" analysis. Thus, predictive distributions can provide the actuary and her client an important tool with which to make business decisions under uncertainty.

1.5.3 BAYESIAN STATISTICAL INFERENCE AND MODERN TIMES

Perhaps, in part, because the frequentist paradigm of statistics dominated the statistical community during the first half of the twentieth century, it remained for Bailey [1950] to rediscover and advance Whitney's ideas. During the second half of the twentieth century, Bayesian methods gained increased adherents. Two of the earliest influential books on Bayesian statistics were Savage [1954] and Raiffa and Schlaifer [1961]. Mayerson [1965] brought together the statistical developments in Bayesian statistical inference and the actuary's credibility problem, reexamining Bailey's results using the concept of a "conjugate prior distribution" and other more modern notation and terminology. Ericson [1970] and Jewell [1974] generalized Mayerson's results. Whereas Whitney and Bailey had considered only the distribution of the *number* of claims, Mayerson, Jones, and Bowers [1968] and Hewitt [1971] considered both the distribution of the *number* of claims and the distribution of the *amount* of those claims. Hewitt used some clever, artificial examples to illustrate the use of a full Bayesian approach to insurance ratemaking. It remained for Klugman [1987 and 1992], who had the advantage of modern computing equipment, to extend Hewitt's ideas and actually apply them to a major practical insurance-ratemaking problem

1.5.4 BAYESIAN STATISTICAL INFERENCE
AND MODERN COMPUTING

With the increased power of 21ˢᵗ-century computing equipment, advances in statistical algorithms (e.g., the EM algorithm and Markov chain Monte Carlo methods) that implement the Bayesian approach, and widely-available software that performs Bayesian inference (i.e., Win-BUGS[3]), a wider class of problems is becoming susceptible to solution via the Bayesian approach.

1.6 EXPLORATORY DATA ANALYSIS

Some of the followers of John Tukey [1977] consider "exploratory data analysis" to be another distinct approach to data analysis[4]. While it is not the intention here to enter this philosophical discussion, it is often important to do substantial exploratory data analysis prior to constructing formal models, doing statistical inference, or carrying out other types of more involved statistical procedures. There are several reasons for doing this. First, substantial insight can often be gained by using simple approaches. In some situations, especially when the actuary thoroughly understands the subject matter, exploratory data analysis may yield a complete solution. As an example, we consider the following table that summarizes the experience of some mortgages insured by the Federal Housing Administration (FHA) – a component of the U. S. Department of Housing and Urban Development.

---

[3] The BUGS (**B**ayesian inference **U**sing **G**ibbs **S**ampling) Project (begun by the MRC Biostatistics unit at Imperial College, London) is concerned with the development of flexible software for Bayesian analysis of complex statistical models using Markov chain Monte Carlo methods. The "**Win**" prefix refers to Microsoft's Windows operating system. For more details about BUGS, actuaries should read David Scollnik [2001]: "Actuarial Modeling with MCMC and BUGS."

[4] In addition to Tukey's seminal reference work, cited above, other (perhaps more refined) references on exploratory data analysis include Mosteller and Tukey [1977] and Velleman and Hoaglin [1981].

EXAMPLE 1.2

Claim Rates[5] through July 1, 1989 on FHA-insured Single-family Mortgages Originated during 1981 Owner-Occupied Only						
Loan-to-value ratio	Mortgage Amount (In Dollars)					
	< 25,000	25,001-35,000	35,001-50,000	50,001-60,000	Over 60,000	Overall
≤ 80.0%	8.38%	6.88%	6.74%	10.01%	6.94%	7.63%
80.1 – 85.0	20.43	12.47	11.92	11.68	8.20	11.39
85.1 - 90.0	24.33	17.43	12.59	11.76	11.43	13.69
90.1 – 95.0	27.70	23.53	18.53	19.10	17.46	19.94
95.1 – 97.0	33.48	32.42	26.76	25.88	23.51	27.77
97.1 – 100.0	42.86	52.05	40.99	31.09	18.42	42.13

Because we know from a companion table that there are only a small number of mortgages whose loan-to-value ratio is in the 97.1 – 100.0% category, we ignore that line of the table. We find a strong pattern indicating that the claim rate goes down as (1) the mortgage amount goes up and (2) as the loan-to-value ratio goes down. In particular, we note that in the roughly eight years covered by the table, more than 27% of the loans having a loan-to-value ratio in excess of 95% resulted in an insurance claim. The message of this table is clear. If you originate mortgages with little or no down-payment, the proportion of mortgages ending up in foreclosure may be substantial. It does not come as a surprise then that, after lenders originated a large number of mortgages with little or no down-payment during the period 2003-2007, a substantial number of these mortgages ended up in foreclosure. Should it come as a surprise that the housing "bubble" burst?

Second, exploratory data analysis often gives useful insight into the process generating the data. Such insight could be critical to the selection of a good model.

[5] Claim rate is defined as the proportion of claims received for a given origination year, on single-family mortgages insured by FHA, i.e.,

$$claim\ rate = \frac{number\ of\ claims}{number\ of\ mortgages\ originated}.$$

Too often large databases/data warehouses have material deficiencies involving erroneous or missing data elements, missing records, and/or duplicate records. Health insurance companies are concerned with avoiding duplicate claim payments to policyholders. Life insurance companies are concerned with (1) making payments to deceased annuitants and (2) failing to pay beneficiaries of life insurance policyholders because they are not aware that the policyholder has died. Hansen and Wang [1991] describe major deficiencies in a wide range of databases. Thus, the existence of material errors is not an unusual occurrence. Exploratory data analyses can often reveal such errors in the database under study. For a more complete discussion of how to prevent, identify, and correct faulty data, the interested reader should see Herzog, Scheuren, and Winkler [2007].

1.7 RECENT APPLICATIONS

We conclude this chapter by citing some recent applications of credibility theory to actuarial problems. Jewell [1989 and 1990] shows how to use Bayesian procedures to calculate incurred but not yet reported reserve requirements. Russo [1995] extends the work of Jewell. In order to estimate insurance reserves, Russo develops continuous time models of claim reporting and payment processes. In so doing, he employs both the Bayesian paradigm and a multistate model of the incurred claims process.

Klugman [1987] uses a full Bayesian approach to analyze actual data on worker's compensation insurance. Klugman investigates two problems. First, he calculates the joint posterior distribution of the relative frequency of claims in each of 133 rating groups. He employs three distinct prior distributions and shows that the results are virtually identical in all three instances. Second, Klugman analyzes the loss ratio for three years of experience in 319 rating classes in Michigan. He uses these data to construct prediction intervals for future observations (i.e., the fourth year). He then compares his predictions to the actual results.

The Bayesian paradigm has been used to graduate (or smooth) various types of mortality data. London [1985], building on the pioneering work of Kimeldorf and Jones [1967], provides a general description of this method. London also provides a Bayesian rationale for the historically popular Whittaker graduation method. A specific application of Bayesian graduation is found in Herzog [1983].

Young [1997, 1998] has done some research on credibility and spline functions. Her work enables the actuary to estimate future claims as a function of a statistic other than the sample mean. For example, Young [1998] argues that the use of a regression model with the predictor variable being a function of the sample geometric mean may lead to a more accurate estimator, i.e., one whose squared error loss is reduced.

As discussed in Chapter 8 of this text, Ericson [1970] and Jewell [1974] have shown that the Bühlmann estimate is equal to the Bayesian estimate of the pure premium when the claim distribution belongs to the exponential family of probability distributions and the conjugate prior is employed. Landsman and Makov [1998a] have extended this result to claim distributions belonging to the "exponential dispersion family" of distributions. Landsman and Makov [1998b] suggest a totally new approach to deal with the situation in which the claim distribution is not a member of either of the two previously-mentioned families of distributions.

Frees, et al., [1999] and Frees, et al., [2001] delineate the relationship between (1) credibility models and (2) parametric statistical models used for panel (longitudinal) data analysis.

Prior to the advent of Markov Chain Monte Carlo (MCMC) numerical methods, it was only feasible to implement a full Bayesian approach for a limited class of models. Scollnik [2001] shows how to implement Bayesian methods in actuarial models using the BUGS software package. Fellingham, Tolley, and Herzog [2005] also use BUGS to construct a Bayesian hierarchical model in order to estimate health insurance claim costs. Finally, Rosenberg and Farrell [2008] use version 1.4 of Win-BUGS to construct a Bayesian statistical model in order to predict the incident and cost of hospitalization for a group of children with cystic fibrosis.

1.8   EXERCISES

1.1 Introduction

1-1   According to Rodermund, what has been the casualty actuaries' most important and enduring contribution to casualty actuarial science?

1.2 Statistical Paradigms

1-2   Name the two major statistical paradigms of current interest.

1.3 What Is Credibility?

1-3   Using Equation (1.1), determine the realization of the compromise estimator C, given that (i) the mean of the current observations is 10, (ii) the prior mean is 6, and (iii) the credibility factor is .25.

1-4   Using Equation (1.1), determine the insurance rate, C, for a particular class of business given that (i) the insurance rate calculated strictly from the experience data of that class of business is $100, (ii) the insurance rate for all classes combined is $200, and (iii) the credibility factor for the class is .40.

1.4 Three Approaches to Credibility

1-5   List the three major approaches to credibility.

CHAPTER 2

MATHEMATICAL PRELIMINARIES

In this chapter we review some basic probability and statistics concepts. In Section 2.1, we first define the term "conditional probability" which forms the basis for Bayes' theorem. Bayes' theorem, in turn, is the foundation of the Bayesian paradigm, a useful tool for solving a wide range of practical problems. After the statement and proof of Bayes' theorem, we present the Theorem of Total Probability, which is often useful in applying Bayes' theorem. In Section 2.2 we consider some examples of the use of Bayes' theorem. The first example is based on the target-shooting example of Philbrick [1981]; the second is taken from Hewitt [1970]. Prior and posterior probabilities are defined in Section 2.3, and the concepts of conditional expectation and unconditional expectation are reviewed in Sections 2.4 and 2.5, respectively. Hewitt's example is used to illustrate the results of Sections 2.4 and 2.5.

Exercises 2-8, 2-9, 2-14, and 2-15 deal with the estimation of the number of future insurance claims, a key component of an insurer's future liability of loss. (The provision for such liability is called the **loss reserve**, and the process of estimating the liability is called loss reserving or **loss development**.) These four exercises are based on material discussed by Brosius [1993].

2.1 BAYES' THEOREM

Definition 2.1

Let A and B represent events such that $P[B] > 0$. Then the **conditional probability of A given B** is defined to be

$$P[A \mid B] = \frac{P[A \text{ and } B]}{P[B]}. \qquad (2.1)$$

The following result is named after the Reverend Thomas Bayes, who lived during the eighteenth century.

**Theorem 2.1
(Bayes' Theorem)**

Let A and B be events such that $P[B] > 0$. Then

$$P[A|B] = \frac{P[B|A] \cdot P[A]}{P[B]}. \qquad (2.2)$$

Proof

By repeated application of the definition of conditional probability, we have

$$P[B|A] = \frac{P[A \text{ and } B]}{P[A]},$$

so that $P[A \text{ and } B] = P[B|A] \cdot P[A]$. Then

$$P[A|B] = \frac{P[A \text{ and } B]}{P[B]} = \frac{P[B|A] \cdot P[A]}{P[B]}.$$

Since the value of $P[B]$ does not depend on A, we can consider $P[A|B]$ to be the product of a constant, c, and the two functions of A, writing

$$P[A|B] = c \cdot P[B|A] \cdot P[A]. \qquad (2.2a)$$

Alternatively we can consider $P[A|B]$ to be proportional to the product of the two functions of A, writing

$$P[A|B] \propto P[B|A] \cdot P[A], \qquad (2.2b)$$

a construct frequently employed in applications appearing later in the text.

The next theorem is often useful in the application of Bayes' theorem.

Theorem 2.2
(Theorem of Total Probability)

Let $A_1, A_2, \ldots$ represent a countable collection of mutually exclusive and exhaustive events, so that

$$A_i \cap A_j = \varnothing \quad \text{for} \quad i \neq j$$

and

$$\bigcup_{i=1}^{\infty} A_i = \Omega$$

where Ω denotes the entire sample space. Then

$$P[B] = \sum_{i=1}^{\infty} P[B \mid A_i] \cdot P[A_i]. \tag{2.3}$$

Proof

We have

$$P[B] = P[B \text{ and } \Omega]$$

$$= P\left[B \text{ and } \bigcup_{i=1}^{\infty} A_i \right] = P\left[\bigcup_{i=1}^{\infty} (B \text{ and } A_i) \right]$$

$$= \sum_{i=1}^{\infty} P[B \text{ and } A_i] = \sum_{i=1}^{\infty} P[B \mid A_i] \cdot P[A_i].$$

The Theorem of Total Probability is widely used in this text. Its first application is found in Example 2.2.

2.2 EXAMPLES OF THE USE OF BAYES' THEOREM

Under the notation of Chapter 1, the Bayesian approach does *not* necessarily produce a linear estimate of the true value. In fact, the Bayesian estimate, B, does not even have to be on the line segment joining R and H, as shown in the following figure.

FIGURE 2.1

This is illustrated in the following example.

EXAMPLE 2.1

Consider an abbreviated form of the "target-shooting" example of Philbrick [1981], where one of two shooters, X or Y, is chosen at random (i.e., with probability ½). The shots of each shooter are uniformly distributed over two non-overlapping circular targets, illustrated in Figure 2.2a.

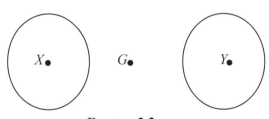

FIGURE 2.2a

The (overall) mean of the two targets is G, the point half-way between the centers of the two circles. (In the terminology of physics, G is known as the **center of gravity**.) A single shot is fired and observed to be at point S on target X, as shown in Figure 2.2b. What is the Bayesian estimate of the next shot?

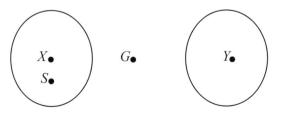

FIGURE 2.2b

SOLUTION

The answer is the center of target X. The reason[1] is that the selected shooter must be shooter X. Since the prior estimate is the point G, half-way between the centers of the two targets, the Bayesian point estimate of the location of the second shot is not on the line segment from G to the location, S, of the first shot. ❑

The following example of the use of Bayes' theorem is taken from the important paper of Hewitt [1970].

EXAMPLE 2.2

A die is selected at random (i.e., with probability ½) from a pair of "honest" dice. It is known that one die, a_1, has one marked face and five unmarked faces and the other die, a_2, has three marked faces and three unmarked faces. Let A denote the random variable representing the selection of the die. Let u denote the outcome if a toss of the die produces an unmarked face, and let m denote the outcome if the result is a marked face. Then

A_1 denotes the event $A = a_1$, the selection of the die with one marked face and five unmarked faces, and

A_2 denotes the event $A = a_2$, the selection of the die with three marked faces and three unmarked faces.

Let T_i denote the random variable representing the result of the ith toss of the selected die, for $i = 1, 2, \ldots$. Then

U_i denotes the event $T_i = u$, the result of having an unmarked face showing on the ith toss for $i = 1, 2, \ldots$, and

M_i denotes the event $T_i = m$, the result of having a marked face showing on the ith toss for $i = 1, 2, \ldots$.

---

[1] While the "reason" is probably intuitive and therefore comfortable, it is not complete. To make the reasoning complete, we must employ a "loss function" (see Chapter 3). In particular, if a squared error loss function is chosen, then the center is the "best" estimate because it minimizes the sum of the squared deviations. The reader may wish to return to this example after reading Chapter 3.

Note that A and T_i denote random variables, whereas A_1, A_2, U_i, and M_i denote events. In calling each die "honest" we simply mean that

$$P[U_i \mid A_1] = \frac{5}{6} \qquad (2.4a)$$

and

$$P[U_i \mid A_2] = \frac{3}{6} \qquad (2.4b)$$

Calculate the value of $P[A_1 \mid U_1]$, the probability that the die with only one marked face has been drawn, given that a die was selected at random, tossed once, and resulted in an unmarked face.

SOLUTION

By Bayes' theorem we have

$$P[A_1 \mid U_1] = \frac{P[A_1 \text{ and } U_1]}{P[U_1]} = \frac{P[U_1 \mid A_1] \cdot P[A_1]}{P[U_1]}.$$

From Equation (2.4a), we have $P[U_1 \mid A_1] = \frac{5}{6}$. Because each die is chosen with probability $\frac{1}{2}$, we have $P[A_1] = \frac{1}{2}$. The value of $P[U_1]$ is computed using the Theorem of Total Probability as

$$P[U_1] = P[A_1 \text{ and } U_1] + P[A_2 \text{ and } U_1]$$

$$= P[U_1 \mid A_1] \cdot P[A_1] + P[U_1 \mid A_2] \cdot P[A_2]$$

$$= \left(\frac{5}{6}\right)\left(\frac{1}{2}\right) + \left(\frac{3}{6}\right)\left(\frac{1}{2}\right) = \frac{2}{3}.$$

Substituting into the Bayes' theorem equation, we obtain the result

$$P[A_1 \mid U_1] = \frac{\left(\frac{5}{6}\right)\left(\frac{1}{2}\right)}{\frac{2}{3}} = \frac{5}{8}. \qquad \Box$$

2.3 PRIOR AND POSTERIOR PROBABILITIES

In Example 2.2, we assumed that $\frac{1}{2}$ was our initial or **prior** (estimate of the) **probability** of event A_1. The word "prior" relates to the fact that this probability was assessed before the experiment of tossing the die was performed. After observing the result of the first toss to be an unmarked face, we revised our estimate of the probability of A_1 to be $\frac{5}{8}$. In symbols, we now have $P[A_1 | U_1] = \frac{5}{8}$. Thus our final or **posterior** (estimate of the) **probability** of A_1 given U_1 is $\frac{5}{8}$. This modification of our prior probability estimate based on recently observed data is the essence of Bayesian statistics.[2] Such modifications are frequently required in order to solve practical actuarial problems such as the calculation of insurance premium rates.

In terms of the probability distribution of the parameter A, our initial assessment was $P[A=a_1] = \frac{1}{2}$ and $P[A=a_2] = \frac{1}{2}$. Under the Bayesian paradigm, parameters are typically considered to be random variables. After observing the result of the first toss to be an unmarked face, we revised our assessment of the probability distribution of the parameter A to be $P[A=a_1 | T_1=u] = \frac{5}{8}$ and $P[A=a_2 | T_1=u] = \frac{3}{8}$. In general, the entire distribution of the prior probabilities of a parameter is called its **prior probability distribution**, and the entire distribution of **posterior probabilities** is called its posterior probability distribution. **Prior and posterior density functions** are similarly defined.

2.4 CONDITIONAL EXPECTATION

We now move on to a concept that is most useful in calculating insurance premium rates.

---

[2] Edwards, Lindman, and Savage (1963) summarize the Bayesian view of statistics as follows:

> "Probability is orderly opinion, and inference from data is nothing other than the revision of such opinion in the light of relevant new information."

Definition 2.2

Let X be a discrete random variable such that $x_1, x_2, \ldots$ are the only values that X takes on with positive probability. Then the **expectation of X**, denoted $E[X]$, is given by

$$E[X] = \sum_{i=1}^{\infty} x_i \cdot P[X = x_i]. \qquad (2.5)$$

Definition 2.3

Using the notation of Definition 2.2, we define the **conditional expectation of X given that event A_1 has occurred**, denoted by $E[X \mid A_1]$, as

$$E[X \mid A_1] = \sum_{i=1}^{\infty} x_i \cdot P[X = x_i \mid A_1]. \qquad (2.6)$$

To illustrate the concept of conditional expectation, we consider the following example, also based on Hewitt [1970].

EXAMPLE 2.3

A spinner is selected at random (i.e., with probability $\frac{1}{2}$) from a pair of spinners. It is known that (a) one spinner, b_1, has six equally likely sectors, five of which are marked "two" and one of which is marked "fourteen," and (b) the other spinner, b_2, has six equally likely sectors, three of which are marked "two" and three of which are marked "fourteen." Let B denote the random variable representing the selection of the spinner. Also let

B_1 denote the event $B = b_1$, the selection of the spinner with five "two's" and one "fourteen," and

B_2 denote the event $B = b_2$, the selection of the spinner with three "two's" and three "fourteen's."

Let S_i denote the random variable representing the result of the ith spin, for $i = 1, 2, \ldots$. Calculate (a) the value of $E[S_1 \mid B_1]$, the conditional expectation of the value of a single spin, given that the spinner with one "fourteen" has been selected, and (b) the value of $E[S_1 \mid B_2]$.

SOLUTION

(a) By the definition of conditional expectation (Definition 2.3) we have

$$E[S_1 \mid B_1] = 2 \cdot P[S_1 = 2 \mid B_1] + 14 \cdot P[S_1 = 14 \mid B_1]$$

$$= 2\left(\frac{5}{6}\right) + 14\left(\frac{1}{6}\right) = 4.$$

(b) In a similar manner we can find

$$E[S_1 \mid B_2] = 2\left(\frac{3}{6}\right) + 14\left(\frac{3}{6}\right) = 8. \qquad \square$$

The following example further illustrates the use of Bayes' theorem.

EXAMPLE 2.4

Calculate the value of $P[B_1 \mid S_1 = 2]$.

SOLUTION

As in Example 2.2, from Bayes' theorem we have

$$P[B_1 \mid S_1 = 2] = \frac{P[S_1 = 2 \mid B_1] \cdot P[B_1]}{P[S_1 = 2]},$$

where $P[S_1 = 2 \mid B_1] = \frac{5}{6}$ and $P[B_1] = \frac{1}{2}$, and, from Theorem 2.2, we find

$$P[S_1 = 2] = P[S_1 = 2 \mid B_1] \cdot P[B_1] + P[S_1 = 2 \mid B_2] \cdot P[B_2]$$

$$= \left(\frac{5}{6}\right)\left(\frac{1}{2}\right) + \left(\frac{1}{2}\right)\left(\frac{1}{2}\right) = \frac{2}{3}.$$

Then we can calculate

$$P[B_1 \mid S_1 = 2] = \frac{\left(\frac{5}{6}\right)\left(\frac{1}{2}\right)}{\frac{2}{3}} = \frac{5}{8}. \qquad \square$$

(The reader is encouraged to calculate other such probabilities.)

2.5 UNCONDITIONAL EXPECTATION

The following theorem is useful in calculating pure premium estimates, as will be demonstrated in Chapter 4.

Theorem 2.3

Let $A_1, A_2, \ldots$ represent a countable collection of mutually exclusive and exhaustive events, and let X be a discrete random variable for which $E[X]$ exists. Then

$$E[X] = \sum_{i=1}^{\infty} E[X \mid A_i] \cdot P[A_i]. \qquad (2.7)$$

Proof

Because X is a discrete random variable, we have from Definition 2.2

$$E[X] = \sum_{j=1}^{\infty} x_j \cdot P[X = x_j]. \qquad (2.5)$$

By the Theorem of Total Probability we have

$$P[X = x_j] = \sum_{i=1}^{\infty} P[X = x_j \mid A_i] \cdot P[A_i].$$

Then we can rewrite Equation (2.5) as

$$E[X] = \sum_{j=1}^{\infty} x_j \sum_{i=1}^{\infty} P[X = x_j \mid A_i] \cdot P[A_i].$$

Interchanging the order of summation we obtain

$$E[X] = \sum_{i=1}^{\infty} \sum_{j=1}^{\infty} x_j \cdot P[X = x_i \mid A_i] \cdot P[A_i]$$

$$= \sum_{i=1}^{\infty} P[A_i] \cdot \sum_{j=1}^{\infty} x_j \cdot P[X = x_j \mid A_i].$$

By the definition of conditional expectation (Definition 2.3), the second summation is $E[X \mid A_i]$, so the last expression may be written as

$$E[X] = \sum_{i=1}^{\infty} P[A_i] \cdot E[X \mid A_i].$$

EXAMPLE 2.5

Calculate the expected value of the random variable S_1 defined in Example 2.3.

SOLUTION

Using Theorem 2.3 and the results of Example 2.3, we obtain

$$E[S_1] = \sum_{i=1}^{2} P[B_i] \cdot E[S_1 \mid B_i] = \left(\frac{1}{2}\right)(4) + \left(\frac{1}{2}\right)(8) = 6. \qquad \square$$

Some more sophisticated and useful applications of Theorem 2.3 will be discussed in Chapter 4.

Theorem 2.4

Let X and Y be discrete random variables and let $g(Y)$ be a function of Y for which $E[g(Y)]$ exists. Then we may write

$$E[g(Y)] = E_Y[g(Y)] = E_X\left[E_Y[g(Y) \mid X]\right], \qquad (2.8)$$

where E_X denotes expectation over the sample space of X.

Proof

By definition of E_Y, we have $E[g(Y)] = E_Y[g(Y)]$.

Since Y is a discrete random variable, then

$$E[g(Y)] = \sum_{i=1}^{\infty} g(y_i) \cdot P[Y = y_i]$$

$$= \sum_{i=1}^{\infty} g(y_i) \cdot \sum_{j=1}^{\infty} P[Y = y_i \mid X = x_j] \cdot P[X = x_j]$$

$$= \sum_{j=1}^{\infty} P[X = x_j] \cdot \sum_{i=1}^{\infty} g(y_i) \cdot P[Y = y_i \mid X = x_j]$$

$$= \sum_{j=1}^{\infty} P[X = x_j] \cdot E_Y[g(Y) \mid X = x_j].$$

The final expression above is the expectation, with respect to X, of the conditional expectation, with respect to Y, of the random variable $g(Y)$, given that $X = x_j$. Thus it can be rewritten as

$$E[g(Y)] = E_X\left[E_Y[g(Y) \mid X]\right].$$

We note that in the last equation the term $E_Y\left[g(Y)|X\right]$ is a function only of X.

EXAMPLE 2.6

Use the result of Theorem 2.4 to compute $E\left[S_1^2\right]$.

SOLUTION
Recall that B is the random variable representing the result of selecting either spinner b_1 or b_2 with equal probability. Then we have

$$E\left[S_1^2\right] = E_B\left[E_{S_1}\left[S_1^2\,|\,B\right]\right]$$

$$= \frac{1}{2}\cdot E_{S_1}\left[S_1^2\,|\,B=b_1\right] + \frac{1}{2}\cdot E_{S_1}\left[S_1^2\,|\,B=b_2\right]$$

$$= \frac{1}{2}\left[(2)^2\left(\frac{5}{6}\right)+(14)^2\left(\frac{1}{6}\right)\right] + \frac{1}{2}\left[(2)^2\left(\frac{1}{2}\right)+(14)^2\left(\frac{1}{2}\right)\right]$$

$$= \frac{1}{2}(36) + \frac{1}{2}(100) = 68.$$

❑

2.6   EXERCISES

2.1 Bayes' Theorem
2.2 Examples of the Use of Bayes' Theorem

2-1   What is $P\left[A_2\,|\,U_1\right]$?

2-2   Let the conditions be as in Example 2.2. As before we select a die at random, but now toss it twice rather than just once. What is the probability that the die with only one marked face has been drawn, if both tosses result in unmarked faces? (Symbolically this is given by $P\left[A_1\,|\,U_1 \text{ and } U_2\right]$.)

2-3 Let the conditions be as in Example 2.2, except that $P[A_1]=\frac{5}{8}$ and $P[A_2]=\frac{3}{8}$. What is $P[A_1\,|\,U_2]$ in this case?

2-4 A box contains 4 red balls and 6 white balls. A sample of size 3 is drawn without replacement from the box. What is the probability of obtaining 1 red ball and 2 white balls, given that at least 2 of the balls in the sample are white?

2-5 Defective items on an assembly line occur independently with probability .05. A random sample of 100 items is taken. What is the probability that the first sampled item is *not* defective, given that at least 99 of the sampled items are *not* defective?

2-6 Box I contains 3 red marbles and 2 blue marbles. Box II contains 3 red marbles and 7 blue marbles. Box I is selected with probability $\frac{2}{3}$ and Box II is selected with probability $\frac{1}{3}$. A box is selected and a red marble is drawn from the selected box. What is the probability that Box I was selected?

2-7 An insured population of individual drivers consists of 1500 youthful drivers and 8500 adult drivers. The probability distribution of claims for individual insureds during a single policy year is as follows:

Number of Claims	Probability for Youth	Adult
0	.50	.80
1	.30	.15
2	.15	.05
3	.05	.00

A particular policy has exactly 1 claim. What is the probability that the insured is a youthful driver?

2-8   A property-casualty insurance company issues automobile policies
       on a calendar year basis only. Let X be a random variable
       representing the number of accident claims reported during calen-
       dar year 2005 on policies issued during calendar year 2005. Let Y
       be a random variable representing the total number of accident
       claims that will eventually be reported on policies issued during
       calendar year 2005. The probability that an individual accident
       claim on a 2005 policy is reported during calendar year 2005 is d.
       Assume that the reporting times of individual claims are mutually
       independent. Assume also that Y has the negative binomial distri-
       bution, with fixed parameters r and p, given by

$$P[Y = y] = \binom{r + y - 1}{y} p^r (1-p)^y, \qquad (2.9)$$

       for $y = 0,1,\dots$. Calculate $P[Y = y \mid X = x]$, the probability that the
       total number of claims reported on 2005 policies is y, given that x
       claims have been reported by the end of the calendar year. [Hint:
       The solution requires the use of Theorems 2.1 and 2.2, and the
       identity $\binom{y}{x}\binom{r+y-1}{y} = \binom{r+x-1}{x}\binom{(r+x)+(y-x)-1}{y-x}$. In all, sub-
       stantial algebraic manipulation is involved.]

2-9   An insurer believes that the number of claims, Y, that will occur
       during calendar year 2005 is uniformly distributed over the set
       $\{2,3,4,5,6\}$, so that

$$P[Y = y] = \begin{cases} .2 & y = 2,3,4,5,6 \\ 0 & \text{elsewhere} \end{cases}.$$

       The insurer further believes that any claim occurring during the ca-
       lendar year has a 50% chance of being reported before the end of the
       calendar year, and that the reporting of one claim does not influence
       the reporting of any other claims. Let X be a random variable
       representing the number of claims occurring during 2005 and re-
       ported before the end of 2005. Calculate the values of
       $P[Y = y \mid X = x]$, for $x = 0,1,\dots,6$ and $y = x, x+1,\dots,6$.

2.3 Prior and Posterior Probabilities
2.4 Conditional Expectation

2-10 Let R_1 and R_2 be stochastically independent random variables, each with probability density function $f(x) = e^{-x}$, for $x \geq 0$. Calculate $E\left[R_1^2 + R_2^2 \mid R_1 = r_1 \right]$, for $r_1 > 0$.

2-11 Let X and Y be stochastically independent random variables each with density function $f(x)$ defined by

$$f(x) = \begin{cases} 0 & x < 0 \\ .25 & x = 0 \\ .75e^{-x} & x > 0 \end{cases}.$$

Calculate the expected value of $X^2 + Y^3$, given that $X = 3$ and $Y > 0$.

2-12 Let X and Y be discrete random variables with joint density function $f(x,y)$ concentrated on the four corners of a unit square $((0,0),(0,1),(1,0)$ and $(1,1))$. Let $f(x,y)$ be defined as follows:

x	y	$f(x,y)$
0	0	.1
0	1	.2
1	0	.3
1	1	.4

Calculate each of the following:

(a) $E_Y\left[Y \mid X = 1\right]$

(b) $E_X\left[X \mid Y = 0\right]$

2-13 Let X and Y be continuous random variables with joint density function

$$f(x,y) = \begin{cases} 6xy + 3x^2, & 0 < x < y < 1 \\ 0 & \text{otherwise} \end{cases}.$$

Find $E[X \mid Y = y]$, for $0 < y < 1$, via the following three steps:
(a) First determine $f(y)$, for $0 < x < y < 1$.
(b) Then determine $f(x \mid y)$, for $0 < x < y < 1$.
(c) Finally calculate $E[X \mid Y = y]$.

2-14 Using the results and notation of Exercise 2-9, calculate each of the following:

(a) The conditional expectation $E[Y \mid X = 3]$, the total expected number of claims on 2005 policies that will be reported in 2006 and beyond, given that 3 claims on such policies were reported during 2005.

(b) $E[Y \mid X = 3] - 3$, the expected number of claims reported after 2005 on policies issued during 2005.

2-15 Show that if X and Y are as defined in Exercise 2-8, then

$$E[Y \mid X = x] = x + (r+x) \cdot \frac{(1-d)(1-p)}{1-(1-d)(1-p)},$$

for $x = 0,1,\ldots$. This result can be restated as follows:

Given that x claims were reported on the 2005 book of business during calendar year 2005, then the expected number of claims that will eventually be reported on the 2005 book of business is $x + (r+x) \cdot \frac{(1-d)(1-p)}{1-(1-d)(1-p)}$, for $x = 0,1,\ldots$. Alternatively, the expected number of claims that will be reported on the 2005 book of business in 2006 and beyond is $\frac{(r+x)(1-d)(1-p)}{1-(1-d)(1-p)}$, for $x = 0,1,\ldots$.
[Hint: The expected value of a random variable having a negative binomial distribution with parameters n and q is $\frac{n(1-q)}{q}$. The distribution of $Y \mid X = x$ is the same as that of $U + X$, where U has a negative binomial distribution with parameters $n = r + x$ and $q = 1 - (1-d)(1-p)$.]

2.5 Unconditional Expectation

2-16 Let the discrete random variables X and Y be defined as in Exercise 2-12. Calculate the unconditional expectation $E[X]$.

2-17 Let the continuous random variables X and Y be defined as in Exercise 2-13.

(a) Show that the marginal probability density function of X is

$$f(x) = \begin{cases} 3x + 3x^2 - 6x^3 & 0 < x < 1 \\ 0 & \text{otherwise} \end{cases}.$$

(b) Calculate the unconditional expectation $E[X]$.

2-18 Assume that the number of insurance claims, R, filed by an individual in a single policy year has a binomial distribution with parameter for Θ for $r = 0,1,2,3$. Assume further that the parameter Θ has density function $g(\theta) = 6(\theta - \theta^2)$, for $0 < \theta < 1$. Determine the unconditional expectation $E[R]$.

CHAPTER 3

LOSS FUNCTIONS

Under the frequentist paradigm of statistics, every parameter, Θ, is assumed to be a fixed, but unknown, quantity with an underlying "true value." Statistical inference involves constructing either (i) a point estimate of Θ or (ii) a confidence interval around Θ.

In contrast, under the Bayesian paradigm, every parameter is assumed to be a random variable. Before any data are observed, Θ is assumed to have a particular prior distribution. After the observation of pertinent data, a revised or posterior distribution can be computed for Θ via Bayes' theorem. We illustrate such computations in Chapter 8.

In order to obtain a point estimate of Θ from its posterior distribution, it is necessary to specify a loss function of Θ, $L(\Theta, \hat{\Theta})$, where we use $\hat{\Theta}$ to denote an estimator of Θ. As in Bayesian decision analysis (see, for example, Berger [1985]), we employ the estimator of Θ that minimizes the expected value of $L(\Theta, \hat{\Theta})$.

In the first three sections of this chapter we consider three loss functions discussed in Hogg and Klugman [1984][1]. In Section 3.4 we consider some other loss functions.

3.1 SQUARED ERROR LOSS FUNCTIONS

Definition 3.1

The loss function

$$L(\Theta, \hat{\Theta}) = (\Theta - \hat{\Theta})^2 \qquad (3.1)$$

is called the **squared error** (or **squared deviation**) loss function.

---

[1] See page 77.

EXAMPLE 3.1

Calculate the expected value of the squared error loss function, given by $L(\Theta,\hat{\Theta}) = (\Theta - \hat{\Theta})^2$, given that $\hat{\Theta} = 0$ and the probability density function of Θ is

$$h(\theta) = \begin{cases} .5 & -1 \le \theta \le 1 \\ 0 & \text{elsewhere} \end{cases},$$

the uniform density function over the closed interval $[-1,1]$.

SOLUTION

$$E_\Theta\left[L(\Theta,\hat{\Theta})\right] = \int_{-\infty}^{\infty} (\theta - \hat{\Theta})^2 \cdot h(\theta)\, d\theta$$

$$= .50\int_{-1}^{1} \theta^2\, d\theta = \frac{\theta^3}{6}\Bigg|_{-1}^{1} = \frac{1}{3}. \qquad \square$$

EXAMPLE 3.2

Calculate the expected value of the squared error loss function given by $L(\Theta,\hat{\Theta}) = (\Theta - \hat{\Theta})^2$, given the vector of observed data $\mathbf{x}$, assuming that

$$\hat{\Theta} = \hat{\Theta}(\mathbf{x}) = \hat{\Theta}(x_1, x_2, ..., x_n) = \frac{1}{n}\sum_{i=1}^{n} x_i = \bar{x}$$

and that the posterior probability density function of Θ given $\mathbf{x}$ has mean $\bar{x}$ and variance σ^2.

SOLUTION

$$E_\Theta\left[L(\Theta,\hat{\Theta})\,|\,\mathbf{x}\right] = E_\Theta\left[(\Theta - \hat{\Theta})^2\,|\,\mathbf{x}\right]$$

$$= E_\Theta\left[(\Theta - \bar{x})^2\,|\,\mathbf{x}\right]$$

$$= Var_\Theta\left[\Theta\,|\,\mathbf{x}\right]$$

$$= \sigma^2,$$

since $\bar{x} = E_\Theta[\Theta\,|\,\mathbf{x}]$. $\qquad \square$

Theorem 3.1

Let $H(\theta)$ denote the probability distribution function of Θ. If the loss function is $(\Theta-\hat{\Theta})^2$, the squared error loss function, then the point estimator, $\hat{\Theta}$, which minimizes the expected value of the loss function is the mean of the distribution of Θ.

Proof

Our goal is to find the value of $\hat{\Theta}$ which minimizes

$$E_{\Theta}\left[(\Theta-\hat{\Theta})^2\right]. \tag{3.2}$$

If the distribution function of Θ is continuous, for example, then we can write

$$E_{\Theta}\left[(\Theta-\hat{\Theta})^2\right] = \int_{-\infty}^{\infty}(\theta-\hat{\Theta})^2 \cdot h(\theta)\,d\theta,$$

where $h(\theta)$ is the probability density function of Θ. In the general case, we can expand Expression (3.2) as

$$E_{\Theta}\left[(\Theta-\hat{\Theta})^2\right] = E_{\Theta}\left[\Theta^2 - 2\Theta\hat{\Theta}+\hat{\Theta}^2\right]$$
$$= E_{\Theta}\left[\Theta^2\right] - 2\hat{\Theta}\cdot E_{\Theta}[\Theta]+\hat{\Theta}^2.$$

To find the value of $\hat{\Theta}$ that minimizes Expression (3.2), we differentiate the expression $E_{\Theta}[\Theta^2]-2\hat{\Theta}\cdot E_{\Theta}[\Theta]+\hat{\Theta}^2$ with respect to $\hat{\Theta}$, set the result equal to zero, and solve for $\hat{\Theta}$. The result is

$$-2E_{\Theta}[\Theta]+2\hat{\Theta} = 0,$$

which solves for

$$\hat{\Theta} = E_{\Theta}[\Theta].$$

Thus we see that $\hat{\Theta}$ is the mean of the distribution of Θ.

> ## Corollary 3.1
>
> Let $h(\theta \,|\, \mathbf{x})$ denote the posterior density function of Θ, given the vector of observed data $\mathbf{x}$. If the loss function is $(\Theta - \hat{\Theta})^2$, then the Bayesian point estimator, $\hat{\Theta}$, which minimizes the expected value of the loss function is the **mean** of the posterior distribution of Θ.
>
> **Proof**
>
> Simply replace $h(\theta)$ by $h(\theta \,|\, \mathbf{x})$ and $E_\Theta[\cdot]$ by $E_\Theta[\cdot \,|\, \mathbf{x}]$ in the proof of Theorem 3.1.

3.2   ABSOLUTE ERROR LOSS FUNCTIONS

> **Definition 3.2**
>
> The loss function
> $$L(\Theta, \hat{\Theta}) = |\Theta - \hat{\Theta}| \qquad (3.3)$$
> is called the **absolute error** (or **deviation**) **loss function**.

EXAMPLE 3.3

Let Θ be uniformly distributed over the closed interval $[-1, 8]$ and let Θ have the probability density function

$$f(\theta) = \begin{cases} \frac{1}{9} & -1 \le \theta \le 8 \\ 0 & \text{elsewhere} \end{cases}.$$

Let Θ's loss function be the absolute error loss function $|\Theta - \hat{\Theta}(\mathbf{x})|$, where the estimator $\hat{\Theta}(\mathbf{x})$ is the median of the sample $x_1, x_2, \ldots, x_n$.

Calculate the expected loss for the following sample of size 5:

$$x_1 = 1.1, \quad x_2 = 6.8, \quad x_3 = -.7, \quad x_4 = 3.0, \quad x_5 = 3.2$$

SOLUTION

$\hat{\Theta}(\mathbf{x})$, the median of $\{x_1, x_2, ..., x_5\}$, is $x_4 = 3.0$. Then

$$E_\Theta\left[L(\Theta,\hat{\Theta})\right] = \int_{-\infty}^{\infty}\left|\theta - \hat{\Theta}(\mathbf{x})\right| \cdot f(\theta)\, d\theta$$

$$= \int_{-1}^{8}\left|\theta - 3\right| \cdot \frac{1}{9}\, d\theta = \int_{-1}^{3}\frac{3-\theta}{9}\, d\theta + \int_{3}^{8}\frac{\theta-3}{9}\, d\theta$$

$$= 2.3. \qquad \square$$

Theorem 3.2

If $E[\theta]$ exists and the absolute error (deviation) loss function, $|\theta - \hat{\theta}|$, is employed, then the point estimator, $\hat{\Theta}$, which minimizes the expected value of the loss function is the median of the distribution of Θ.

Proof

We restrict the proof to the case where Θ has a continuous distribution function, $F(\theta)$. The proof should extend, with minor modifications, to other types of distribution functions. We begin with the equation

$$E_\Theta\left[|\Theta - m|\right] = \int_{-\infty}^{m}(m-\theta)\cdot dF(\theta) + \int_{m}^{\infty}(\theta-m)\cdot dF(\theta). \quad (3.4)$$

Integrating by parts it follows that

$$\int_{-\infty}^{m}(m-\theta)\, dF(\theta) = \int_{-\infty}^{m}F(\theta)\, d\theta \qquad (3.5)$$

and

$$\int_{m}^{\infty}(\theta-m)\, dF(\theta) = \int_{m}^{\infty}\left(1-F(\theta)\right) d\theta. \qquad (3.6)$$

Equations (3.5) and (3.6) allow us to rewrite Equation (3.4) as

$$E_\Theta\left[|\Theta - m|\right] = \int_{-\infty}^{m}F(\theta)\, d\theta + \int_{m}^{\infty}\left(1-F(\theta)\right) d\theta. \qquad (3.7)$$

Differentiating Equation (3.7) with respect to m and setting the result to zero, we obtain

$$F(m) - \left(1-F(m)\right) = 0, \quad \text{or} \quad F(m) = \tfrac{1}{2}.$$

This demonstrates that the minimum of $E_\Theta[|\Theta - m|]$ is indeed attained when m is the median of $F(\theta)$.

Corollary 3.2

Let $F(\theta \mid \mathbf{x})$ denote the posterior distribution of Θ, given the vector of observed data $\mathbf{x}$. If the loss function is $|\Theta - \hat{\Theta}|$, the absolute error (deviation), then the Bayesian point estimator, $\hat{\Theta}$, which minimizes the expected value of the loss function is the **median** of the posterior distribution of Θ.

Proof
Simply replace $F(\theta)$ by $F(\theta \mid \mathbf{x})$ and $E_\Theta[\cdot]$ by $E_\Theta[\cdot \mid \mathbf{x}]$ in the proof of Theorem 3.2.

3.3 ALMOST CONSTANT LOSS FUNCTIONS

Definition 3.3

The loss function

$$L(\Theta, \hat{\Theta}) = \begin{cases} c & \hat{\Theta} \neq \Theta \\ 0 & \hat{\Theta} = \Theta \end{cases} \tag{3.8}$$

is called the **almost constant loss function**.

EXAMPLE 3.4

Calculate the expected loss if $L(\Theta, \hat{\Theta})$ is defined by Equation (3.8) with $c = 4$, Θ has a Poisson distribution with mean λ, and $\hat{\Theta} = 3$.

SOLUTION

$$E_\Theta\left[L(\Theta, \hat{\Theta})\right] = \sum_{k=0}^{\infty} L(k, \hat{\Theta}) \cdot P[\Theta = k]$$

$$= \sum_{\substack{k=0 \\ k \neq 3}}^{\infty} c \cdot P[\Theta = k] = 4 \cdot \sum_{\substack{k=0 \\ k \neq 3}}^{\infty} \frac{e^{-\lambda}\lambda^k}{k!} = 4\left[1 - \frac{e^{-\lambda}\lambda^3}{3!}\right]$$

❏

Theorem 3.3

If for a non-negative real number c, the loss function, denoted by $L(\Theta, \hat{\Theta})$, is given by Equation (3.8), then the point estimator, $\hat{\Theta}$, which minimizes the expected value of the loss function is the **mode** of the distribution of Θ.

Proof

Our goal is to minimize $E_\Theta[L(\Theta, \hat{\Theta})]$, where $L(\Theta, \hat{\Theta})$ is defined by Equation (3.8). Here we have

$$E_\Theta[L(\Theta, \hat{\Theta})] = E_\Theta[c] - c \cdot P[\Theta = \hat{\Theta}]$$

$$= c - c \cdot P[\Theta = \hat{\Theta}]$$

$$= c\left(1 - P[\Theta = \hat{\Theta}]\right).$$

The last expression achieves its minimum value when $P[\Theta = \hat{\Theta}]$ achieves its maximum value. This occurs when the estimator $\hat{\Theta}$ is the mode of the distribution of Θ. Note, however, that the mode of the distribution of Θ is not necessarily unique. Note also that if Θ is a continuous random variable, then we have the results $P[\Theta = \hat{\Theta}] = 0$ and $E_\Theta[L(\Theta, \hat{\Theta})] = c$.

Corollary 3.3

If for a non-negative real number c, the loss function, denoted $L(\Theta, \hat{\Theta})$, is given by Equation (3.8), then the Bayesian point estimator, $\hat{\Theta}$, which minimizes the expected value of the loss function is the mode of the posterior distribution of Θ.

Proof

Simply replace $E_\Theta[\cdot]$ and $P[\cdot]$ by $E_\Theta[\cdot \,|\, \mathbf{x}]$ and $P[\cdot \,|\, \mathbf{x}]$, respectively, in the proof of Theorem 3.3.

3.4   OTHER LOSS FUNCTIONS

EXAMPLE 3.5

Let Θ denote the amount of taxes owed by John Q. Taxpayer. John Q is charged interest of $100a\%$ per period for each dollar of income tax he underpays and loses interest on his cash of $100b\%$ per period for each dollar of tax he overpays. Let $\hat{\Theta}$ be John Q's estimator of Θ, the amount of estimated taxes paid. What is John Q's loss function for one period?

SOLUTION
The loss function is

$$L(\Theta,\hat{\Theta}) = \begin{cases} a(\Theta-\hat{\Theta}) & \Theta > \hat{\Theta} \\ b(\hat{\Theta}-\Theta) & \Theta < \hat{\Theta} \end{cases}.$$

Note that this is a generalization of Example 3.3. If $a = b = 1$, then the loss function above is the absolute error loss function of Section 3.2. ❑

EXAMPLE 3.6

Calculate the expected value of the loss function in Example 3.5, if $a = .06$, $b = .02$, $\hat{\Theta} = 10,000$ and the density function of Θ is

$$h(\theta) = \begin{cases} \frac{1}{5000} & 8,000 < \theta < 13,000 \\ 0 & \text{elsewhere} \end{cases}.$$

SOLUTION
(Note that all calculations are in thousands of dollars.)

$$E_\Theta[L(\Theta,\hat{\Theta})] = \int_8^{13} L(\theta,\hat{\Theta}) \cdot h(\theta)\, d\theta$$

$$= b\int_8^{10} (\hat{\Theta}-\theta) \cdot h(\theta)\, d\theta + a\int_{10}^{13} (\theta-\hat{\Theta}) \cdot h(\theta)\, d\theta$$

$$= .02\int_8^{10} \frac{10-\theta}{5}\, d\theta + .06\int_{10}^{13} \frac{\theta-10}{5}\, d\theta = .062,$$

or $62. ❑

The following example uses a loss function known as a **0-1 loss func-tion**. Here we employ the concept of a **decision rule**, $\delta(\Theta)$, in place of an estimator, $\hat{\Theta}$. A decision rule is an algorithm for choosing between two alternative courses of action.

EXAMPLE 3.7

Let

$$L\big(\Theta,\delta(\Theta)\big) = \begin{cases} 0 & a < \Theta < b \\ 1 & \Theta \le a \ \text{ or } \ \Theta \ge b \end{cases}.$$

Calculate the expected loss if Θ has a standard normal distribution and $a = -1.645$ and $b = 1.645$.

SOLUTION

$$E_\Theta\big[L\big(\Theta,\delta(\Theta)\big)\big] = \int_{-\infty}^{a} 1 \cdot h(\theta)\, d\theta + \int_{a^+}^{b^-} 0 \cdot h(\theta)\, d\theta$$

$$+ \int_{b}^{\infty} 1 \cdot h(\theta)\, d\theta$$

$$= P[\Theta \le a] + 0 + P[\Theta \ge b]$$

$$= 1 - P[a < \Theta < b]$$

$$= 1 - P[-1.645 < \Theta < 1.645] = 1 - .90 = .10.$$

❑

Note that this is just the probability of rejecting the null hypothe-sis $H_0 : a < \Theta < b$ when H_0 is true.

3.5 FURTHER REMARKS

The concept of a statistical loss function is important and, unfortunately, underutilized. One use of loss functions is to help select the "best" of several competing stochastic models. Several different loss functions should be employed to determine the relative appropriateness of compet-ing models. Herzog [1990] shows that different loss functions can lead to different model selections. Berger [1985] argues that loss functions should be employed instead of frequentist tests of significance. Herzog [1990; page 293] warns that "one should not mechanically apply fre-quentist tests of significance without thinking carefully about the data and how they should best be analyzed." Finally, Berger [1985; page 21] argues that "a 'statistically significant' difference between the true parameter (or true model) and the null hypothesis can be an unimportant difference practically. Likewise a difference that is not statistically significant can nevertheless be very important practically."

3.6 EXERCISES

3.1 Squared Error Loss Functions

3-1 Assuming that the distribution function of Θ is continuous, give an alternate proof of Theorem 3.1 by interchanging the order of integration and differentiation.

3-2 Determine the point estimator $\hat{\Theta}$ which minimizes the expected value of the loss function of the paramenter of interest, given the five observations 1, −3, 4, 0, and −1. Use the squared error loss function, and assume that the mean of the posterior distribution of the parameter is equal to its sample value.

3-3 Calculate the expected value of the squared error loss function, assuming $\hat{\theta} = .20$ (as in Exercise 3-2) and the probability density function

$$f(\theta) = \begin{cases} \frac{1}{9} & -1 \leq \theta \leq 8 \\ 0 & \text{elsewhere} \end{cases}.$$

3-4 Calculate the minimum expected value of the squared error loss function, given the probability density function of Exercise 3-3 and the five observations .3, 2.1, 6.4, −.7, and 6.9.

3.2 Absolute Error Loss Functions

3-5   Using the absolute error loss function, determine the point estima-
       tor $\hat{\Theta}$ which minimizes the expected value of the loss function of
       the parameter of interest, given the observations of Exercise 3-2.
       Assume that the median of the posterior distribution of the parame-
       ter is equal to its sample value.

3-6   Calculate the expected value of the absolute error loss function
       under the conditions of Exercise 3-5, using the probability density
       function of Example 3.3. Use the result $\hat{\theta} = 0$ from Exercise 3-5.

3.3 Almost Constant Loss Functions

3-7   Calculate the expected loss if (i) $L(\Theta, \hat{\Theta})$ is defined by Equation
       (3.8) with $c = 2$, (ii) Θ has a binomial distribution with parameters
       $n = 8$ and p, and (iii) $\hat{\Theta} = 4$.

3-8   Let Θ have the probability density function of Example 3.3 and
       the loss function of Example 3.5 with $a = 1$ and $b = 5$. Calculate
       the expected loss function with $\hat{\Theta} = 0$.

3.4 Other Loss Functions

3-9   Rework Example 3.7 with $a = -1.96$ and $b = 2.33$.

3-10   Let the loss function be that of Example 3.5. Determine the Baye-
       sian point estimator, $\hat{\Theta}$, which minimizes the expected value of
       the loss function. (Assume that the parameter Θ has a continuous
       distribution function.)

3-11 Let the loss function be that of Example 3.5 with $a = 1$ and $b = 2$. Show that the Bayesian point estimator, $\hat{\Theta}$, which minimizes the expected value of the loss function is the $33\frac{1}{3}^{rd}$ percentile of the posterior distribution of Θ. (Assume that the parameter Θ has a continuous distribution function.) [Hint: This is a special case of Exercise 3-10.)

3.5   Further Remarks

3-12 Which of the following statements are true?

I.   A statistically significant difference may not be important practically.

II. A difference that is not statistically significant can never be very important practically.

III. It is usually appropriate to use a single loss function to select the best of several competing statistical models.

CHAPTER 4

DISCRETE FREQUENCY-SEVERITY
INSURANCE MODEL UNDER INDEPENDENCE

This chapter presents a simple two-stage model of an insurance operation, based on Examples 2.2 and 2.3. Specifically, we assume that there is a single insured whose claim experience is modeled in the following manner. First, a die and spinner are selected independently and at random. Then using the notation of Chapter 2,

$$P[A_i \text{ and } B_j] = P[A_i] \cdot P[B_j]$$
$$= \left(\frac{1}{2}\right)\left(\frac{1}{2}\right) = \frac{1}{4}, \tag{4.1}$$

for $i = 1, 2$ and $j = 1, 2$. (Once selected, the die and spinner are not replaced.) These are used to determine the risk characteristics of the insured. The random claims process begins when the selected die is rolled. If a marked face appears, a claim has occurred; if not, there is no claim. Then if there is a claim, the selected spinner is spun to determine the amount of the claim. Each roll of the die and spin of the spinner, if necessary, constitutes a single period of observation. We let X_i denote the random variable representing the amount of the claim, if any, during the ith period of observation, $i = 1, 2, \dots$.

In this chapter, we first compute the initial **pure** (net) **premium**, $E[X_i]$, using the initial (i.e., prior) probabilities $P[A_i \text{ and } B_j]$. Then, having observed the result of the first period of observation, we compute a revised pure premium estimate, $E[X_2 \mid X_1]$, based on the revised (i.e., posterior) probabilities $P[A_i \text{ and } B_j \mid X_1]$ given the result of the first period of observation.

4.1 INITIAL PURE PREMIUM ESTIMATES

Since X_1 can take only the values 0, 2, and 14 with positive probability, we may write $E[X_1]$ as

$$E[X_1] = 0 \cdot P[X_1 = 0] + 2 \cdot P[X_1 = 2] + 14 \cdot P[x_1 = 14]. \quad (4.2)$$

Recalling the definitions of U_1 and M_1 from Example 2.2, we find

$$P[X_1=0] = P[U_1]$$
$$= P[U_1 \mid A_1] \cdot P[A_1] + P[U_1 \mid A_2] \cdot P[A_2]$$
$$= \left(\frac{5}{6}\right)\left(\frac{1}{2}\right) + \left(\frac{1}{2}\right)\left(\frac{1}{2}\right) = \frac{2}{3}, \quad (4.3)$$

and

$$P[X_1=2] = P[M_1 \text{ and } (S_1=2)]$$
$$= P[M_1] \cdot P[S_1=2]$$
$$= \left(P[M_1 \mid A_1] \cdot P[A_1] + P[M_1 \mid A_2] \cdot P[A_2] \right)$$
$$\times \left(P[S_1=2 \mid B_1] \cdot P[B_1] + P[S_1=2 \mid B_2] \cdot P[B_2] \right)$$
$$= \left[\left(\frac{1}{6}\right)\left(\frac{1}{2}\right) + \left(\frac{1}{2}\right)\left(\frac{1}{2}\right) \right] \times \left[\left(\frac{5}{6}\right)\left(\frac{1}{2}\right) + \left(\frac{1}{2}\right)\left(\frac{1}{2}\right) \right]$$
$$= \frac{2}{9}. \quad (4.4)$$

Finally,

$$P[X_1=14] = 1 - P[X_1=0] - P[X_1=2]$$
$$= 1 - \frac{2}{3} - \frac{2}{9} = \frac{1}{9}. \quad (4.5)$$

The initial (prior) probabilities obtained above are summarized in column (2) of Table 4.1.

TABLE 4.1

Initial Pure Premium Estimate		
(1)	(2)	(3)
Value of x	Initial Probability $P[X_1=x]$	$x \cdot P[X_1=x]$ $(1) \times (2)$
0	6/9	0
2	2/9	4/9
14	1/9	14/9
Totals	1	2

By adding the entries in column (3) of Table 4.1, we find the initial estimate of the pure premium to be $E[X_1] = 2$.

Alternatively, we can determine $E[X_1]$ using the conditional expectation
results of Chapter 2.

$$E[X_1] = \sum_{i=1}^{2}\sum_{j=1}^{2} E[X_1 \mid A_i \text{ and } B_j] \cdot P[A_i \text{ and } B_j] \qquad (4.6)$$

where $E[X_1 \mid A_i \text{ and } B_j]$ is the mean claim amount, given the pair of
events A_i and B_j. It, in turn, is equal to the product of (a) the mean
number of claims, and (b) the mean severity amount, given that a claim
occurs. Symbolically this is expressed as

$$E[X_1 \mid A_i \text{ and } B_j] = E[I_1 \mid A_i \text{ and } B_j] \cdot E[S_1 \mid A_i \text{ and } B_j]$$
$$= E[I_1 \mid A_i] \cdot E[S_1 \mid B_j],$$

where

$$I_1 = \begin{cases} 1 & \text{if the first toss of the die produces a marked side.} \\ 0 & \text{if otherwise} \end{cases}$$

Thus it follows that $E[I_1 \mid A_i] = P[M_1 \mid A_i]$. From Examples 2.2 and 2.3
we obtain the results shown in Table 4.2. Substituting the pure premium
values from column (4), along with the probabilities $P[A_i \text{ and } B_j] = \frac{1}{4}$,
into Equation (4.6), we again obtain the result $E[X_1] = 2$.

TABLE 4.2

Pure Premium by Type of Die and Spinner			
(1)	(2)	(3)	(4)
Type of Die and Spinner	Frequency $E[I_1 \mid A_i]$	Severity $E[S_1 \mid B_j]$	$E[X_1 \mid A_i \text{ and } B_j]$ $(2) \times (3)$
A_1 and B_1	1/6	4	2/3
A_1 and B_2	1/6	8	4/3
A_2 and B_1	1/2	4	2
A_2 and B_2	1/2	8	4

4.2 REVISED PURE PREMIUM ESTIMATES AND PREDICTIVE DISTRIBUTIONS

In this section we estimate the pure premium for the second period of observation, given the result of the first period. Symbolically we seek the values of $E[X_2 \mid X_1=k]$, for $k = 0, 2$, and 14. The method of solution also yields the conditional probabilities of X_2, given the value of X_1. These conditional probabilities constitute the **predictive distribution of the random variable X_2 given the value of the random variable X_1.**

Since (a) once a die has been chosen, the result of each toss of that die is independent of the results of all other tosses, and (b) once a spinner has been selected, the result of each spin of that spinner is independent of the results of all other spins, then the random variable X_2 depends only on the result of the first period of observation through the joint probabilities of A_i and B_j. In other words, the only effect is through the revised die-spinner probabilities $P[A_i \text{ and } B_j \mid X_1=k]$.

By analogy with Equation (4.2), we may write

$$
\begin{aligned}
E[X_2 \mid X_1=k] \;=\; & 0 \cdot P[X_2=0 \mid X_1=k] \\
& + 2 \cdot P[X_2=2 \mid X_1=k] \\
& + 14 \cdot P[X_2=14 \mid X_1=k],
\end{aligned}
\tag{4.7}
$$

for $k = 0, 2$, and 14. Our goal is to calculate the conditional expected claim amount (pure premium) for the second period of observation, after having observed a claim amount of k during the first period of observation. For the reasons given in the preceding section, we may write

$$P[X_2=m \mid X_1=k] = \sum_{i=1}^{2}\sum_{j=1}^{2} P[X_2=m \mid A_i \text{ and } B_j]$$
$$\times P[A_1 \text{ and } B_j \mid X_1=k], \quad (4.8)$$

for $m = 0, 2$, and 14. The reader should note that the result

$$P[X_2=m \mid A_i \text{ and } B_j] = P[X_1=m \mid A_i \text{ and } B_j],$$

follows from the conditions of the model.

We first calculate the probabilities $P[X_1=R \mid A_i \text{ and } B_j]$, starting with $R = 0$. In this case we have

$$P[X_1=0 \mid A_i \text{ and } B_j] = P[X_1=0 \mid A_i] = P[U_1 \mid A_i]. \quad (4.9)$$

The values of $P[U_1 \mid A_1]=\frac{5}{6}=\frac{30}{36}$ and $P[U_1 \mid A_2]=\frac{1}{2}=\frac{18}{36}$ are already known. Next, we consider $P[X_1=2 \mid A_i \text{ and } B_j]$. We know that

$$P[X_1=2 \mid A_i \text{ and } B_j] = P[M_1 \mid A_i] \cdot P[S_1=2 \mid B_j], \quad (4.10)$$

so these values can be easily calculated, as shown in Table 4.3.

TABLE 4.3

$P[X_1 = 2 \mid A_i \text{ and } B_j]$			
(1)	(2)	(3)	(4)
Type of Die and Spinner	$P[M_1 \mid A_i]$	$P[S_1=2 \mid B_j]$	$P[X_1=2 \mid A_i \text{ and } B_j]$ (2)×(3)
A_1 and B_1	1/6	5/6	5/36
A_1 and B_2	1/6	1/2	3/36
A_2 and B_1	1/2	5/6	15/36
A_2 and B_2	1/2	1/2	9/36

The calculation of $P[X_1{=}14\,|\,A_i \text{ and } B_j]$ is left to the reader as Exercise 4-2. The results of Equation (4.9), Equation (4.10), and Exercise 4-2 are summarized in Table 4.4. Note that the $R=2$ column comes from column (4) of Table 4.3.

TABLE 4.4

Probability of Claim Outcome Given Die and Spinner $P[X_1{=}R\,|\,A_i \text{ and } B_j]$				
Type of Die and Spinner	Value of R			
	0	2	14	Total
A_1 and B_1	30/36	5/36	1/36	1
A_1 and B_2	30/36	3/36	3/36	1
A_2 and B_1	18/36	15/36	3/36	1
A_2 and B_2	18/36	9/36	9/36	1

In order to evaluate the right side of Equation (4.8), we need the values of $P[A_i \text{ and } B_j \,|\, X_1{=}k]$, for $k=0,2,$ and 14. From Bayes' theorem we have

$$P[A_i \text{ and } B_j \,|\, X_1{=}k]$$
$$= \frac{P[X_1{=}k\,|\,A_i \text{ and } B_j]\cdot P[A_i \text{ and } B_j]}{P[X_1 = k]}. \qquad (4.11)$$

Since (a) $P[A_i \text{ and } B_j]=\frac{1}{4}$ for all i and j, (b) the values of the initial probabilities $P[X_1 = k]$ are given in column (2) of Table 4.1, and (c) the values of $P[X_1{=}k\,|\,A_i \text{ and } B_j]$ are given in Table 4.4, we can easily evaluate $P[A_i \text{ and } B_j \,|\, X_1{=}k]$, for $k=0,2,$ and 14. For example, Equation (4.11) produces

$$P[A_1 \text{ and } B_2 \,|\, X_1{=}14] = \frac{P[X_1{=}14\,|\,A_1 \text{ and } B_2]\cdot P[A_1 \text{ and } B_2]}{P[X_1 = 14]}$$
$$= \frac{\left(\frac{3}{36}\right)\left(\frac{1}{4}\right)}{\frac{1}{9}} = \frac{3}{16}.$$

All of the results from Equation (4.11) are summarized in the following table.

TABLE 4.5

Posterior Distribution of Die-Spinner Combinations $P[A_i \text{ and } B_j \mid X_1=k]$			
Type of Die and Spinner	Value of k		
	1	2	14
A_1 and B_1	5/16	5/32	1/16
A_1 and B_2	5/16	3/32	3/16
A_2 and B_1	3/16	15/32	3/16
A_2 and B_2	3/16	9/32	9/16

Tables 4.4 and 4.5 give the results needed to evaluate the conditional probabilities of Equation (4.8). For example

$$P[X_2=2 \mid X_1=14] = \sum_{i=1}^{2} \sum_{j=1}^{2} P[X_2=2 \mid A_i \text{ and } B_j] \cdot P[A_i \text{ and } B_j \mid X_1=14]$$

$$= \left(\frac{5}{36}\right)\left(\frac{1}{16}\right) + \left(\frac{3}{36}\right)\left(\frac{3}{16}\right) + \left(\frac{15}{36}\right)\left(\frac{3}{16}\right) + \left(\frac{9}{36}\right)\left(\frac{9}{16}\right)$$

$$= \frac{35}{144}.$$

Table 4.6 summarizes the values of the conditional probabilities of X_2 given X_1. These values constitute the predictive distribution of the random variable X_2, given the value of X_1. That is, given the result of the first period of observation, the appropriate column of Table 4.6 gives the probability of each possible outcome for the second period.

TABLE 4.6

Predictive Distribution of X_2 Given X_1 $P[X_2=m \mid X_1=k]$			
	Value of k		
m	0	2	14
0	51/72	168/288	84/144
2	14/72	85/288	35/144
14	7/72	35/288	25/144
Totals	1	1	1

Finally, we can use Equation (4.7) and the entries of Table 4.6 to calculate the conditional expectations of X_2, given X_1. For example, for $k = 2$,

$$E[X_2 \mid X_1=2] = 2 \cdot P[X_2=2 \mid X_1=2] + 14 \cdot P[X_2=14 \mid X_1=2]$$
$$= 2\left(\frac{85}{288}\right) + 14\left(\frac{35}{288}\right) = \frac{55}{24}.$$

The results for all three values of k are given in the following table.

TABLE 4.7

k	$E[X_2 \mid X_1=k]$
0	42/24
2	55/24
14	70/24

An alternative approach to find $E[X_2 \mid X_1=k]$ is to directly calculate the joint probabilities $P[X_2=m$ and $X_1=k]$, and to then obtain the entries of Table 4.6 by using the definition of conditional probability

$$P[X_2=m \mid X_1=k] = \frac{P[X_2=m \text{ and } X_1=k]}{P[X_1=k]}. \tag{4.12}$$

4.3 ADDITIONAL REMARKS

The reader should compare the prior probability estimates of Table 4.1 with the probability estimates of the predictive distribution given in Table 4.6. The reader should also compare the initial pure premium estimate of $E[X_1] = 2$ with those of Table 4.7, and note how the observed claim amount in the first period of observation modifies the claim amount expected in the second period.

In this work, **predictive distribution** refers only to that of a random variable given previous outcomes of one or more random variables, as in Table 4.6. We use the term **posterior distribution** to refer to other conditional distributions, such as those involving one or more parameters. For example, in Section 9.2, we derive the predictive distribution of X_{m+1}, given the previous outcomes of the random variables $X_1, X_2, ..., X_m$. To complete this derivation, we have to calculate the posterior distribution of a parameter Θ, given the previous outcomes of the random variables $X_1, X_2, ..., X_m$.

The notion of the distribution of a parameter is a crucial difference between the Bayesian paradigm and the frequentist paradigm. In the Bayesian paradigm, each parameter is assumed to be a random variable with a probability distribution. By contrast, under the frequentist paradigm, each parameter is assumed to be a fixed, but unknown, quantity. Therefore, under the frequentist paradigm, we typically seek a point estimate or a confidence interval for each parameter, but not an entire probability distribution.

In this chapter, we have used the observed outcome of the random variable X_1 to modify the joint prior distribution of the random variables A and B. The result was the joint posterior distribution of the random variables A and B. We then used this joint posterior distribution to compute the conditional (or predictive) distribution of X_2 given X_1. Under the Bayesian paradigm, we may consider A and B to be parameters, similar to the parameter θ discussed earlier. Additional applications of the Bayesian paradigm are presented in Chapters 8 and 14.

4.4 EXERCISES

4.1 The Initial Pure Premium
4.2 Revised Pure Premium Estimates and
     Predictive Distributions

4-1   Show that $P[X_2=m \mid A_i \text{ and } B_j] = P[X_1=m \mid A_1 \text{ and } B_j]$.

4-2   Verify the results for $P[X_1=14 \mid A_i \text{ and } B_j]$ shown in Table 4.4.

4-3   Calculate $P[A_1 \mid X_2=0 \text{ and } X_1=0]$.

4-4   Calculate $P[B_2 \mid X_2=0 \text{ and } X_1=0]$

4-5   Calculate $P[A_1 \text{ and } B_2 \mid X_2=0 \text{ and } X_1=0]$.

4-6   Show that $P[X_2 = 14 \mid X_1 = 2] = \frac{95}{288}$.

4-7　Show that $E[X_2 \mid X_1 = 0] = \frac{42}{24}$ and $E[X_2 \mid X_1 = 14] = \frac{70}{24}$.

4-8　Calculate $E[X_3 \mid X_2 = 0$ and $X_1 = 0]$.

4-9　Calculate $Var(X_1)$, the unconditional variance of X_1.

4-10　Calculate $Var(X_2 \mid X_1 = k)$ for $k = 0, 2$, and 14.
　　　This is the conditional variance of X_2 given $X_1 = k$.

4-11　Using only the information contained in Tables 4.1 and 4.7, show that $E[X_2] = 2$. (It has already been shown in the text that $E[X_1] = 2$.)

4-12　Let one of two coins be selected with probability of .50. One coin is a "fair" coin with one side having "heads" and the other "tails"; the second coin has heads on both sides.

　　(a) For $n > 0$, calculate the probability that the $(n+1)^{st}$ toss will be heads given that the first n tosses are all heads. [Note that one coin is selected and tossed throughout the entire process.]

　　(b) Calculate the limit as $n \to \infty$ of the result in part (a).

　　(c) Calculate the (conditional) variance of the indicator variable for the event described in part (a).

　　(d) Calculate the limit as $n \to \infty$ of the result in part (c).

4.3 Additional Remarks

4-13　(a) Does $F(x_2 \mid X_1 = x_1)$ denote a posterior distribution or a predictive distribution? Explain.

　　(b) Does $F(\theta \mid X_1, X_2)$ denote a posterior distribution or a predictive distribution? Explain.

4-14　(a) How is a parameter treated under the frequentist paradigm of statistics?

　　(b) How is a parameter treated under the Bayesian paradigm of statistics?

CHAPTER 5

LIMITED FLUCTUATION
CREDIBILITY APPROACH

5.1 INTRODUCTION

The goal of the limited fluctuation approach is to find a compromise estimator, C, of the form

$$C = ZR + (1-Z)H, \qquad (1.1)$$

as defined in Chapter 1. The limited fluctuation credibility approach is one of the oldest, going back at least as far as Mowbray [1914] and Perryman [1932]. More modern treatments are found in Longley-Cook [1962] and in Chapter 8 of Hossack, Pollard, and Zehnwirth [1983]. Outside North America this approach is sometimes called "American credibility."

We begin, in Section 5.2, with some mathematical preliminaries needed to derive the main results of the chapter. Under the limited fluctuation approach to full credibility (i.e., $Z = 1$), described in Section 5.3, frequentist models are used to determine the expected number of claims, λ_F, required for full credibility. Likewise, under the limited fluctuation approach to partial credibility (i.e., $Z < 1$), described in Section 5.4, frequentist methods are used to determine the credibility factor Z. Section 5.5 concludes the chapter with a brief discussion of the advantages and disadvantages of this approach to credibility.

5.2 MATHEMATICAL PRELIMINARIES

Let N be a random variable representing the number of claims from an insurance portfolio. Thus N takes only non-negative integer values with positive probability, so that

$$\sum_{i=0}^{\infty} P[N = i] = 1. \qquad (5.1)$$

For $i = 1, 2, \ldots,$ let X_i denote the random variable representing the amount of the ith claim and S denote the aggregate claim amount, so that

$$S = \sum_{i=1}^{N} X_i. \tag{5.2}$$

Then we have the following important theorem.

Theorem 5.1

If the several values of X_i are mutually independent with identical first and second moments, and if the number of claims, N, is independent of the claim amounts, then the expected value of the random variable S is given by

$$E[S] = E[N] \cdot E[X_1]. \tag{5.3a}$$

Proof

We first write S as the random sum of N random variables, so that

$$S = \sum_{j=1}^{N} X_j.$$

Then

$$E[S] = E\left[\sum_{j=1}^{N} X_j \right].$$

By Theorem 2.3, with A_i replaced by $N = i$, we obtain

$$E[S] = E\left[\sum_{j=0}^{N} X_j \right] = \sum_{i=0}^{\infty} P[N=i] \cdot E\left[\sum_{j=0}^{N} X_j \mid N=i \right]$$

$$= \sum_{i=0}^{\infty} P[N=i] \cdot E\left[\sum_{j=1}^{i} X_j \right]$$

$$= \sum_{i=0}^{\infty} P[N=i] \cdot \sum_{j=1}^{i} E[X_j]$$

$$= \sum_{i=0}^{\infty} P[N=i] \cdot i \cdot E[X_1]$$

$$= \left(\sum_{i=0}^{\infty} i \cdot P[N=i] \right) \cdot E[X_1] = E[N] \cdot E[X_1].$$

EXAMPLE 5.1

Let N have a Poisson distribution with mean 5, and let X_i, for $i = 1, 2, \ldots$, have a normal distribution with mean 30 and variance 7. Let N and the X_i's be mutually independent. Use Theorem 5.1 to find the mean of

$$S = \sum_{i=1}^{N} X_i.$$

SOLUTION

Since N is Poisson, then $E[N] = Var(N) = 5$. We are also given the values $E[X_1] = 30$ and $Var(X_1) = 7$. By Equation (5.3a) we have

$$E[S] = E[N] \cdot E[X_1] = (5)(30) = 150. \qquad \square$$

Theorem 5.2

If X and Y are random variables, then

$$Var(Y) = E_X[Var_Y(Y \mid X)] + Var_X\left(E_Y[Y \mid X]\right).\ ^1$$

Proof

$$E_X\left[Var_Y(Y \mid X)\right] = E_X\left[E_Y[Y^2 \mid X]\right] - E_X\left[\left(E_Y[Y \mid X]\right)^2\right]$$

$$= E_Y[Y^2] - E_X\left[\left(E_Y[Y \mid X]\right)^2\right]$$

We now add and subtract $\left(E_Y[Y]\right)^2$ to the right side of this last equation, yielding

$$E_X[Y^2] - \left(E_Y[Y]^2\right) - \left\{E_X\left[\left(E_Y[Y \mid X]\right)^2\right] - \left(E_Y[Y]\right)^2\right\}$$

$$= Var_Y(Y) - \left\{E_X\left[\left(E_Y[Y \mid X]\right)^2\right] - \left(E_X\left[E_Y[Y \mid X]\right]\right)^2\right\}$$

$$= Var_Y(Y) - Var_X\left(E_Y[Y \mid X]\right).$$

We have now shown that

$$E_X\left[Var_Y[Y \mid X]\right] = Var_Y(Y) - Var_X\left(E_Y[Y \mid X]\right),$$

which is equivalent to

$$Var_Y(Y) = E_X\left[Var_Y(Y \mid X)\right] + Var_X\left(E_Y[Y \mid X]\right).$$

---

[1] In words, the variance of Y is the mean of the conditional variance plus the variance of the conditional mean.

Theorem 5.3

Under the conditions and notation of Theorem 5.1,

$$Var(S) = E[N] \cdot Var(X_1) + Var(N) \cdot (E[X_1])^2. \qquad (5.3b)$$

Proof

Applying Theorem 5.2 with $Y = S$ and $X = N$, we obtain

$$Var(S) = E_N\left[Var_S(S \mid N)\right] + Var_N\left(E_S[S \mid N]\right)$$

$$= E_N\left[Var\left(\sum_{i=1}^{N} X_i \mid N\right)\right] + Var_N\left(E\left[\sum_{i=1}^{N} X_i \mid N\right]\right)$$

$$= E_N\left[N \cdot Var(X_1)\right] + Var_N\left(N \cdot E[X_1]\right)$$

$$= E_N[N] \cdot Var(X_1) + Var_N(N) \cdot (E[X_1])^2.$$

EXAMPLE 5.2

Using the notation and assumptions of Example 5.1, calculate $Var(S)$.

SOLUTION
From Equation (5.3b) we have

$$Var(S) = E[N] \cdot Var(X_1) + Var(N) \cdot (E[X_1])^2$$

$$= (5)(7) + (5)(30)^2$$

$$= 4535. \qquad \square$$

5.3 THE FULL CREDIBILITY APPROACH

5.3.1 THE RATIONALE FOR FULL CREDIBILITY

Large insureds experiencing favorable claim results usually want their future insurance premiums to be based solely on their own experience, which is what we mean by **full credibility**. Then the question naturally arises as to when the insured's experience is large enough to be assigned full credibility (i.e., $Z = 1$). In this approach, "experience" is specifically measured by the expected number of claims during the next period of observation. Under the limited fluctuation approach, the answer to the question concerning full credibility proceeds along the following lines, using the notation and assumptions of Theorem 5.1. As mentioned in Chapter 1, the limited fluctuation approach is an application of the frequentist paradigm.

5.3.2 THE FULL CREDIBILITY FORMULA

The basic assumption is that the insurer is willing to assign full credibility to the estimator of aggregate claims, S, based solely on the observed data, provided S is within, say, $100c\%$ of its true value, s, with probability $1 - \alpha$. Symbolically, we want

$$P[-cs < S-s < cs] = 1-\alpha, \tag{5.4a}$$

or

$$P\left[\frac{-cs}{\sqrt{Var(S)}} < \frac{S-s}{\sqrt{Var(S)}} < \frac{cs}{\sqrt{Var(S)}}\right] = 1-\alpha. \tag{5.4b}$$

In this context c is called the **range parameter** and $(1-\alpha)$ is the **probability level**.

Under the limited fluctuation approach, the assumption is also made that N has a Poisson distribution. We let λ denote the mean of N. For a Poisson random variable we also know that $Var(N) = E[N] = \lambda$. As stated in Theorem 5.1, the expected value and variance of the loss severity or claim amount, X_i, are assumed constant over all values of i, and are denoted by

$$E[X_i] = m \tag{5.5a}$$

and

$$Var(X_i) = \sigma^2, \tag{5.5b}$$

respectively. Then by Equation (5.3a) we have

$$E[S] = E[N] \cdot E[X_i] = \lambda m \tag{5.6a}$$

and by Equation (5.3b) we have

$$Var(S) = E[N] \cdot Var(X_1) + Var(N) \cdot (E[X_1])^2$$
$$= \lambda\sigma^2 + \lambda m^2 = \lambda(\sigma^2 + m^2). \tag{5.6b}$$

According to the Central Limit Theorem[2], if the experience is reasonably large, then the random variable $\frac{S-s}{\sqrt{Var(S)}}$ is approximately distributed as a normal random variable with mean zero and standard deviation one. Then from Equation (5.4b) we have

$$\frac{cs}{\sqrt{Var(S)}} = x_\alpha, \tag{5.7}$$

where x_α is the point on the standardized normal curve such that the area between $-x_a$ and x_α is equal to $1 - \alpha$.

Substituting λm for s and $\lambda(\sigma^2 + m^2)$ for $Var(S)$ in Equation (5.7) we obtain

$$\frac{c\lambda m}{\sqrt{\lambda(\sigma^2 + m^2)}} = x_\alpha,$$

or, rearranging terms,

$$\frac{\sqrt{\lambda}}{\sqrt{1 + \left(\frac{\sigma}{m}\right)^2}} = \frac{x_\alpha}{c}.$$

(Note that the substitution of λm for s assumes that S is an unbiased estimator.)

Then squaring both sides and solving for λ, we obtain in the general case

$$\lambda = \lambda_F = \frac{x_\alpha^2}{c^2}\left[1 + \left(\frac{\sigma}{m}\right)^2\right], \tag{5.8}$$

where λ_F is the minimum number of expected claims during the next period of observation required for full credibility. The ratio of the standard deviation to the mean, $\frac{\sigma}{m}$, is called the **coefficient of variation**.

---

[2] See, for example, Section 4.4 of Hogg, McKean, and Craig [2005].

5.3.3 NUMERICAL EXAMPLES

EXAMPLE 5.3

Show how to determine λ_F if $c = .03$ and $1-\alpha = .95$.

SOLUTION
Equations (5.4a) and (5.4b), respectively, produce

$$P[.97s < S < 1.03s] = .95$$

and

$$P\left[\frac{-.03s}{\sqrt{Var(S)}} < \frac{S-s}{\sqrt{Var(S)}} < \frac{.03s}{\sqrt{Var(S)}}\right] = .95.$$

From a table of standardized normal values we obtain $x_a = 1.96$.
Then from Equation (5.8) we have

$$\lambda_F = \left(\frac{1.96}{.03}\right)^2\left[1+\left(\frac{\sigma}{m}\right)^2\right] = 4268\left[1+\left(\frac{\sigma}{m}\right)^2\right]. \qquad \square$$

The value of the coefficient 4268 in Example 5.3 is a direct result of the choice of the range parameter $c = .03$ and the probability level $(1-\alpha) = .95$. Both of these choices are arbitrary. It should be apparent to the reader that, in determining the expected number of claims required for full credibility, we are just determining the sample size required to produce a $100(1-\alpha)\%$ confidence interval for a particular value of c.

EXAMPLE 5.4

Show that if $X_i = d$, a positive constant, for $i = 1, 2, ...$, so that $P[X_i = d] = 1$, then the coefficient of variation of the loss severity (i.e., claim size) distribution is zero.

SOLUTION
Since all claim sizes are constant, it follows that $\sigma = \sqrt{Var(X_i)} = 0$ and the coefficient of variation, σ / m, is equal to zero as well. $\qquad \square$

EXAMPLE 5.5

Show that if $P[X_i=d]=1$ for $i=1,2,...$, then the minimum number of expected claims required for full credibility is $\frac{x_\alpha^2}{c^2}$.

SOLUTION

Since $\frac{\sigma}{m}=\lambda_0$, the second factor on the right side of Equation (5.8) is equal to 1. Then we are left with

$$\lambda_F \;=\; \frac{x_\alpha^2}{c^2} \tag{5.9a}$$

as the minimum number of expected claims required for full credibility, in the case where we are only concerned with the number of claims. We use λ_0 to denote this result, so we have

$$\lambda_0 \;=\; \frac{x_\alpha^2}{c^2}. \tag{5.9b}$$

❑

EXAMPLE 5.6

A full credibility standard is employed so that the total number of claims is within 5% of the expected number with a probability of 98%. If the full credibility standard just determined were applied to the total cost of claims, then the actual total cost would be within $100c\%$ of the expected cost with 95% probability. Determine the value of c under the following assumptions:

1. The loss frequency distribution is Poisson which can be approximated by a normal distribution.

2. The coefficient of variation of the loss severity distribution is .894.

3. The aggregate loss distribution can be approximated by a normal distribution.

SOLUTION

In the first situation, where we are concerned only with the *number* of claims, the parameters are $c=.05$ and $x_\alpha=2.327$. Then

from Equation (5.9b) it follows that $\lambda_0 = \left(\frac{2.327}{.05}\right)^2 = 2165.972$.
In the second situation, where we are concerned with the total
cost of claims, we have $x_\alpha = 1.96$ and $\frac{\sigma}{m} = .894$. Then by
Equation (5.8) we find

$$\lambda_F = \left(\frac{1.96}{c}\right)^2 \left[1 + (.894)^2\right] = \frac{6.912}{c^2}.$$

Since the full credibility standard is the same in both situations,
we have

$$\frac{6.912}{c^2} = 2165.972,$$

from which we find $c = .0565$. ❑

5.3.4 MINIMUM NUMBER OF EXPECTED CLAIMS REQUIRED FOR FULL CREDIBILITY

Values of the ratio $\lambda_0 = \frac{x_\alpha^2}{c^2}$, for various pairs of c and $1 - \alpha$, are shown
in Table 5.1. These values show the minimum number of expected
claims required for full credibility based solely on the frequency
component of claims (i.e., ignoring the loss severity of claims). The entry
of 1082, corresponding to the pair of parameter values $c = .05$ and
$(1 - \alpha) = .90$, is frequently cited in the actuarial literature as the minimum
number of expected claims required for full credibility.

TABLE 5.1

Values of λ_0					
Probability Level, $1 - \alpha$	Range Parameter, c				
	.30	.20	.10	.05	.01
.900	30	68	271	1082	27,060
.950	43	96	384	1537	38,416
.990	74	166	664	2654	66,358
.999	120	271	1083	4331	108,274

5.3.5 SUMMARY OF THE FULL CREDIBILITY APPROACH

Goal: To determine λ_F, the minimum number of expected claims during the next period of observation required for full credibility.

Step 1: Select the range parameter, c.

Step 2: Select the probability level, $1 - \alpha$.

Step 3: Estimate the value of the coefficient of variation for the loss severity distribution.

Step 4: Use Equation (5.8) to calculate λ_F.

Assumption 1: The number of claims, N, has a Poisson distribution.

Assumption 2: The mean and variance of the loss severity, X_i, are constant for all values of i.

Assumption 3: The Central Limit Theorem applies.

5.4 THE PARTIAL CREDIBILITY APPROACH

5.4.1 THE RATIONALE FOR PARTIAL CREDIBILITY

For some insureds, the number of claims expected during the next period of observation, λ, is insufficient to assign full credibility of $Z = 1$. In this case, we need to determine the appropriate value of the partial credibility factor $Z < 1$. Longley-Cook [1962] suggests choosing the credibility factor to be equal to $\sqrt{\lambda / \lambda_F}$, where λ_F is specified by Equation (5.8).

5.4.2 THE PARTIAL CREDIBILITY FORMULA

The basic assumption in this case is that the estimator $ZS - Zs$ must be in the interval $[-cs, cs]$ with probability $1 - \alpha$. Symbolically, we require

$$P[-cs < ZS - Zs < cs] = 1 - \alpha, \tag{5.10a}$$

or, equivalently,

$$P\left[\frac{-cs}{Z\sqrt{Var(S)}} < \frac{S-s}{\sqrt{Var(S)}} < \frac{cs}{Z\sqrt{Var(S)}}\right] = 1 - \alpha. \tag{5.10b}$$

As in the previous section, if the experience is sufficiently large we can appeal to the Central Limit Theorem, and thereby assume that the random variable $\frac{S-s}{Var(S)}$ is approximately distributed as a standardized normal random variable. Then from Equation (5.10b) we have

$$\frac{cs}{Z\sqrt{Var(S)}} = x_\alpha, \tag{5.11}$$

where x_α is as defined in Section 5.3. Substituting λm for s and $\lambda(\sigma^2 + m^2)$ for $Var(S)$ in Equation (5.11), we obtain

$$\frac{c\lambda m}{Z\sqrt{\lambda(\sigma^2 + m^2)}} = x_\alpha.$$

Solving for Z we obtain

$$Z = \frac{\sqrt{\lambda}}{\frac{x_\alpha}{c}\sqrt{1 + \left(\frac{\sigma}{m}\right)^2}}. \tag{5.12}$$

But by Equation (5.8), the denominator of the right side of Equation (5.12) is $\sqrt{\lambda_F}$, so we can rewrite Equation (5.12) as

$$Z = \sqrt{\frac{\lambda}{\lambda_F}}. \tag{5.13}$$

Therefore the (partial) credibility factor, Z, is equal to the square root of the ratio of the expected number of claims for the risk, λ, to the minimum number of expected claims required for full credibility λ_F.

5.4.3 PARTIAL CREDIBILITY EXAMPLE

EXAMPLE 5.7

The following information for a group of insureds is available:

Prior estimate of total losses	20,000,000
Observed total losses	25,000,000
Expected number of claims during next period	10,000
Minimum number of claims for full credibility	17,500

Using the partial credibility formula specified by Equation (5.13), estimate S, the total losses for the group during the next period of observation.

SOLUTION
We first calculate Z from Equation (5.13), obtaining

$$Z = \sqrt{\lambda / \lambda_F} = \sqrt{10,000 / 17,500} = .756.$$

Then from Equation (1.1), with C replaced by S, we find

$$S = ZR + (1-Z)H$$
$$= (.756)(25,000,000) + (.244)(20,000,000) = 23,780,000.$$

∎

5.4.4 SUMMARY OF THE PARTIAL CREDIBILITY APPROACH

Goal: To calculate the partial credibility factor, Z.

Step 1: Select the range parameter, c.

Step 2: Select the probability level, $1 - \alpha$.

Step 3: Estimate the value of the coefficient of variation for the loss severity distribution.

Step 4: Use Equation (5.8) to calculate λ_F.

Step 5: Estimate the number of claims, λ, expected during the next period of observation.

Step 6: Use Equation (5.13) to calculate Z, provided, of course, that $\lambda < \lambda_F$.

Assumption 1: The number of claims, N, has a Poisson distribution.

Assumption 2: The mean and variance of the loss severity, X_i, are constant over all values of i.

Assumption 3: The Central Limit Theorem applies.

5.5 FURTHER REMARKS AND SUMMARY

This chapter has described the limited fluctuation approach to both full and partial credibility, summarized in Sections 5.3.5 and 5.4.4, respectively. The main advantage of the limited fluctuation approach is that it is relatively simple to use.

The main disadvantages of this approach are the following:

(1) The same weight, $1 - Z$, is given to the prior mean, H, regardless of the analyst's view of the accuracy of H.

(2) According to Sundt [1992], there is an internal inconsistency in the limited fluctuation approach to full credibility. He notes that the criterion for replacing the old premium rate is based on the assumption that the old premium rate is correct. This leads to the following conundrum: if the old premium rate is correct, then why replace it? Sundt [1992; page 110] concludes with the observation that "This seems to be the most unclear issue with limited fluctuation credibility."

(3) No weight is given to the prior mean, H, and all the weight is given to the observed data, R, in the case of full credibility. This raises the philosophical question of whether it makes sense to talk about full (i.e., 100%) credibility since more data can generally be obtained. Some actuaries believe that no data are entitled to full credibility, so that the credibility curve should approach 1 asymptotically, without ever reaching it.

(4) Bühlmann, as reported in Hickman and Heacox [1999], "felt that the mathematical reasoning behind the [limited fluctuation approach] as presented by Longley-Cook [1962], was not convincing." Bühlmann noted that

- The reasoning for the limited fluctuation approach was under the frequentist paradigm of statistics and so ignored prior data;

- The approach began by deriving the minimum volume of risks required for full credibility;

- The derivation was performed using a confidence interval;

- The approach used a standard deviation argument to go from full credibility to partial credibility for a smaller volume of risks.

This lead Buhlmann to ask the following penetrating question:

"[W]hy should a confidence interval that, by definition, includes the true value with a probability of less than one, guarantee full credibility?"

Venter [198; pages 409-416] extends the discussion of the limited fluctuation approach by dropping the assumption that the Central Limit Theorem applies. Nevertheless, this extension suffers from the same failings as does the basic approach presented here.

5.6 EXERCISES

5.1 Introduction
5.2 Mathematical Preliminaries

5-1　Let N have a Poisson distribution with mean 8. For $i = 1, 2, \ldots$, let

$$E[X_i] = 5 \text{ and } Var[X_i] = 10. \text{ Let } S = \sum_{i=1}^{N} X_i.$$

Find $E[S]$ and $Var[S]$.

5-2　Let Y be a Poisson random variable whose distribution depends on a parameter (mean), Θ. We assume that Θ, in turn, is also a random variable with mean, $E[\Theta] = 1$, and variance, $Var[\Theta] = 4$. Find the unconditional variance of Y, $Var[Y]$.

5-3   Using the notation of Theorem 5.1, show that

$$E\left[\sum_{j=1}^{N} X_j^2\right] = E[N] \cdot E\left[X_1^2\right].$$

5-4   Using the notation and assumptions of Theorem 5.1, show that

$$E\left[\sum_{j=1}^{N}\sum_{k=1}^{N} X_j X_k\right] = \left(E[X_1]\right)^2 \cdot \left(E[N^2] - E[N]\right).$$
$$\scriptstyle j \neq k$$

5-5   Using the notation, assumptions, and results of Exercises 5-3 and 5-4, show that

$$Var(S) = E[N] \cdot Var(X_1) + Var(N) \cdot \left(E[X_1]\right)^2.$$

Hint:

$$E[S^2] = E\left[\left(\sum_{j=1}^{N} X_j\right)^2\right]$$
$$= E\left[\left(\sum_{j=1}^{N} X_j^2 + \sum_{j=1}^{N}\sum_{k=1}^{N} X_j X_k\right)\right]$$
$$\scriptstyle j \neq k$$

5.3 The Full Credibility Approach

5-6   What is the standard for full credibility of the claim frequency corresponding to a 90% probability level and a 5% range parameter?

5-7   What is the minimum number of expected claims required for the pure premium to be fully credible, assuming

(i)   a 90% probability level,
(ii)   a 5% range parameter,
(iii)   an average claim cost of $500, and
(iv)   a standard deviation of claim cost of $1000?

(Hint: Use the result of Exercise 5-6.)

5-8   If the severity of claims is constant, then the minimum number of expected claims required for full credibility is 2670. What is the minimum number of claims required for full credibility if the claim severity has a lognormal distribution with mean 1000 and variance 1,500,000?

5-9   Let X denote the expected number of claims required for full credibility assuming a probability level of 90% and a range parameter of 5%. Let Y denote the expected number of claims required for full credibility assuming a probability level of 90% and a range parameter of 10%. What is the value of $\frac{X}{Y}$?

5-10 Which of the following statements are true?

I.   The normal distribution may be approximated by the Poisson distribution.

II.   All actuaries believe that there exists a certain number of expected claims that deserves a credibility of 1.

III. The Poisson distribution may be approximated by the normal distribution.

5.4 The Partial Credibility Approach

5-11 Show that 2401 expected automobile accident claims are required for full credibility assuming a 95% probability level and a 4% range parameter. Then, assuming 40,000 car-years of exposure and an average claim frequency of .0441, show that the credibility factor is $Z = .86$.

5-12 The actuary for the XYZ Insurance Company has just developed a new rate for a particular class of insureds. The new rate has a loss cost provision of $125.

(a) Assuming that the old rate had a loss cost provision of $100 and that the loss cost in the experience period was $200, show that the credibility factor is $Z = .25$.

(b) During the experience period there were 10,000 insureds with an average claim frequency of .021. Determine the expected number of claims required for full credibility, assuming zero inflation.

5-13 The Slippery Rock Insurance Company is reviewing its rates. It wants the expected number of claims required for full credibility, λ_F, to be based on a probability level of 90% and a range parameter of 5%. It estimates that individual claim losses are mutually independent and identically distributed according to the probability density function $f(x) = \frac{1}{200,000}$, for $0 < x < 200,000$. Assume that the number of claims follows a Poisson distribution.

(a) Show that the variance of aggregate claims, $Var(S)$, is equal to $\lambda_F (200,000)^2 \left(\frac{1}{3}\right)$.

(b) Assuming that the most recent period of observation contains 1082 claims, show that the credibility factor for that period is $Z = .866$. (Use the normal approximation to the Poisson.)

5-14 Which of the following statements are true?

I. The limited fluctuation approach to credibility requires a separate mechanism for handling partial credibility.

II. The limited fluctuation approach to credibility is related to the concept of confidence intervals.

5.5 Further Remarks and Summary

5-15 Which of the following statements are true?

    I. Under the limited fluctuation approach to credibility, the analyst directly determines the weight given to the prior mean, H.

    II. According to Sundt, the limited fluctuation approach to full credibility suffers from the inconsistency that the criterion for replacing the old premium rate is based on the assumption that the old premium rate is correct.

    III. All actuaries believe that there exists a certain finite number of expected claims that deserves a credibility of 1.

CHAPTER 6

BÜHLMANN'S APPROACH

6.1 INTRODUCTION

In this chapter we describe Bühlmann's credibility approach. The essence of Bühlmann's approach is discussed in Section 6.2, where we present the basic credibility formula, the variance of the hypothetical means, and the expected value of the process variance. In Section 6.3 we discuss the characteristics of the credibility factor, Z. The examples of Section 6.4 supplement those given in Section 6.2. In Section 6.5 we show that the total variance is equal to the sum of (a) the expected value of the process variance and (b) the variance of the hypothetical means. In Section 6.6 we provide an alternative method for calculating $k = \dfrac{expected\ value\ of\ process\ variance}{variance\ of\ hypothetical\ means}$ in practical situations, and in Section 6.7 we describe two equivalent ways to calculate Z. We conclude the chapter in Section 6.8 with some brief remarks about the Bayesian version of the Kalman filter model.

6.2 BASIC ELEMENTS OF BÜHLMANN'S APPROACH

6.2.1 BÜHLMANN'S CREDIBILITY FORMULA

If the actuary has sufficient prior knowledge and substantial technical and computational resources, then he or she should probably construct a predictive distribution for aggregate claims during the next period of observation, given prior aggregate claim amounts. An alternative, frequentist approach that does not explicitly require prior information to calculate the credibility factor Z, and does not require as many resources, has been suggested by Bühlmann [1967]. His approach is to employ a point estimator, C, of the form

$$C = ZR + (1-Z)H, \tag{1.1}$$

as defined in Chapter 1, where R is the mean of the current observations, H is the prior mean, and the credibility factor Z is defined by

$$Z = \frac{n}{n+k}, \tag{6.1}$$

and satisfies $0 \le Z \le 1$. In Equation (6.1), n is the number of independent trials (or exposure units), and

$$k = \frac{expected\ value\ of\ process\ variance}{variance\ of\ hypothetical\ means}, \tag{6.2}$$

where the numerator and denominator of Equation (6.2) are defined in Sections 6.2.5 and 6.2.3, respectively. Henceforth we will refer to credibility estimators satisfying Equations (1.1), (6.1), and (6.2) as **Bühlmann credibility estimators**.

Such estimators are of interest because, among other properties, they are the "best" linear approximations to the Bayesian estimators. More is said about this in Chapter 10 where we also justify the use of Expressions (6.1) and (6.2).

In the material that follows, we use the adjectives **process** and **hypothetical** as synonyms for the term **conditional**.

6.2.2 HYPOTHETICAL MEANS

In general, each **hypothetical mean** refers to the average frequency, average severity, or average aggregate claim amount (i.e., pure premium) of an individual combination of risk characteristics. The hypothetical mean is the conditional expectation, given that particular combination of risk characteristics. For instance, in computing premium rates for individual automobile insurance policies, automobile insurers typically partition their policyholders according to such characteristics as age, gender, and location where the automobile is normally garaged.

As an initial example, we consider the target-shooting example of Philbrick [1981], introduced in abbreviated form in Example 2.1. One of four individual shooters, *W*, *X*, *Y*, and *Z*, is selected at random (i.e., with probability ¼). The selected shooter (whose identity is unknown to us) fires a shot at a target some distance away. Our task is to estimate the location on the target that the shooter will hit with his next shot.

Additional prior information is available. The results of each of the four shooters firing a large number of shots at an identical target have been tabulated. Based on these results, it is assumed that the shots of each shooter are uniformly distributed over four non-overlapping circular targets as shown in Figure 6.1. The positions marked *W*, *X*, *Y*, and *Z*, represent the center (or, equivalently, the mean) of each circular target. The (overall) mean of the four targets is *G*, the center of gravity.

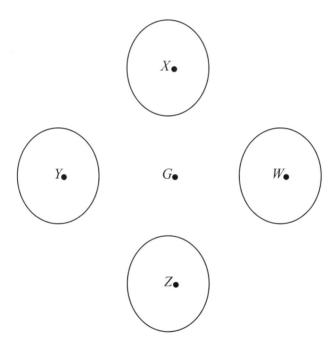

FIGURE 6.1

Each of the four target centers is the hypothetical mean of the corresponding shooter, and the center of gravity, *G*, is the average of the hypothetical means. Prior to the observation of any shots, the "best" estimate of the location of the next shot would be *G*.

After the observation of a single shot at location S on target W, for example, the "best" estimate for the next shot, based on Bühlmann's credibility approach, is on the line segment joining G and S, as shown in Figure 6.2. (It was noted in Example 2.1 that the Bayesian estimate would be point W, the center of target W, since the targets do not overlap.)

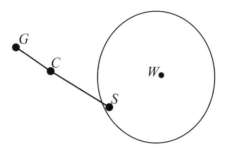

FIGURE 6.2

Some readers may be uncomfortable with the position of the Bühlmann estimate outside the target. This is a result of the trade-off inherent in Bühlmann's approach: a less accurate estimate in exchange for a simpler calculation.

6.2.3 Variance of the Hypothetical Means

The variance of the hypothetical means in the target-shooting example presented in Section 6.2.2 is a function of the distances among the means of the four targets. To be more specific, suppose that (a) each of the four targets has a diameter of one unit, and (b) each of the target centers is a distance of one unit from point G.

If we were to move the targets so that each target center was a distance of two units from G, this would increase the distance among the centers of the targets and therefore increase the variance of the hypothetical means.

On the other hand, if we were to place each target center a distance of one-half unit from G, as shown in Figure 6.3, then the distance among the hypothetical means would decrease, and the variance of the hypothetical means would decrease as well. In Figure 6.3, the targets overlap, so it may be harder to determine the identity of the shooter, having observed a small number of shots. For example, if a single shot is observed at location S, as shown in Figure 6.4, then the shooter may be X or Y. Thus, as the targets move closer together, the variance of the hypothetical means decreases. In the limiting case, if all of the targets are centered at G, then all of the hypothetical means are at G.

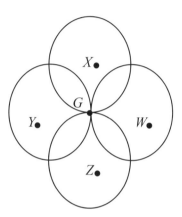

FIGURE 6.3

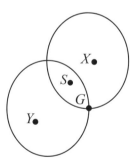

FIGURE 6.4

In this case all of the targets are identical, so the variance of the hypothetical means is zero. Then using Equation (6.2) we find that k is infinite, and, in turn, Equation (6.1) implies that Z is zero. Consequently, all of the information is contained in the prior estimate, H, which in this case is simply G, the center of gravity. Therefore the Bühlmann estimate of the location of the next shot is $C = H = G$, since $Z = 0$ and $1 - Z = 1$.

Next let us compare the situations illustrated by Figures 6.1 and 6.3. In Figure 6.1, after having observed the location of a single shot, you can identify the shooter. This is not necessarily the case in Figure 6.3, as demonstrated by the example shown in Figure 6.4. Hence the variance of the hypothetical means (and hence the credibility factor Z) is larger for Figure 6.1 than for Figure 6.3. This is why more weight should be given to the observed data in the case of Figure 6.1 than in the case of Figure 6.3.

We next consider some simple examples to illustrate the computation of the formulas of Section 6.2.1. We begin with the die example of Section 2.2, in which one of two dice is selected, each with probability $\frac{1}{2}$, and then tossed once. We assume that we have a claim for $1 if a marked face appears; otherwise, there is no claim. There are two combinations (or sets) of risk characteristics, one corresponding to each die. The (hypothetical) mean amount of claims is equal to $\frac{1}{6}$ for the die with one marked face and five unmarked faces, and $\frac{1}{2}$ for the die with three marked and three unmarked faces. Because each die is selected with equal probability of $\frac{1}{2}$, the expected claim amount (i.e., the expected value of the hypothetical means) is

$$\left(\frac{1}{2}\right)\left(\frac{1}{6}\right) + \left(\frac{1}{2}\right)\left(\frac{1}{2}\right) = \frac{1}{3}. \tag{6.3a}$$

and therefore the variance of the hypothetical means is

$$\frac{1}{2}\left(\frac{1}{6} - \frac{1}{3}\right)^2 + \frac{1}{2}\left(\frac{1}{2} - \frac{1}{3}\right)^2 = \frac{1}{36}. \tag{6.4a}$$

In other words, the variance of the hypothetical means is the variance of the conditional expectations over all the various sets of risk characteristics.

To provide more detail on this calculation of the variance of the hypothetical means, we recalculate it using the notation of Example 2.2 and Section 4.1. Using this notation, the hypothetical means can be represented as

$$E_X[X \mid A = a_1] = E[X \mid A_1]$$
$$= 0 \cdot P[X = 0 \mid A_1] + 1 \cdot P[X = 1 \mid A_1]$$
$$= 0 + \frac{1}{6} = \frac{1}{6}$$

and

$$E_X[X \mid A = a_2] = E[X \mid A_2]$$
$$= 0 \cdot P[X = 0 \mid A_2] + 1 \cdot P[X = 1 \mid A_2]$$
$$= 0 + \frac{1}{2} = \frac{1}{2}.$$

Since each die is selected with equal probability, then

$$E[X] = E_X[X] = E_A[E_X[X \mid A]]$$
$$= \sum_{i=1}^{2} P[A_i] \cdot E_X[X \mid A_i]$$
$$= P[A_1] \cdot E_X[X \mid A_1] + P[A_2] \cdot E_X[X \mid A_2]$$
$$= \left(\frac{1}{2}\right)\left(\frac{1}{6}\right) + \left(\frac{1}{2}\right)\left(\frac{1}{2}\right) = \frac{1}{3}. \qquad (6.3b)$$

Thus we see that $E_X[X]$ represents the expected value of the hypothetical means, previously calculated by Equation (6.3a).

We next compute $Var_A(E_X[X \mid A])$, the variance of the hypothetical means, as

$$Var_A(E_X[X \mid A]) = \sum_{i=1}^{2} P[A_i] \cdot \{E_X[X \mid A_i] - E_X[X]\}^2$$
$$= P[A_1] \cdot \left\{E_X[X \mid A_1] - \frac{1}{3}\right\}^2 + P[A_2] \cdot \left\{E_X[X \mid A_2] - \frac{1}{3}\right\}^2$$
$$= \frac{1}{2}\left(\frac{1}{6} - \frac{1}{3}\right)^2 + \frac{1}{2}\left(\frac{1}{2} - \frac{1}{3}\right)^2 = \frac{1}{36}, \qquad (6.4b)$$

as previously calculated by Equation (6.4a).

In the die-spinner example of Chapter 4, the hypothetical means are the pure premium estimates for each of the four die-spinner combinations (or combinations of risk characteristics), given in column (4) of Table 4.2. The variance of the hypothetical means is the weighted sum of the squared differences between each of the four pure premium estimates and the prior mean, $E[X_1] = 2$. (Note that the prior mean is the expected value of the hypothetical means.) Each weight is equal to $\frac{1}{4}$, so the variance of the hypothetical means is

$$\frac{1}{4}\left[\left(\frac{2}{3}-2\right)^2 + \left(\frac{4}{3}-2\right)^2 + (2-2)^2 + (4-2)^2\right] = \frac{14}{9}. \qquad (6.5)$$

6.2.4 PROCESS VARIANCE

In general, each **process variance** refers to the variance of the frequency, severity, or aggregate claim amount of an individual combination of risk characteristics. The term "process" refers to the process generating the number of claims and/or the amount of the claims. Therefore the process variance is the conditional variance, given the combination of risk characteristics.

For an initial example, we return to the target-shooting example discussed in Sections 6.2.2 and 6.2.3, and begin by considering Figure 6.1. The process variance of shooter W refers simply to the variation in the location of W's shots around target W. Similar remarks apply to the process variance of each of the other three shooters.

6.2.5 EXPECTED VALUE OF THE PROCESS VARIANCE

The expected value of the process variance for the target-shooting example is simply the arithmetic mean (since each shooter has equal probability of being selected) of the four individual process variances.

Now suppose all four shooters take lessons at the local police academy and become much better shooters, in the sense that their shots are all restricted to the smaller targets shown in Figure 6.5. Since each shooter's shots cluster more closely around their respective target centers (or means), there is now a lot less process variation. Therefore each process variance is smaller, and so is the (overall) expected process variance. In fact, for the situation of Figure 6.5, it is much easier to identify the shooter after observing a single shot than in the case of Figure 6.3. Since the expected process variance is smaller in Figure 6.5 than in Figure 6.3, then Equation (6.2) shows that k decreases from Figure 6.3 to Figure 6.5, and Equation (6.1) shows that the credibility factor, Z, increases from Figure 6.3 to Figure 6.5. Hence, because of the decrease in the process variance, the observed data, R, are given more weight in Figure 6.5 than in Figure 6.3.

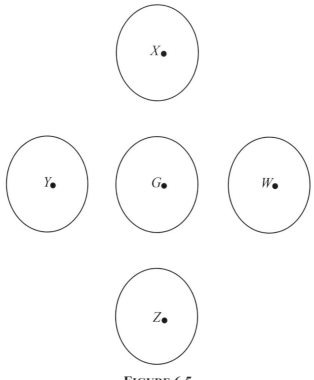

FIGURE 6.5

Next we again consider the die-spinner example of Chapter 4. We recall that for each die the number of claims has a binomial distribution. Then for a single toss of the die with one marked face the process (i.e., conditional) variance is

$$npq = (1)\left(\frac{1}{6}\right)\left(\frac{5}{6}\right) = \frac{5}{36}$$

For a single toss of the die with three marked faces, the process variance is

$$npq = (1)\left(\frac{1}{2}\right)\left(\frac{1}{2}\right) = \frac{1}{4}.$$

Since each die is selected with probability $\frac{1}{2}$, the expected value of the process variance is

$$\left(\frac{1}{2}\right)\left(\frac{5}{36}\right)+\left(\frac{1}{2}\right)\left(\frac{1}{4}\right) = \frac{7}{36}. \tag{6.6a}$$

Using the more formal notation of Section 6.2.3, we can calculate the expected value of the process variance, denoted by $E_A\left[Var_X(X\,|\,A)\right]$, as

$$\begin{aligned}
E_A\left[Var_X(X\,|\,A)\right] &= \sum_{i=1}^{2}P[A_i]\cdot Var_X(X\,|\,A_i) \\
&= P[A_1]\cdot Var_X(X\,|\,A_1)+P[A_2]\cdot Var_X(X\,|\,A_2) \\
&= \left(\frac{1}{2}\right)\left(\frac{5}{36}\right)+\left(\frac{1}{2}\right)\left(\frac{1}{4}\right) = \frac{7}{36}.
\end{aligned} \tag{6.6b}$$

The calculations required to compute the process variance for each die-spinner combination in the die-spinner example are summarized in Table 6.1, and described in the following discussion.

The mean frequencies of column (3) come directly from column (2) of Table 4.2. Since the variance of a single trial of a Bernoulli random variable is pq, the variances of column (4) are easily calculated as

$$Var(I_1\,|\,A_1) = \left(\frac{1}{6}\right)\left(\frac{5}{6}\right) = \frac{5}{36} \tag{6.7a}$$

and

$$Var(I_1\,|\,A_2) = \left(\frac{3}{6}\right)\left(\frac{3}{6}\right) = \frac{1}{4}. \tag{6.7b}$$

The variances of the severity, $Var(S_1\,|\,B_j)$ for $j=1,2$, which constitute column (5), are calculated as

$$Var(S_1 \mid B_j) = \left(2 - E[S_1 \mid B_j]\right)^2 \cdot P[S_1 = 2 \mid B_j]$$
$$+\left(14 - E[S_1 \mid B_j]\right)^2 \cdot P[S_1 = 14 \mid B_j].$$

Then for $j = 1$ we have

$$Var(S_1 \mid B_1) = (2-4)^2 \left(\frac{5}{6}\right) + (14-4)^2 \left(\frac{1}{6}\right) = 20, \qquad (6.8a)$$

and for $j = 2$ we have

$$Var(S_1 \mid B_2) = (2-8)^2 \left(\frac{3}{6}\right) + (14-8)^2 \left(\frac{3}{6}\right) = 36, \qquad (6.8b)$$

where the mean severities, $E[S_1 \mid B_j]$, used to calculate the variances shown in column (5) as well as the entries of column (6), are taken from column (3) of Table 4.2.

Finally, using Equation (5.3b) given by Theorem 5.3, we calculate the process variances shown in column (7) as

$$E[I_1 \mid A_i] \cdot Var(S_1 \mid B_j) + Var(I_1 \mid A_i) \cdot \left(E[S_1 \mid B_j]\right)^2.$$

TABLE 6.1

Process Variance of the Die-Spinner Example						
		Frequency		Severity		
(1)	(2)	(3)	(4)	(5)	(6)	(7)
Type of Die and Spinner	Die-Spinner Probability $P[A_iB_j]$	Mean $E[I_1 \mid A_i]$	Variance $Var(I_1 \mid A_i)$	Variance $Var(S_1 \mid B_j)$	Mean Squared $\left(E[S_1 \mid B_j]\right)^2$	(3)(5)+(4)(6) Process Variance
A_1B_1	$\frac{1}{4}$	$\frac{1}{6}$	$\frac{5}{36}$	20	16	$\frac{50}{9}$
A_1B_2	$\frac{1}{4}$	$\frac{1}{6}$	$\frac{5}{36}$	36	64	$\frac{134}{9}$
A_2B_1	$\frac{1}{4}$	$\frac{1}{2}$	$\frac{1}{4}$	20	16	14
A_2B_2	$\frac{1}{4}$	$\frac{1}{2}$	$\frac{1}{4}$	36	64	34

The expected value of the process variance is obtained by multiplying the process variance of each die-spinner combination, given in column (7), by the corresponding die-spinner probability, given in column (2), and summing the results. Thus we find the expected value of the process variance to be

$$\frac{1}{4}\left(\frac{50}{9} + \frac{134}{9} + 14 + 34\right) = \frac{154}{9}. \tag{6.9}$$

6.2.6 Credibility Estimates

Substituting the results given by Equations (6.5) and (6.9) into Equation (6.2), we find, for the die-spinner example,

$$k = \frac{\frac{154}{9}}{\frac{14}{9}} = 11.$$

For one observation $(n = 1)$, the credibility factor is given by Equation (6.1) as

$$Z = \frac{n}{n+k} = \frac{1}{1+11} = \frac{1}{12}.$$

Finally, using Equation (1.1) with $Z = \frac{1}{12}$ and $H = E[X_1] = 2$, we can compute the Bühlmann estimate, C, given the result, R, of the first trial. For $R = 14$, for example, we have

$$C = ZR + (1-Z)H = \left(\frac{1}{12}\right)(14) + \left(\frac{11}{12}\right)(2) = 3.$$

All three of the Bühlmann estimates, corresponding to each of the three possible outcomes of the first trial, are given in the following table.

TABLE 6.2

Bühlmann Credibility Estimates	
Outcome R,	Bühlmann Estimate, C
0	11/6
2	2
14	3

The Bühlmann credibility estimates of Table 6.2 are shown in the following figure. Note that all three points lie on a straight line, demonstrating that the Bühlmann credibility estimator is indeed a linear estimator.

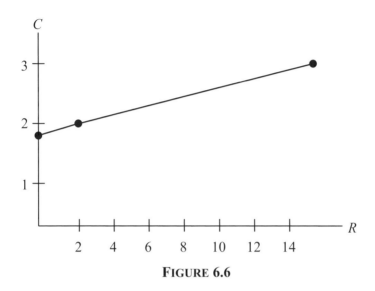

FIGURE 6.6

EXAMPLE 6.1

The number of claims, N_i, during the ith policy year $i = 1, 2$ for an individual insured has a Poisson distribution with parameter Θ. The prior distribution of Θ is the uniform distribution over the interval $(0,1)$. An individual insured has exactly one claim during the first policy year. Use Bühlmann's model to estimate the insured's expected number of claims during the second policy year.

SOLUTION

Note first that the prior density function of Θ is $f(\theta) = 1$, for $0 < \theta < 1$, and $f(\theta) = 0$ elsewhere. The first two moments of Θ are

$$E[\Theta] = \int_0^1 \theta \cdot f(\theta)\, d\theta = \frac{\theta^2}{2}\bigg|_0^1 = \frac{1}{2}$$

and

$$E[\Theta^2] = \int_0^1 \theta^2 \cdot f(\theta) \, d\theta = \left. \frac{\theta^3}{3} \right|_0^1 = \frac{1}{3}.$$

Since the number of claims, N, has a Poisson distribution, the expected value of the process variance is

$$E_\Theta \left[Var_N (N \mid \Theta) \right] = E_\Theta[\Theta] = \frac{1}{2}.$$

The variance of the hypothetical means is

$$Var_\Theta \left(E_N[N \mid \Theta] \right) = Var_\Theta(\Theta) = E[\Theta^2] - \left(E[\Theta] \right)^2 = \frac{1}{12}.$$

Then

$$k = \frac{expected \ value \ of \ the \ process \ variance}{variance \ of \ the \ hypothetical \ means} = \frac{\frac{1}{2}}{\frac{1}{12}} = 6.$$

The number of observations is $n = 1$, so, by Equation (6.1), we have

$$Z = \frac{n}{n+k} = \frac{1}{1+6} = \frac{1}{7}.$$

Finally, since $R = 1$ and $H = E_N[N] = E_\Theta \left[E_N[N \mid \Theta] \right] = E_\Theta[\Theta] = \frac{1}{2}$, we have by Equation (1.1) that the Bühlmann estimate of the expected number of claims during the second policy year is

$$C = ZR + (1-Z)H = \left(\frac{1}{7} \right)(1) + \left(\frac{6}{7} \right)(.50) = .571. \qquad \square$$

6.2.7 SUMMARY OF THE BÜHLMANN APPROACH

Goal: To determine the compromise estimate, C.

Step1: Determine n, the number of periods of observation.

Step2: Compute the variance of the hypothetical means.

Step3: Compute the expected process variance.

Step4: Calculate $k = \dfrac{expected\ process\ variance}{variance\ of\ the\ hypothetical\ means}$.

Step5: Compute the credibility factor, $Z = \dfrac{n}{n+k}$.

Step6: Compute the compromise estimate, $C = ZR + (1-Z)H$.

6.3 CHARACTERISTICS OF THE CREDIBILITY FACTOR

We note the following important characteristics of the Bühlmann credibility factor $Z = \frac{n}{n+k}$.

(1) Z is an increasing function of n. In the limiting case as n approaches infinity, Z approaches one.

(2) Since Z is a decreasing function of k, Z is also a decreasing function of the expected value of the process variance, with a lower limit of zero. Thus, the larger the variation associated with the individual combinations of risk characteristics, the less weight given to the current observations, R, and the more weight given to the prior mean, H.

(3) Finally, Z is an increasing function of the variance of the hypothetical means, with upper limit one. Thus, Z increases with the variation in the expected values of the various combinations of risk characteristics.

6.4 FURTHER EXAMPLES OF BÜHLMANN ESTIMATES

The starting point for the calculation of k is the individual combination of risk characteristics. For each combination of risk characteristics, appropriate expected values (i.e., means) and variances can be calculated. The variance, over the entire population of risk characteristics, of these expected values is called the variance of the hypothetical means. The expected value, over the population, of the individual variances is called the expected value of the process variance. Thus, if the distributions of the individual means and variances are known, k can be calculated directly from the moments of these distributions. This was illustrated in Section 6.2 for the die-spinner example. Two additional examples are presented in this section.

EXAMPLE 6.2

For a group of individual risks, the distribution of the aggregate claim amount for each risk, X, has a mean of M and a variance of V. Further it is known that (a) M, in turn, is selected at random from a distribution with mean $\frac{r}{a}$ and variance $\frac{r}{a^2}$ and (b) V is chosen at random from a distribution with mean $\frac{q}{b}$ and variance $\frac{q}{b^2}$. Find the pure premium for each risk and the value of k.

SOLUTION
The pure premium for each risk is

$$E_X[X] = E_M\left[E_X[X\,|\,M]\right] = E_M[M] = \frac{r}{a},$$

the expected value over all of the conditional means, $E_X[X\,|\,M]$. The variance of the conditional means is

$$Var_M\left(E_X[X\,|\,M]\right) = Var_M(M) = \frac{r}{a^2}.$$

The expected value of the individual conditional variances is

$$E_V\left[Var_X(X\,|\,V)\right] = E_V[V] = \frac{q}{b}.$$

Then we have

$$k = \frac{expected\ value\ of\ the\ conditional\ variances}{variance\ of\ the\ conditional\ means}$$

$$= \frac{\frac{q}{b}}{\frac{r}{a^2}} = \frac{qa^2}{br}. \qquad \qquad \square$$

EXAMPLE 6.3

Suppose each individual risk has a Poisson distribution, $P(\Lambda)$, where the parameter Λ is uniformly distributed over the interval $(.07, .13)$. The severity component is assumed to follow the discrete distribution B_1 40% of the time and the discrete distribution B_2 60% of the time, where the discrete distributions B_1 and B_2 are defined as follows:

Severity	Severity Probabilities	
	B_1	B_2
2	5/6	1/2
14	1/6	1/2

Assume that the frequency of loss and the severity of loss are independent, given the ordered pair (Λ, B_i). Calculate k and Z for aggregate claims over three periods of observation.

SOLUTION

The risk characteristics are denoted by the ordered pair (Λ, B_i) where $.07 < \Lambda < .13$ and $i = 1, 2$. (The reader will recognize B_1 and B_2 as the spinner severity distributions of Example 2.3.) Table 6.3, similar to Table 6.1, summarizes the data for this example. As in the discussion of the die-spinner example of Section 6.2.5, we use Equation (5.3b) of Theorem 5.3 to calculate the process variance.

TABLE 6.3

Development of the Process Variance					
Risk Characteristics	Frequency		Severity		Process Variance
	Mean	Variance	Variance	Mean Squared	
(Λ, B_1)	Λ	Λ	20	16	36Λ
(Λ, B_2)	Λ	Λ	36	64	100Λ

Since Λ is uniformly distributed with p.d.f.

$$f(\lambda) = \begin{cases} \frac{1}{.06} & .07 < \lambda < .13 \\ 0 & \text{otherwise} \end{cases}.$$

then

$$E[\Lambda] = \int_{.07}^{.13} \frac{\lambda}{.06} d\lambda = \frac{\lambda^2}{(2)(.06)} \Big|_{.07}^{.13} = .10,$$

and

$$E[\Lambda^2] = \int_{.07}^{.13} \frac{\lambda^2}{.06}\, d\lambda = \frac{\lambda^3}{(3)(.06)}\Big|_{.07}^{.13} = .0103.$$

Now we can calculate the expected value of the process variance as

$$(.40)\cdot E[36\Lambda]+(.60)E[100\Lambda]$$
$$= (.40)(36)\cdot E[\Lambda]+(.60)(100)\cdot E[\Lambda]$$
$$= (74.4)\cdot E[\Lambda] = (74.4)(.10) = 7.44$$

For the ordered pair of risk characteristics (Λ, B_1) the hypothetical (conditional) mean is 4Λ (since $E[S_1\,|\,B_1]=4$), and for (Λ, B_2) it is 8Λ. Then the expected value of the hypothetical means is

$$(.40)\cdot E[4\Lambda]+(.60)\cdot E[8\Lambda] = (6.4)\cdot E[\Lambda] = (6.4)(.10) = .64.$$

The second moments of the hypothetical means are $E[16\Lambda^2]$ and $E[64\Lambda^2]$ for (Λ, B_1) and (Λ, B_2), respectively, so the expected value of the second moments of the hypothetical means is

$$(.40)\cdot E[16\Lambda^2]+(.60)\cdot E[64\Lambda^2] = (44.8)\cdot E[\Lambda^2]$$
$$= (44.8)(.0103) = .46144.$$

Then the variance of the hypothetical means is

$$.46144-(.64)^2 = .05184,$$

leading to

$$k = \frac{expected\ process\ variance}{variance\ of\ the\ hypothetical\ means} = \frac{7.44}{.05184} = 143.52.$$

Finally, for three periods of observation we have

$$Z = \frac{n}{n+k} = \frac{3}{3+143.52} = .02. \qquad \square$$

6.5 COMPONENTS OF THE TOTAL VARIANCE

In Theorem 5.2 we developed the important equation

$$Var(Y) = E_X\left[Var_Y(Y \mid X)\right] + Var_X\left(E_Y[Y \mid X]\right). \qquad (6.10)$$

In words, Equation (6.10) is saying that

$$\text{Total Variance} = \begin{array}{c}\textit{Expected Value of}\\ \textit{the Process Variance}\end{array} + \begin{array}{c}\textit{Variance of the}\\ \textit{Hypothetical Means}\end{array}.$$

EXAMPLE 6.4

For $i = 1, 2, ..., k$, let the random variable N_i have a Poisson distribution with mean Λ_i, where, in turn, Λ_i has mean μ and variance σ^2.

(a) Calculate the process variance of N_i, given Λ_i, for $i = 1, 2, ..., k$.

(b) Calculate the unconditional variance of N_i, for $i = 1, 2, ..., k$.

SOLUTION

(a) Because N_i has a Poisson distribution given Λ_i, the conditional variance of N_i given Λ_i is equal to the conditional expected value of N_i given Λ_i. In mathematical notation,

$$Var_{N_i}(N_i \mid \Lambda_i) = E_{N_i}\left[N_i \mid \Lambda_i\right] = \Lambda_i,$$

for $i = 1, 2, ..., k$. (This result is used in Section 6.6.)

(b) By Equation (6.10) with Y replaced by N_i and X replaced by Λ_i we have

$$\begin{aligned} Var(N_i) &= E_{\Lambda_i}\left[Var(N_i \mid \Lambda_i)\right] + Var_{\Lambda_i}\left(E_{N_i}[N_i \mid \Lambda_i]\right)\\ &= E_{\Lambda_i}[\Lambda_i] + Var_{\Lambda_i}(\Lambda_i)\\ &= \mu + \sigma^2. \qquad \square \end{aligned}$$

6.6 PRACTICAL APPLICATIONS OF BÜHLMANN'S MODEL

In the examples presented in Sections 6.1-6.5, all of the required probability distributions are assumed to be completely known. In this section, we take the opposite perspective. We assume, as many analysts do in practical situations, that we know nothing about such probability distributions. These analysts feel more comfortable in relying exclusively on the data, rather than making subjective judgments about the prior mean and other parameter values. These analysts estimate the parameters of interest using the available data. Such procedures are often called **empirical Bayesian procedures**, a term coined in the 1960s by Professor Herbert Robbins, then of Columbia University. An early application of empirical Bayesian procedures to insurance problems are found in Morris and van Slyke [1979]. This application is the subject of Chapter 15 in our book.

Before describing the general approach, we present the following definitions which are required in the discussion that follows.

Definition 6.1

For $n \geq 2$, the random variables $X_1, X_2, ..., X_n$ are said to be **mutually independent** if, for any n-tuple of real numbers $(x_1, x_2, ..., x_n)$, we have

$$P\big[(X_1 \leq x_1) \cap (X_2 \leq x_2) \cap \cdots \cap (X_n \leq x_n)\big]$$
$$= P[X_1 \leq x_1] \cdot P[X_2 \leq X_2] \cdot \cdots \cdot P[X_n \leq x_n].$$

Definition 6.2

For $n \geq 2$, the random variables $X_1, X_2, ..., X_n$ are said to be **conditionally independent given the parameter** Θ if, for any n-tuple of real numbers $(x_1, x_2, ..., x_n)$, we have

$$P\big[(X_1 \geq x_1) \cap (X_2 \leq x_2) \cap \cdots \cap (X_n \leq x_n) \mid \Theta\big]$$
$$= P[X_1 \leq x_1 \mid \Theta] \cdot P[X_2 \leq x_2 \mid \Theta] \cdot \cdots \cdot P[X_n \leq x_n \mid \Theta].$$

6.6.1 GENERAL APPROACH

The following general approach might be adopted as an empirical Bayesian procedure. Given n policy years of experience data on r group policyholders[1], $n \geq 2$ and $r \geq 2$, let X_{ij} denote the random variable representing the aggregate loss amount of the ith policyholder during the jth policy year for $i = 1, 2, ..., r$ and $j = 1, 2, ..., n+1$. The goal is to estimate $E[X_{i,n+1} \mid X_{i,1} = x_{i,1}, X_{i,2} = x_{i,2}, ..., X_{i,n} = X_{i,n}]$, the conditional expectation for policyholder i, given the realizations of the random variables $X_{i,1} = x_{i,1}$, $X_{i,2} = x_{i,2}, ..., X_{i,n} = X_{i,n}$ for the n prior policy years.

Let $\mathbf{X_i} = (X_{i,1}, X_{i,2}, ..., X_{i,n})$ denote the random vector of aggregate claim amounts for the ith policyholder. We make the following assumptions:

(1) The random vectors $\mathbf{X_1}, \mathbf{X_2}, ..., \mathbf{X_r}$ are assumed to be mutually independent. In other words, the experience of one policyholder should not influence that of another distinct policyholder.

(2) For $i = 1, 2, ..., r$, the distribution of each element of $\mathbf{X_i}$ depends on an (unknown) risk parameter θ_i, where θ_i is a realization of the random variable Θ_i.

(3) The random variables $\Theta_1, \Theta_2, ..., \Theta_r$ are mutually independent and identically distributed.

(4) Given i and Θ_i, the random variables $X_{i,1}, X_{i,2}, ..., X_{i,n}$ are mutually conditionally independent.

(5) Each combination of policy year and policyholder has an equal number of underlying exposure units.

---

[1] Group insurance is insurance that covers a group of people, usually (1) employees of a company, (2) members of a union, association, or society, or (3) professionals in a common group. For a company, the size of its group health insurance policy would typically be the number of its employees who are covered under the policy. The employer would be the (group) policyholder.

For $i = 1, 2, ..., r$ and $j = 1, 2, ..., n$, we define

$$\mu(\Theta_i) = E[X_{ij} \mid \Theta_i]$$

and

$$v(\Theta_i) = Var(X_{ij} \mid \Theta_i).$$

Then we let

$$\mu = E[\mu(\Theta_i)]$$

denote the overall hypothetical mean,

$$v = E[v(\Theta_i)]$$

denote the expected process variance, and

$$a = Var(\mu(\Theta_i))$$

denote the variance of the hypothetical means. We employ the following estimators for $\mu, v,$ and a, respectively:

$$\hat{\mu} = \bar{x}.. = \frac{1}{r}\sum_{i=1}^{r}\bar{x}_i. = \frac{1}{rn}\sum_{i=1}^{r}\sum_{j=1}^{n}x_{ij}, \qquad (6.11)$$

where $\bar{x}_i. = \frac{1}{n}\sum_{j=1}^{n}x_{ij}$,

$$\hat{v} = \frac{1}{r}\sum_{i=1}^{r}\hat{v}_i = \frac{1}{r(n-1)}\sum_{i=1}^{r}\sum_{j=1}^{n}(x_{ij}-\bar{x}_i.)^2, \qquad (6.12)$$

where $\hat{v}_i = \frac{1}{n-1}\sum_{j=1}^{n}(x_{ij}-\bar{x}_i.)^2$, and

$$\hat{a} = \frac{1}{r-1}\sum_{i=1}^{r}(\bar{x}_i.-\bar{x}..)^2 - \frac{\hat{v}}{n}$$

$$= \frac{1}{r-1}\sum_{i=1}^{r}(\bar{x}_i.-\bar{x}..)^2 - \frac{1}{rn(n-1)}\sum_{i=1}^{r}\sum_{j=1}^{n}(x_{ij}-\bar{x}_i.)^2. \qquad (6.13)$$

It turns out that $\hat{\mu}, \hat{v}$, and $\hat{a}$ are unbiased estimators of μ, v, and a, respectively.[2] The estimators of k and Z are then $\hat{k} = \frac{\hat{v}}{\hat{a}}$ and $\hat{Z} = \frac{n}{n + \hat{k}}$, where neither $\hat{k}$ nor $\hat{Z}$ is an unbiased estimator. Moreover, $\hat{v}$ and $\hat{a}$ are not the only possible estimators of v and a, respectively. Finally, the Bühlmann estimate of $E\left[X_{i,n+1} \mid X_{i,1} = x_{i,1}, X_{i,2} = x_{i,2}, ..., X_{i,n} = x_{i,n}\right]$ is

$$\hat{C}_i = \hat{Z}\bar{x}_i. + (1-\hat{Z})\hat{\mu}, \qquad (6.14)$$

for $i = 1, 2, ..., r$. It is possible, as shown in Exercise 6-19, that $\hat{a}$ can be negative, an undesirable result since variances must, of course, be nonnegative. The above procedure is illustrated in the following example.

EXAMPLE 6.5

An insurance company has two group workers' compensation policies. The aggregate claim amounts in millions of dollars for the first three policy years are summarized in the table below. Use Bühlmann's model to estimate the aggregate claim amount during the fourth policy year for each of the two group policies. Do not make any assumptions about the probability distribution of aggregate claim amounts. Assume no inflation and an equal number of exposure units for each of the six combinations of group policy and policy year.

Aggregate Claim Amounts		
Group Policy	Policy Year	
	1	2	3
1	5	8	11
2	11	13	12

SOLUTION

Since there are two group policies and three years of experience data for each, we have $r = 2$ and $n = 3$. The observed claim vectors are $\mathbf{x_1} = (x_{11}, x_{12}, x_{13}) = (5, 8, 11)$ and $\mathbf{x_2} = (x_{21}, x_{22}, x_{23}) = (11, 13, 12)$ respectively, for the two policies. Since

---

[2] We use $\hat{\mu}, \hat{v}$ and $\hat{a}$ to denote both the estimators and their realizations. We hope the reader can distinguish between the two from the context.

$$\bar{x}_1. = \frac{1}{n}\sum_{j=1}^{n}x_{1j} = \frac{5+8+11}{3} = 8$$

and

$$\bar{x}_2. = \frac{1}{n}\sum_{j=1}^{n}x_{2j} = \frac{11+13+12}{3} = 12,$$

then the estimate of the overall prior mean, $\hat{\mu}$, is

$$\hat{\mu} = \bar{x}.. = \frac{1}{r}\sum_{i=1}^{r}\bar{x}_i. = \frac{8+12}{2} = 10.$$

Furthermore, since

$$\hat{v}_1 = \frac{1}{n-1}\sum_{j=1}^{n}(x_{1j}-\bar{x}_1.)^2 = \frac{1}{2}\left[(5-8)^2+(8-8)^2+(11-8)^2\right] = 9$$

and

$$\hat{v}_2 = \frac{1}{n-1}\sum_{i=1}^{n}(x_{2j}-\bar{x}_2.)^2$$

$$= \frac{1}{2}\left[(11-12)^2+(13-12)^2+(12-12)^2\right] = 1,$$

then the estimate of the expected process variance is

$$\hat{v} = \frac{1}{r}\sum_{i=1}^{r}\hat{v}_i = \frac{1}{2}(9+1) = 5.$$

The estimate of the variance of the hypothetical means is

$$\hat{a} = \frac{1}{r-1}\sum_{i=1}^{r}(\bar{x}_i.-\bar{x}..)^2 - \frac{\hat{v}}{n}$$

$$= \frac{1}{1}\left[(8-10)^2+(12-10)^2\right] - \frac{5}{3} = \frac{19}{3}.$$

Then we have

$$\hat{k} = \frac{\hat{v}}{\hat{a}} = \frac{5}{\frac{19}{3}} = .78947.$$

Next, the estimated credibility factor for each group policy is

$$\hat{Z} = \frac{n}{n+\hat{k}} = \frac{3}{3+.78947} = .79167.$$

Finally, the estimated aggregate claim amounts for the two group policies are

$$\hat{Z}\bar{x}_1. + (1-\hat{Z})\hat{\mu} = (.79167)(8)+(.20833)(10) = 8.41666$$

and

$$\hat{Z}\bar{x}_2. + (1-\hat{Z})\hat{\mu} = (.79167)(12)+(.20833)(10) = 11.58334,$$

respectively. ❑

6.6.2 SUMMARY OF THE GENERAL APPROACH

Goal: To determine the compromise estimate of the aggregate claim amount for each of the r policyholders.

Step 1: Determine the number of policyholders, $r \geq 2$.

Step 2: Determine the number of policy years of experience, $n \geq 2$.

Step 3: Compute the aggregate claim amount, x_{ij}, for each policyholder during each policy year.

Step 4: Compute the average claim amount, $\bar{x}_i.$, over all policy years for each policyholder.

Step 5: Compute the estimated overall mean, $\hat{\mu}$.

Step 6: Compute the estimated expected process variance, $\hat{v}$,

Step 7:   Compute the estimated variance of the hypothetical means, $\hat{a}$.

Step 8:   Calculate $\hat{k} = \frac{\hat{v}}{\hat{a}}$.

Step 9:   Compute the credibility factor, $\hat{Z} = \frac{n}{n+\hat{k}}$.

Step 10:   Compute the Bühlmann compromise estimate, $\hat{C}_i$, of the aggregate claim amount for each policyholder.

6.6.3 USING WIDELY-AVAILABLE SOFTWARE TO COMPUTE BÜHLMANN ESTIMATES

Bühlmann estimates can be computed using widely-available statistical software, such as R, SAS or SPSS, together with a few additional elementary arithmetic operations. In this section we describe how such work can be carried out.

When we perform one-factor analysis of variance, we customarily obtain the following two sums of squares:

(1) The within-sample sum of squares

$$\sum_{j=1}^{n}\sum_{i=1}^{r}(X_{ij} - \overline{X}_i.)^2 \tag{6.15}$$

(2) The between-samples sum of squares

$$n\sum_{i=1}^{r}(\overline{X}_i. - \overline{X}..)^2 \tag{6.16}$$

We recall that the estimator $\hat{v}$, employed in the Bühlmann model of Section 6.6.1 is

$$\hat{v} = \frac{1}{r}\sum_{j=1}^{n}\sum_{i=1}^{r}\frac{(X_{ij} - \overline{X}_i.)^2}{n-1}. \tag{6.17}$$

This is just Expression (6.15) multiplied by $\frac{1}{r(n-1)}$ Moreover, the estimator $\hat{a}$, which is also employed in the model of Section 6.6.1, is

$$\hat{a} = \sum_{i=1}^{r} \frac{(\overline{X}_i. - \overline{X}..)^2}{r-1} - \frac{\hat{v}}{n}. \tag{6.18}$$

The first term of Expression (6.18) is just Expression (6.16) multiplied by $\frac{1}{n(r-1)}$. Thus if we have readily-available analysis-of-variance software, it is a simple matter to apply the appropriate factor to the output of such software to produce the estimates needed for the model of Section 6.6.1.

6.6.4 AD HOC METHODS

In certain instances, the functional relationship among the three parameters μ, v, and a, facilitates their estimation. For example, if the number of claims, N, has a Poisson distribution with mean $\mu(\Theta)$, then the overall hypothetical mean, μ, is equal to the expected value of the process variance, v. This result is established as

$$\mu = E\big[\mu(\Theta)\big] = E_\Theta\big[E[N\,|\,\Theta]\big] = E_\Theta\big[Var(N\,|\,\Theta)\big] = E_\Theta\big[v(\Theta)\big] = v.$$

In this situation it is sufficient to estimate only two parameters, say, μ and a, since $\mu = v$. As shown in Example 6.6, this allows us to calculate Bühlmann estimates even though we have only one group policyholder.

Before presenting this example involving the Poisson distribution, we first describe the following alternate procedure for calculating k in practical applications.

(1) A separate sample variance is calculated from the available data on each combination of risk characteristics. The average of these sample variances is then calculated and used as the estimate of the expected value of the process variance.

(2) The available data on each individual risk are then used to calculate the total sample variance, which is used as the estimate of the total variance.

(3) Since Theorem 5.2 established that

$$\frac{Total}{Variance} = \frac{Expected\ Value\ of}{the\ Process\ Variance} + \frac{Variance\ of\ the}{Hypothetical\ Means},$$

then the variance of the hypothetical means can be obtained by subtracting the result of (1) from that of (2).

(4) Then k is found by dividing the result of (1) by that of (3).

Although this is a direct method of calculating k, it is not necessarily optimal. In fact, the estimated variance of the hypothetical means produced by this method may be negative. Moreover, the estimator of the variance of the hypothetical means in step (3) above is not an unbiased estimator. Several refinements of this procedure have been developed for its practical application.

The following example makes use of this ad hoc procedure for calculating k, as well as the result that $\mu = v$ for the Poisson distribution.

EXAMPLE 6.6

The number of losses arising from 300 individual insureds over a single period of observation is distributed as follows:

Number of Losses:	0	1	2	3	4	5
Number of Insureds:	123	97	49	21	8	2

Each loss has a severity of one unit. The number of losses for each insured follows a Poisson distribution, but the mean of each such distribution may be different for individual insureds. Show how to estimate k.

SOLUTION
We first estimate the average expected loss as

$$\frac{(1)(97)+(2)(49)+(3)(21)+(4)(8)+(5)(2)}{300} = 1.0.$$

This is the (estimated) expected value of the 300 individual risk means. Under the Poisson distribution, the individual risk variances are equal to their means, so

$$\begin{aligned} \text{\textit{Estimated Expected Value}} &= \text{\textit{Estimated Expected Value}} \\ \text{\textit{of the Process Variance}} &\quad \text{\textit{of Individual Risk Variances}} \\ &= \text{\textit{Estimated Expected Value}} \\ &\quad \text{\textit{of Individual Means}} \\ &= 1.0. \end{aligned}$$

The (estimated) expected value of the squares of the losses is

$$\frac{(1)^2(97)+(2)^2(49)+(3)^2(21)+(4)^2(8)+(5)^2(2)}{300} = 2.2.$$

The total variance of the losses is estimated to be $2.2-(1.0)^2 =1.2$. Then by Equation (6.10) the variance of the hypothetical means can be estimated as

$$\begin{array}{l} \text{\textit{Estimated}} \\ \text{\textit{Total Variance}} \end{array} - \begin{array}{l} \text{\textit{Estimated Expected}} \\ \text{\textit{Process Variances}} \end{array} = 1.2-1.0 = .2,$$

leading to

$$k = \frac{1.0}{.2} = 5. \qquad \square$$

6.7   TWO EQUIVALENT WAYS TO CALCULATE Z

EXAMPLE 6.7

Four urns contain balls marked either 0 or 1 in the following proportions:

Urn	Percentage of Balls in Urn Marked	
	0	1
A	70%	30%
B	70	30
C	30	70
D	20	80

An urn is selected at random (i.e., with probability $\frac{1}{4}$) and four balls are selected from the urn with replacement. The total of the values is 2. Four more balls are selected from the same urn. Calculate the expected total of the second set of four balls using Bühlmann's credibility formula.

SOLUTION

Using the binomial distribution for each urn, we calculate the expected value of the process variance as

$$\frac{1}{4}\left[(4)(.7)(.3)+(4)(.7)(.3)+(4)(.3)(.7)+(4)(.2)(.8)\right] = .79.$$

The expected value of the hypothetical means is

$$\frac{1}{4}\left[(4)(.3)+(4)(.3)+(4)(.7)+(4)(.8)\right] = 2.10.$$

The second moment of the hypothetical means is

$$\frac{1}{4}\left[\left[(4)(.3)\right]^2+\left[(4)(.3)\right]^2+\left[(4)(.7)\right]^2+\left[(4)(.8)\right]^2\right] = 5.24.$$

The variance of the hypothetical means is

$$5.24-(2.10)^2 = .83.$$

Then we have

$$k = \frac{.79}{.83} = .95$$

and

$$Z = \frac{n}{n+k} = \frac{1}{1+.95} = .51.$$

Finally, the compromise Bühlmann estimate is

$$C = ZR+(1-Z)H = (.51)(2)+(.49)(2.10) = 2.049. \qquad \square$$

The next example is a slight modification of Example 6.7.

EXAMPLE 6.8

Let the four urns be as in Example 6.7. Again an urn is selected at random, four balls are selected from the urn with replacement, and the total of the values is found to be 2. This time just one additional ball is drawn from the selected urn. What is the expected value of the next draw using Bühlmann's credibility formula?

SOLUTION
The expected value of the process variance is

$$\frac{1}{4}\left[(.7)(.3)+(.7)(.3)+(.3)(.7)+(.2)(.8)\right] = .1975,$$

using the binomial distribution. The expected value of the hypothetical means is

$$\frac{1}{4}(.3+.3+.7+.8) = .525.$$

The second moment of the hypothetical means is

$$\frac{1}{4}\left[(.3)^2+(.3)^2+(.7)^2+(.8)^2 = .3275.\right]$$

The variance of the hypothetical means is

$$.3275-(.525)^2 = .051875.$$

Then we have

$$k = \frac{.1975}{.051875} = 3.8072$$

and

$$Z = \frac{n}{n+k} = \frac{4}{4+3.8072} = .51.$$

(Note that $n=4$ here because only one ball is drawn during an individual period of observation. The four balls correspond to four periods of observation.) Finally, the compromise Bühlmann estimate is

$$C = ZR + (1-Z)H \quad (.51)(.5)+(.49)(.525) = .51225. \quad \square$$

We note here that in Examples 6.7 and 6.8 the values of Z are identical and the Bühlmann estimate of Example 6.7 is exactly $n = 4$ times that of Example 6.8, since four times as many balls are to be drawn. This leads us to the following theorem.

Theorem 6.1

Suppose that (1) in a single period of observation there are n independent trials, $X_1, X_2, ..., X_n$, each with probability distribution function $F(x\,|\,\Theta)$, and (2) in each of n periods of observation there is a single trial, X_i, $i = 1, 2, ..., n$, where the X_i's are independent and identically distributed with probability distribution function $F(x\,|\,\Theta)$, where Θ is a random vector of parameter values. Then the credibility factor of case (1) is equal to the credibility factor of case (2).

Proof

The credibility factor of case (1) is

$$\frac{1}{1 + \dfrac{E_\Theta[Var(X_1 + X_2 + \cdots + X_n|\Theta)]}{Var_\Theta(E[X_1 + X_2 + \cdots + X_n|\Theta])}} = \frac{1}{1 + \dfrac{E_\Theta[n \cdot Var(X_1|\Theta)]}{Var_\Theta(E[n \cdot E[X_1|\Theta])}}$$

$$= \frac{1}{1 + \dfrac{n \cdot E_\Theta[Var(X_1|\Theta)]}{n^2 \cdot Var_\Theta(E[X_1|\Theta])}}$$

$$= \frac{n}{n + \dfrac{E_\Theta[Var(X_1|\Theta)]}{Var_\Theta(E[X_1|\Theta])}},$$

which is the credibility factor of case (2), as desired.

6.8 FURTHER COMMENTS

In Section 6.6, we considered the problem of computing a single credibility factor, Z, for r distinct group policyholders. The question arises as to how similar these groups need to be for this procedure to produce reasonable results. The answer is that this decision must be left to the subjective judgment of the actuary. We present an example to illustrate this.

Efron and Morris [1975] consider the batting averages of 18 major league baseball players during the 1970 season. Their goal is to use the averages based on the first 45 at bats to predict the averages for the entire season. Efron and Morris used a shrinkage procedure similar to credibility theory to do this. Why did Efron and Morris think this was reasonable? Because they felt that they had prior knowledge of baseball player performance. They felt, for example, that it was likely that Roberto Clemente (an outfielder for the Pittsburgh Pirates), whose average was .400 after 45 at bats would end the season with an average less than .400. (Clemente in fact ended up the 1970 season with a .352 average.) They also felt that Thurmon Munson, the catcher for the New York Yankees, was a good hitter and would end the season with an average much higher than the .178 he was hitting after 45 at bats. (Munson ended the season at .274.) Efron and Morris were pleased with the results of their work.

In all of the examples discussed here (including the last), we assume that the parameter values (e.g., the probability of obtaining a "1") do not change over time. In some applications, this may not be a realistic assumption and other types of models may be required in order to obtain useful results. One model which could be used in this situation is the Kalman filter model.

As mentioned earlier, under the Bayesian paradigm certain parameters are assumed to have probability distributions. In order to obtain reasonable results, some of these probability distributions must be assumed to change over time. The Bayesian version of the Kalman filter model can be used in such situations. This type of modeling is discussed in Chapter 4 of Klugman [1992] and in Meinhold and Singpurwalla [1983].

6.9 EXERCISES

6.1 Introduction
6.2 Basic Elements of Bühlmann's Approach

6-1 You are given that
(i) the Bühlmann credibility factor of an individual risk's experience is $\frac{1}{3}$ based on a single observation, and
(ii) the individual risk's underlying expected loss is constant over time.

Determine the Bühlmann credibility factor for the individual risk's experience after four observations.

6-2 Let $n = 2, k = \frac{154}{11}$, and $H = E[X_2 \mid X_1 = 0]$, where X_1 and X_2 are as defined in Chapter 4. Use Equation (1.1) and Table 4.7 to estimate $E[X_3 \mid X_2 = R]$, for $R = 0, 2$, and 14.

6-3 Two urns each contain balls marked with 0, 1, or 2, in the following proportions:

Urn	Percentage of Balls in Urn Marked		
	0	1	2
A	20%	40%	40%
B	70	20	10

An urn is selected at random with probability $\frac{1}{2}$, and two balls are drawn, with replacement, from the urn. The sum of the marks on the two balls is 2. Two more balls are drawn, with replacement, from the selected urn. Using Bühlmann's credibility approach with $n = 1$, determine each of the following.

(a) The variance of the hypothetical means.
(b) The expected value of the process variance.
(c) The value of k.
(d) The credibility factor Z.
(e) The expected total of the marks on the two balls.

6-4 An insured population of automobile drivers can be partitioned into two groups of equal size. Each member of the first group has a 20% chance of getting into an accident each year, and the corresponding probability for members of the other group is 40%. No one can have more than one accident per year. Everyone in the population has the following severity distribution:

Probability	Size of Loss
.80	$100
.10	200
.10	400

Assuming that the drivers within each group are mutually independent, calculate each of the following.

(a) The variance of the hypothetical means.
(b) The expected value of the process variance.
(c) The value of k.
(d) The credibility factor for an individual insured's experience.

6-5 There is a new brand of chocolate chip cookies on the market. You buy a box of 50 cookies and find a total of 265 chips. Your prior research has led you to expect 4.80 chips per cookie, with a variance among brands of .20. (i.e., the variance of the hypothetical means is .20.) For a given brand, the number of chips in each cookie is assumed to have a Poisson distribution. Using Bühlmann's model, estimate the average number of chips per cookie for the new brand.

6-6 Each individual within a homogeneous class of insureds has a Poisson distribution with a constant mean of .10. Under Bühlmann's approach, what is the credibility factor to be assigned to the experience of an individual insured within this class of risks? (Hint: First calculate the variance of the hypothetical means.)

6-7   Assume that the number of insurance claims, R, filed by an individual in a single policy year has a binomial distribution with parameters $n = 3$ and Θ, where Θ has density function

$$g(\theta) = \begin{cases} 6(\theta-\theta^2) & 0 < \theta < 1 \\ 0 & \text{otherwise} \end{cases}.$$

Given that a single claim is filed by the individual during that policy year, determine the Bühlmann credibility factor.

6-8   You are given that (i) $X_1, X_2, \ldots, X_n$ are mutually independent and identically distributed random variables with mean M and variance V, (ii) M has mean 2 and variance 4, and (iii) V has mean 8 and variance 32. Determine the value of the Bühlmann credibility factor after observing realizations of the first three random variables X_1, X_2, and X_3.

6.3 Characteristics of the Credibility Factor

6-9   Choose exactly one of the words or values in parentheses in each of the following statements.

(a) Z is a (increasing/decreasing) function of n.
(b) In the limiting case as $n \to \infty$, Z approaches (0/1).
(c) Z is a (increasing/decreasing) function of k.
(d) Z is a (increasing/decreasing) function of the expected value of the process variance.
(e) Z is a (increasing/decreasing) function of the variance of the hypothetical means.

6.4 Further Examples of Bühlmann Estimates

6-10 The number of claims per policy year for a single risk has a Poisson distribution with parameter A. In turn, A has a prior gamma distribution with density function $g(a) = a \cdot e^{-a}$, for $0 < a < \infty$. Determine the Bühlmann credibility factor to be assigned to a single observation.

6-11   The number of claims per policy year for an individual insured has a Poisson distribution with parameter A. The prior distribution of A is the uniform distribution over the interval $(1,3)$. An individual insured has exactly one claim during the first policy year. Use Bühlmann's model to estimate the insured's expected number of claims during the next policy year.

6-12   For each member of a class of insureds the probability of a claim within a policy year is uniformly distributed over the closed interval $[.07,.13]$. Each insured can have no more than one claim during the policy year. The following two severity distributions apply:

Severity	Amount of Claim		
Distribution	$5	$10	$20
Type 1	$\frac{1}{3}$	$\frac{1}{2}$	$\frac{1}{6}$
Type 2	$\frac{1}{2}$	$\frac{1}{4}$	$\frac{1}{4}$

Assume that:

(i) the frequency and severity distributions are stochastically independent, and
(ii) 60% of the risks are of Type 1 and 40% are of Type 2.

Calculate each of the following.

(a) The variance of the hypothetical means.
(b) The expected value of the process variance.
(c) The value of k.
(d) The credibility factor for a single insured's experience.

6-13   The number of claims, N_i, during the ith policy year for an individual insured has a Poisson distribution. The expected annual claim frequency of the entire population of insureds is uniformly distributed over $(0, 1)$. An individual's claim frequency is constant over time. A particular insured filed a total of three claims during the first three policy years, so that $N_1 + N_2 + N_3 = 3$. Using Bühlmann's credibility model, estimate the expected annual claim frequency for the fourth policy year.

6.5 Components of the Total Variance

6-14 Determine the total variance if:
   (i) the expected value of the process variance is 6.5, and
   (ii) the variance of the hypothetical means is 4.2.

6-15 Using the notation of Theorem 5.2, determine the variance of the hypothetical means given $Var(Y) = 8$ and $E_X\left[Var_Y(Y \mid X) = 3.\right]$

6-16 Let $E[X]$ denote the expected value of the random variable X and let $g(Y)$ be a function of the random variable Y for which $E[Y]$ exists. Which of the following are true?

   I. $E[X] = E_Y\left[E(X \mid Y)\right]$

   II. $Var(X) = E_Y\left[VarX \mid Y)\right] + Var_Y\left(E[X \mid Y]\right)$

   III. $E\left[g(Y)\right] = E_Y\left[E_X\left[g(Y) \mid X\right]\right]$

6.6 Practical Applications of Bühlmann's Model

6-17 A group of 340 insureds in a high-crime area submitted the following 210 theft claims during a one-year period of observation.

Number of Claims	Number of Insureds
0	200
1	80
2	50
3	10

For each insured the number of thefts is assumed to follow a Poisson distribution, but the mean of each distribution may vary among insureds. An individual insured experienced two claims during the one-year period of observation. Calculate each of the following.

(a) The average number of claims observed per insured.

(b) The expected value of the process variance.

(c) The variance of the hypothetical means.

(d) The value of k.

(e) The credibility factor for an individual insured's experience.

(f) The Bühlmann credibility estimate of the number of claims for this insured during the next one-year period of observation.

6-18 For a large sample of insureds, the observed relative frequency of claims during an observation period is as follows.

Number of Claims	Relative Frequency of Claims
0	61.9%
1	28.4
2	7.8
3	1.6
4	.3
5 or more	0

Assume that the underlying distribution is Poisson and is constant over time. Calculate each of the following:

(a) The average number of claims observed per insured.

(b) The expected value of the process variance.

(c) The variance of the hypothetical means.

(d) The value of k.

(e) The credibility factor for an individual insured's experience.

(f) The expected number of claims during period $n+1$ for an insured who had no claims during period n.

6-19 An insurance company has two group workers' compensation policies. The aggregate claim amounts in millions of dollars for the first three policy years are summarized in the table below. Use Bühlmann's model to attempt to estimate the aggregate claim amount during the fourth policy year for each of the two group policies. Do not make any assumptions about the probability distribution of aggregate claim amounts. Assume no inflation. Show that $\hat{a} < 0$ so that the procedure breaks down.

Aggregate Claim Amounts			
Group Policy	Policy Year		
	1	2	3
1	5	8	11
2	2	8	14

6-20 An insurance company has two group workers' compensation policies. The aggregate claim amounts in millions of dollars for the first four policy years are summarized in the table below. Use Bühlmann's model to estimate the aggregate claim amount during the fifth policy year for each of the two group policies. Do not make any assumptions about the probability distribution of aggregate claim amounts. Assume no inflation.

Aggregate Claim Amounts				
Group Policy	Policy Year			
	1	2	3	4
1	4	10	8	6
2	12	14	13	13

6.7 Two Equivalent Ways to Calculate Z

6-21 Three urns each contain balls marked with 0 or 1, in the following proportions:

	Percentage of Balls in Urn Marked	
Urn	0	1
A	10%	90%
B	60	40
C	80	20

An urn is selected at random with probability $\frac{1}{3}$, and three balls are drawn, with replacement, from the selected urn. The total of the marks on the three balls is 1. Three more balls are drawn, with replacement, from the selected urn. Using Bühlmann's credibility model with $n = 1$, calculate the expected total of the marks on the three balls. Recalculate the expected total of the marks using $n = 3$. According to Theorem 6.1, the results should be the same.

6-22 Rework Exercise 6-3 using $n = 2$.

6-23 One of three multisided dice is selected at random, with probability $\frac{1}{3}$. One die has four sides (numbered 1, 2, 3, and 4), the second die has the usual six sides (numbered $1, 2, ..., 6$), and the third die has eight sides (numbered $1, 2, ..., 8$). Each die is fair, so that each side has an equal chance of being rolled. The selected die is rolled once, the result is observed, and the die is rolled a second time. We wish to estimate the result of the second roll.

(a) Using Bühlmann's model, estimate the result of the second roll if the result of the first roll is a 7.

(b) Using Bayes' Theorem, determine the predictive distribution of the second roll, R_2, if the result of the first roll, R_1, is a 7.

(c) What is the Bayesian point estimate of the result of the second roll if the squared error loss function is specified?

(d) What is the Bayesian point estimate of the result of the second roll if the absolute error loss function is specified?

(e) Rework parts (c) and (d) assuming that $P[R_2 = i] = \frac{i}{36}$, for $i = 1, 2, ..., 8$.

(f) What is the Bayesian point estimate of the result of the second roll, given that the first roll is a 7, the probability distribution of part (e) applies, and the almost constant loss function is specified?

CHAPTER 7

BÜHLMANN-STRAUB MODEL

7.1 INTRODUCTION

The Bühlmann-Straub model, a generalization of the Bühlmann model of Chapter 6, is of major practical interest. A deficiency of the Bühlmann model is that it does not allow different numbers of exposure units or different distributions of claim sizes across past policy years. Thus in group insurance, for example, the Bühlmann model would not be able to handle changes in the number of insured members of the group over two or more periods of observation. The Bühlmann-Straub model addresses this deficiency.

7.2 MODEL FOR ONE POLICYHOLDER WITH KNOWN UNDERLYING PROBABILITY DISTRIBUTIONS

7.2.1 BASIC ELEMENTS

For $1 = 1,2,...,n+1$, let X_i denote the aggregate claim amount of a single policyholder during the ith period of observation (e.g., the ith policy year). As before, we want to estimate the expected value of the random variable X_{n+1} for period $n+1$, given the realizations $X_1 = x_1$, $X_2 = x_2,...,X_n = x_n$, for the n prior periods. This expected value is denoted by $E[X_{n+1} \mid X_1 = x_1, X_2 = x_2,..., X_n = x_n]$. We make the following assumptions for this version of the Bühlmann-Straub model:

(1) For $j = 1,2,...,n+1$, the distribution of each X_j depends on a parameter Θ.

(2) Given Θ, the random variables $X_1, X_2,..., X_{n+1}$ are conditionally independent and identically distributed

These assumptions imply that the random variables $X_1, X_2, ..., X_{n+1}$ are identically distributed. Note, however, that they are not necessarily unconditionally independent.

We generalize the Bühlmann model of Chapter 6 by requiring that

$$\mu(\Theta) = E[X_j \mid \Theta]$$

and

$$v(\Theta) = m_j \cdot Var(X_j \mid \Theta),$$

for $j = 1, 2, ..., n+1$, where m_j is a known constant representing the amount of exposure during the jth observation period. We assume that neither $\mu(\Theta)$ nor $v(\Theta)$ depends on the observation period j. We set

$$m = \sum_{j=1}^{n} m_j.$$

(Recall that in Chapter 6 all of the weights, m_j, were required to be equal.) Another difference between the Chapter 6 model and the Bühlmann-Straub model is that here the X_j's represent the *average* claim amount per exposure unit, rather than the *aggregate* claim amount as employed earlier in the text.

Under the Bühlmann-Straub model, our goal is to produce a point estimate of $E\big[\mu(\Theta) \mid X_1 = x_1, X_2 = x_2, ..., X_n = x_n,\big]$ the conditional expectation of $\mu(\Theta)$, given $X_1 = x_1, X_2 = x_2, ..., X_n = x_n$. As will be shown in Theorem 8.4 of Chapter 8, this is equivalent to producing a point estimate of $E[X_{n+1} \mid X_1 = x_1, X_2 = x_2, ..., X_n = x_n]$, the conditional expectation of X_{n+1}, given the realizations $X_1 = x_1, X_2 = x_2, ..., X_n = x_n$, since $E[X_{n+1} \mid \Theta] = \mu(\Theta)$. As with the Bühlmann model, we choose a linear estimator of the conditional expectation of $\mu(\Theta)$ of the form

$$a_0 + a_1 X_1 + a_2 X_2 + \cdots + a_n X_n.$$

The linear estimator chosen is the one whose coefficients, i.e., the quantities $a_0, a_1, a_2, ..., a_n$, minimize

$$E\Big[\big(\mu(\Theta) - a_0 - a_1 X_1 - a_2 X_2 - \cdots - a_n X_n\big)^2\Big]. \tag{7.1}$$

The coefficients $a_0, a_1, a_2, ..., a_n$ are obtained by differentiating Expression (7.1) $n+1$ times, first with respect to a_0, then with respect to a_1, and so on, and finally with respect to a_n, and setting each derivative equal to zero. The resulting $n+1$ equations in $n+1$ unknowns are then solved for $a_0, a_1, a_2, ..., a_n$. The results are

$$a_0 = (1-Z) \cdot E[\mu(\Theta)],$$

where

$$Z = \frac{\Sigma m_j}{\Sigma m_j + \dfrac{E[v(\Theta)]}{Var(\mu(\Theta))}},$$

and

$$a_j = \frac{m_j}{\Sigma m_j + \dfrac{E[v(\Theta)]}{Var(\mu(\Theta)}}$$

for $j = 1, 2, ..., n$. Thus the point estimator of the conditional expectation of $\mu(\Theta)$ is

$$Z \cdot \bar{X} + (1-Z) \cdot E[\mu(\Theta)], \qquad (7.2)$$

where

$$\bar{X} = \frac{\Sigma m_j X_j}{\Sigma m_j}$$

and Z is as defined above. Expression (7.2) is of the same form as Equation (1.1) with $R = \bar{X}$ and $H = E[\mu(\Theta)]$. Note that the estimator of Expression (7.2) is a linear function of the random variables $X_1, X_2, ..., X_n$, since $\bar{X}$ is a linear function of $X_1, X_2, ..., X_n$.

7.2.2 EXAMPLES

In the two examples that follow we apply the Bühlmann-Straub model described in Section 7.2.1. In these examples we assume that all of the requisite probability distributions are known so that we can obtain results for a single policyholder. As discussed in Section 7.3, when such distributions cannot be employed, we need experience data on at least two policyholders to obtain the desired results.

EXAMPLE 7.1

Consider Example 6.8, which dealt with the four urns. Suppose that, during the first observation period, we drew four balls of which exactly two were marked 1. If five balls are to be drawn during the second period of observation, what is the best estimate under the Bühlmann-Straub model for one policyholder of the number of balls marked 1 drawn during the second period?

SOLUTION

Let C_1 and C_2 denote the *total* number of balls marked 1, drawn during each of the first two observation periods, respectively. Let X_1 and X_2 denote the *average* number of balls marked 1, drawn during the same two observation periods, respectively. For $i = 1, 2, ..., 9$, let Y_i denote the result of the ith draw from the urn so that

$$X_1 = \frac{C_1}{4} = \frac{Y_1 + Y_2 + Y_3 + Y_4}{4}$$

and

$$X_2 = \frac{C_2}{5} = \frac{Y_5 + Y_6 + Y_7 + Y_8 + Y_9}{5}.$$

In this example we have $n = 1$ (prior) period for which we have observed the results. The numbers of exposure units are $m_1 = 4$ for the first observation period and $m_2 = 5$ for the second observation period, whose outcome we are attempting to forecast. The total number of exposure units during all past observation periods (of which there is only one) is $m = m_1 = 4$. Because we are given that $C_1 = 2$, it follows that $X_1 = \frac{C_1}{m_1} = \frac{2}{4} = \frac{1}{2}$. We seek the Bühlmann-Straub estimate of $E[C_2|C_1 = 2]$, or, equivalently,

$$E\left[m_2 X_2 \mid X_1 = \frac{1}{2} \right] = m_2 \cdot E\left[X_2 \mid X_1 = \frac{1}{2} \right].$$

Recall from Example 6.8 that the expected value of the hypothetical means, μ, is .525, so that for $j = 1, 2$ and $i = 1, 2, ..., 9$ we have

$$.525 = \mu = E_\Theta \left[\mu(\Theta) \right] = E_\Theta \left[E\left[X_j \,|\Theta \right] \right] = E_\Theta \left[E\left[Y_i \,|\Theta \right] \right],$$

where the parameter Θ represents the selected urn. Also, from Example 6.8, the variance of the hypothetical means is

$$.051875 = Var\left(\mu(\Theta) \right) = Var_\Theta \left(E\left[Y_i \,|\Theta \right] \right)$$

and the expected value of the process variance is

$$.1975 = E_\Theta \left[v(\Theta) \right] = E_\Theta \left[Var\left(Y_i \,|\Theta \right) \right],$$

so that, as in Example 6.8, $k = 3.8072$ and $Z = .51$. The Bühlmann-Straub compromise estimate of $E\left[X_2 \,|\, X_1 = \tfrac{1}{2} \right]$ is

$$ZR + (1-Z)\mu = (.51)(.50) + (.49)(.525) = .51225,$$

where $R = X_1 = .50$. Hence the Bühlmann-Straub compromise estimate of $E\left[C_2 \,|\, C_1 = 2 \right] = m_2 \cdot E\left[X_2 \,|\, X_1 = \tfrac{1}{2} \right]$, is m_2 times the Bühlmann-Straub compromise estimate of $E\left[X_2 \,|\, X_1 = \tfrac{1}{2} \right]$, namely

$$(5)(.51225) = 2.56125. \qquad \square$$

In the next example, we expand on the previous example to give a better feel for the Bühlmann-Straub model.

EXAMPLE 7.2

Let the conditions be as in Example 7.1, except that we have now observed $X_2 = \tfrac{3}{5}$. If six balls are to be drawn during the third period of observation, what is the best estimate under the Bühlmann-Straub model for one policyholder of the number of balls marked 1 drawn during that period?

SOLUTION

In this example there are $n = 2$ observation periods. The numbers of exposure units are $m_1 = 3$ and $m_2 = 5$ for the first two observation periods, respectively, and $m_3 = 6$ for the third observation period, whose outcome we are attempting to forecast. The total number of exposure units during all past observation periods combined (of which there are two) is $m = m_1 + m_2 = 4+5 = 9$. Finally, we have the results $X_1 = \frac{1}{2}$ and $X_2 = \frac{3}{5}$. Then

$$R = \frac{m_1 X_1 + m_2 X_2}{m} = \frac{4\left(\frac{1}{2}\right) + 5\left(\frac{3}{5}\right)}{9} = \frac{5}{9},$$

and

$$Z = \frac{m}{m+k} = \frac{9}{9+3.8072} = .7027,$$

where $k = 3.8072$ is again taken from Example 6.8. The Bühlmann-Straub compromise estimate of $E\left[X_3 | X_1 = \frac{1}{2}, X_2 = \frac{3}{5}\right]$ is

$$ZR + (1-Z)\mu = (.7027)\left(\frac{5}{9}\right) + (.2973)(.525) = .5465.$$

Hence, the Bühlmann-Straub compromise estimate of C_3, the number of balls marked 1 to be drawn during the third observation period, denoted by

$$E[C_3 | C_1 = 2, C_2 = 3] = m_3 \cdot E\left[X_3 | X_1 = \frac{1}{2}, X_2 = \frac{3}{5}\right],$$

is

$$(6)(.5465) = 3.279. \qquad \square$$

7.3 MODEL FOR TWO OR MORE POLICYHOLDERS

7.3.1 BASIC ELEMENTS

In this section we discuss the application of the Bühlmann-Straub model without using any underlying probability distributions. This model generalizes both the model for one policyholder described in Section 7.2 and the model requiring equal numbers of exposure units described in Section 6.6.1. For ease of discussion, we couch the language in terms of a common insurance setting.

Let n_i represent the number of years of available experience data on the ith group policyholder where $i = 1, 2, ..., r$ and $r\ (r \geq 2)$ is the number of group policyholders. Let m_{ij} denote the number of exposure units for the ith policyholder during the jth policy year, $i = 1, 2, ..., r$ and $j = 1, 2, ..., n_i + 1$. Let X_{ij} denote the random variable representing the average claim amount per exposure unit of the ith policyholder during the jth policy year.

Let $\mathbf{X}_i = (X_{i,1}, X_{i,2}, ..., X_{i,n_i})$ be the random vector of average claim amounts for the ith policyholder, $i = 1, 2, ..., r$. We make the following assumptions:

(1) The random vectors $\mathbf{X}_1, \mathbf{X}_2, ..., \mathbf{X}_r$ are assumed to be mutually independent. In other words, the experience of one policyholder does not influence that of another distinct policyholder.

(2) For $i = 1, 2, ..., r$, the distribution of each element of $\mathbf{X}_i$ depends on an (unknown) risk parameter θ_i, where θ_i is a realization of the random variable Θ_i.

(3) The random variables $\Theta_1, \Theta_2, ..., \Theta_r$ are mutually independent and identically distributed.

(4) Given i and Θ_i, the random variables $X_{i,1}, X_{i,2}, ..., X_{i,n_i}$ are mutually conditionally independent.

These assumptions are similar to those of the model of Section 6.6.1. Here, however, we generalize the Bühlmann model of Section 6.6.1 by only requiring that

$$\mu(\Theta_i) = E[X_{ij} | \Theta_i]$$

and

$$\nu(\Theta_i) = m_{ij} \cdot Var(X_{ij} | \Theta_i),$$

for $i = 1, 2, ..., r$ and $j = 1, 2, ..., n_i$. As in Section 7.2.1, we assume that neither $\mu(\Theta_i)$ nor $\nu(\Theta_i)$ depend on the observation period j. The total number of exposure units attributable to the ith policyholder during the first n_i policy years is

$$m_i. = \sum_{j=1}^{n_i} m_{ij}$$

and the overall number of exposure units is

$$m = \sum_{i=1}^{r} m_i..$$

Recall that assumption (5) of the model of Section 6.6.1 required that $m_{ij} = 1$ for all i and j. Thus the assumptions of this section are less restrictive than those of Section 6.6.1. Then the estimators of the hypothetical mean (μ), the expected process variance (v), and the variance of the hypothetical means (a) are, respectively,

$$\hat{\mu} = \overline{X}.. = \frac{1}{m}\sum_{i=1}^{r} m_i.\overline{X}_i. = \frac{1}{m}\sum_{i=1}^{r}\sum_{j=1}^{n_i} m_{ij} X_{ij}, \qquad (7.3)$$

where

$$\overline{X}_i. = \frac{1}{m_i.}\sum_{j=i}^{n_i} m_{ij} X_{ij},$$

$$\hat{v} = \frac{\sum_{i=1}^{r}\sum_{j=1}^{n_i} m_{ij}(X_{ij}-\overline{X}_i.)^2}{\sum_{i=1}^{r}(n_i-1)}, \qquad (7.4)$$

and

$$\hat{a} = \left\{m - \frac{1}{m}\sum_{i=1}^{r} m_i^2.\right\}^{-1}\left\{\sum_{i=1}^{r} m_i.(\overline{X}_i.-\overline{X}..)^2 - \hat{v}(r-1)\right\}, \qquad (7.5)$$

where $\hat{v}$ is defined in Equation (7.4).

It can be shown that $\hat{\mu}, \hat{v}$, and $\hat{a}$ are all unbiased estimators of μ, v, and a, respectively. It is possible that $\hat{a}$ be negative, an undesirable result since variances must, of course, be nonnegative.

The estimator of k is then $\hat{k} = \frac{\hat{v}}{\hat{a}}$, and the estimator of the credibility factor for the ith policyholder, Z_i, is

$$\hat{Z}_i = \frac{m_i.}{m_i.+\hat{k}}.$$

The Bühlmann-Straub compromise estimator of the average claim amount per exposure unit for the ith policyholder is

$$\hat{\overline{X}}_{i\cdot} = \hat{Z}_i \overline{X}_{i\cdot} + (1-\hat{Z}_i)\hat{\mu}, \qquad (7.6)$$

for $i = 1,2,...,r$. The Bühlmann-Straub compromise estimator of the aggregate claim amount for the ith policyholder is

$$\hat{C}_i = m_{i,n_{i+1}} \cdot \hat{\overline{X}}_{i\cdot}.$$

for $i = 1,2,...,r$.

7.3.2 EXAMPLES

We illustrate the procedure of Section 7.3.1 in the following examples.

EXAMPLE 7.3

Compute the estimated aggregate claim amount to be observed during the fourth policy year on each of the two groups whose first three years of experience data are presented in Table 7.1. The aggregate claim amounts are in millions of dollars. Assume no inflation.

TABLE 7.1

Group Policyholder		Policy Year			
		1	2	3	4
1	Aggregate Claim Amount	8,000	11,000	15,000	–
	Size of Group	40	50	70	75
2	Aggregate Claim Amount	20,000	24,000	19,000	–
	Size of Group	100	120	115	95

SOLUTION

Because there are two group policyholders, $r = 2$. We first compute the average claim amount per person during each policy year for each of the two group policyholders. Since we have three years of experience data for each policyholder, we set $n_1 = 3$ and $n_2 = 3$.

For Policyholder 1, the exposure measures are $m_{11} = 40$, $m_{12} = 50$, $m_{13} = 70$, and $m_{14} = 75$, so that

$$m_1. = \sum_{j=1}^{3} m_{1j} = 40 + 50 + 70 = 160$$

and the average claim amounts are

$$x_{11} = \frac{8,000}{40} = 200,$$

$$x_{12} = \frac{11,000}{50} = 220,$$

and

$$x_{13} = \frac{15,000}{70} = 214.29.$$

Then

$$\overline{x}_{i.} = \frac{1}{m_{1.}} \sum_{j=1}^{3} m_{1j} x_{1j} = \frac{8,000 + 11,000 + 15,000}{160} = 212.50.$$

For Policyholder 2, we have $n_2 = 3$ years of experience and exposure measures $m_{21} = 100$, $m_{22} = 120$, $m_{23} = 115$, and $m_{24} = 95$, so that

$$m_2. = \sum_{j=1}^{3} m_{2j} = 100 + 120 + 115 = 335$$

and the average claim amounts are

$$x_{21} = \frac{20,000}{100} = 200,$$

$$x_{22} = \frac{24,000}{120} = 200,$$

and

$$x_{23} = \frac{19,000}{115} = 165.22.$$

Then

$$\bar{x}_{2.} = \frac{1}{m_{2.}} \sum_{j=1}^{3} m_{2j} x_{2j} = \frac{20,000 + 24,000 + 19,000}{335} = 188.06.$$

The overall number of exposure units for the first three policy years is

$$m = m_{1.} + m_{2.} = 160 + 335 = 495.$$

The estimate of the overall (prior) mean, by Equation (7.3), is

$$\hat{\mu} = \bar{x}_{..} = \frac{1}{m} \sum_{i=1}^{2} m_{i.} \bar{x}_{i.}$$

$$= \frac{1}{495} \left[(160)(212.50) + (335)(188.06) \right] = 195.96.$$

The estimate of the expected process variance, by Equation (7.4), is

$$\hat{v} = \frac{\displaystyle\sum_{i=1}^{2} \sum_{j=1}^{3} m_{ij} (x_{ij} - \bar{x}_{i.})^2}{\displaystyle\sum_{i=1}^{2} (3-1)}$$

$$= \frac{\begin{array}{c}(40)(200-212.5)^2 + (50)(220-212.5)^2 + (70)(214.29-212.5)^2 \\ + (100)(200-188.06)^2 + (120)(200-188.06)^2 \\ + (115)(165.22-188.06)^2\end{array}}{2+2}$$

$$= 25,160.58.$$

The estimate of the variance of the hypothetical means, by Equation (7.5), is

$$
\begin{aligned}
\hat{a} &= \left\{ m - \frac{1}{m}\sum_{i=1}^{2}m_i^2 \right\}^{-1} \left\{ \sum_{i=1}^{r}m_i.(\bar{x}_i.-\bar{x}..)^2 - \hat{v}(r-1) \right\} \\
&= \left\{ 495 - \frac{1}{495}\left[(160)^2+(335)^2\right] \right\}^{-1} \left\{(160)(212.5-195.96)^2 \right. \\
&\qquad\qquad\qquad\qquad \left. +(335)(188.06-195.96)^2 - 25,160.58(1) \right\} \\
&= 182.48.
\end{aligned}
$$

Then the estimate of k is

$$
\hat{k} = \frac{\hat{v}}{\hat{a}} = \frac{25,160.58}{182.48} = 137.88,
$$

and the estimated credibility factors for the two policyholders are

$$
\hat{Z}_1 = \frac{m_1.}{m_1.+\hat{k}} = \frac{160}{160+137.88} = .537
$$

and

$$
\hat{Z}_2 = \frac{m_2.}{m_2.+\hat{k}} = \frac{335}{335+137.88} = .708.
$$

Next the Bühlmann-Straub estimates of the average claim amounts per exposure unit for the two group policyholders, by Equation (7.6), are

$$
\hat{\bar{X}}_1. = \hat{Z}_1\bar{X}_1.+(1-\hat{Z}_1)\hat{\mu}
$$

$$
= (.537)(212.50)+(.463)(195.96) = 204.84
$$

and

$$
\hat{\bar{X}}_2. = \hat{Z}_2\bar{X}_2.+(1-\hat{Z}_2)\hat{\mu}
$$

$$
= (.708)(188.06)+(.292)(195.96) = 190.37.
$$

Finally, the Bühlmann-Straub estimates of the aggregate claim amounts for the two group policyholders during the fourth policy year are

$$\hat{C}_1 = m_{14} \cdot \hat{\bar{X}}_1 = (75)(204.84) = 15,363.00$$

and

$$\hat{C}_2 = m_{24} \cdot \hat{\bar{X}}_2 = (95)(190.37) = 18,085.15. \qquad \square$$

EXAMPLE 7.4

Compute the estimated aggregate claim amount to be observed during the fourth policy year on each of the two groups whose first three years of experience data are presented in Table 7.2. (Note that this is the same as Example 7.3, except that Policy Year 1 data are not available for Policyholder 1.)

TABLE 7.2

Group Policyholder		Policy Year			
		1	2	3	4
1	Aggregate Claim Amount	–	11,000	15,000	–
	Size of Group	–	50	70	75
2	Aggregate Claim Amount	20,000	24,000	19,000	–
	Size of Group	100	120	115	95

SOLUTION

Because there are two group policyholders, $r = 2$. We first compute the average claim amount per person during each policy year for each of the two group policyholders.

For Policyholder 1, we have $n_1 = 2$ years of experience. Because it is immaterial which past years' data we have for Policyholder 1, we denote the exposure measures of Policyholder 1 to be $m_{11} = 50, m_{12} = 70$, and $m_{13} = 75$, so that

$$m_{1.} = \sum_{j=1}^{2} m_{1j} = 50 + 70 = 120$$

and the average claim amounts are

$$x_{11} = \frac{11,000}{50} = 220$$

and

$$x_{12} = \frac{15,000}{70} = 214.29.$$

Then

$$\bar{x}_{1.} = \frac{1}{m_{1.}} \sum_{j=1}^{2} m_{1j} x_{1j} = \frac{11,000 + 15,000}{120} = 216.67.$$

For Policyholder 2, we have $n_2 = 3$ years of experience and exposure measures $m_{21} = 100, m_{22} = 120, m_{23} = 115,$ and $m_{24} = 95,$ so that

$$m_{2.} = \sum_{j=1}^{3} m_{2j} = 100 + 120 + 115 = 335$$

and the average claim amounts are

$$x_{21} = \frac{20,000}{100} = 200,$$

$$x_{22} = \frac{24,000}{120} = 200,$$

and

$$x_{23} = \frac{19,000}{115} = 165.22.$$

Then, just as in Example 7.3,

$$\bar{x}_{2.} = \frac{1}{m_{2.}} \sum_{j=1}^{3} m_{2j} x_{2j} = \frac{20,000 + 24,000 + 19,000}{335} = 188.06.$$

The overall number of exposure units is

$$m = m_1. + m_2. = 120 + 335 = 455.$$

The estimate of the overall (prior) mean, by Equation (7.3), is

$$\hat{\mu} = \overline{x}.. = \frac{1}{m}\sum_{i=1}^{2} m_i.\overline{x}_i.$$

$$= \frac{1}{455}\left[(120)(216.67) + (335)(188.06)\right] = 195.61.$$

The estimate of the expected process variance, by Equation (7.4), is

$$\hat{v} = \frac{\sum_{i=1}^{2}\sum_{j=1}^{n_i} m_{ij}(x_{ij} - \overline{x}_{i.})^2}{\sum_{i=1}^{2}(n_i - 1)}$$

$$= \frac{\begin{array}{c}(50)(220 - 216.67)^2 + (70)(214.29 - 216.67)^2 \\ + (100)(200 - 188.06)^2 + (120)(200 - 188.06)^2 \\ + (115)(165.22 - 188.06)^2\end{array}}{1 + 2}$$

$$= 30,768.83.$$

The estimate of the variance of the hypothetical means, by Equation (7.5), is

$$\hat{a} = \left\{ m - \frac{1}{m}\sum_{i=1}^{2} m_i^2. \right\}^{-1} \left\{ \sum_{i=1}^{2} m_i.(\overline{x}_{i.} - \overline{x}..)^2 - \hat{v}(r-1) \right\}$$

$$= \left\{ 455 - \frac{1}{455}\left[(120)^2 + (335)^2\right] \right\}^{-1} \left\{ (120)(216.67) - 195.6)^2 \right.$$
$$\left. + (335)(188.06 - 195.61)^2 - (30,768.83)(1) \right\} = 235.14.$$

Then the estimate of k is

$$\hat{k} = \frac{\hat{v}}{\hat{a}} = \frac{30,768.83}{233.14} = 130.85.$$

and the estimated credibility factors for the two policyholders are

$$\hat{Z}_1 = \frac{m_1.}{m_1. + \hat{k}} = \frac{120}{120 + 130.85} = .478$$

and

$$\hat{Z}_2 = \frac{m_2.}{m_2. + \hat{k}} = \frac{335}{335 + 130.85} = .719.$$

Next, the Bühlmann-Straub estimates of the average claim amount per exposure unit for the two group policyholders, by Equation (7.6), are

$$\hat{\bar{X}}_1. = \hat{Z}_1 \bar{X}_1. + (1 - \hat{Z}_1) \hat{\mu}$$

$$= (.478)(216.67) + (.522)(195.61)$$

$$= 205.68$$

and

$$\hat{\bar{X}}_2. = \hat{Z}_2 \bar{X}_2. + (1 - \hat{Z}_2) \hat{\mu}$$

$$= (.719)(188.06) + (.281)(195.61)$$

$$= 190.18.$$

Finally, the Bühlmann-Straub estimates of the aggregate claim amounts for the two group policyholders during the fourth policy year are

$$\hat{C}_1 = m_{13} \cdot \hat{\bar{X}}_1. = (75)(205.68) = 15,426.00$$

and

$$\hat{C}_2 = m_{24} \cdot \hat{\bar{X}}_2. = (95)(190.18) = 18,067.10 \qquad \square$$

7.3.3 SUMMARY

The Bühlmann-Straub approach for two or more group policyholders can be summarized as follows:

Goal: To determine the compromise estimate of the aggregate claim amount for each of the r policyholders.

Step 1: Determine the number of group policyholders, $r \geq 2$.

Step 2: Determine the number of periods of observation, n_i, for each of the r policyholders.

Step 3: Determine the exposure measures, m_{ij}, for each policyholder during each observation period.

Step 4: Compute the average claim amount, x_{ij}, for each policyholder during each observation period.

Step 5: Compute the average claim amount, $\bar{x}_i.$, over all observation periods for each policyholder.

Step 6: Compute the estimated overall mean, $\hat{\mu}$.

Step 7: Compute the estimated expected process variance, $\hat{v}$.

Step 8: Compute the estimated variance of the hypothetical means, $\hat{a}$.

Step 9: Calculate $\hat{k} = \dfrac{\hat{v}}{\hat{a}}$.

Step 10: Compute the credibility factor, $\hat{Z}_i$, for each policyholder.

Step 11: Compute the Bühlmann-Straub compromise estimate, $\hat{\bar{X}}_i.$, of the average claim amount per exposure unit for each policyholder.

Step 12: Compute the Bühlmann-Straub compromise estimate, $\hat{C}_i$, of the aggregate claim amount for each policyholder.

7.3.4 WHAT IF THE ESTIMATE OF THE VARIANCE IS NEGATIVE?

The estimate of the variance of the hypothetical means could be negative. A common practice is to use an estimate of zero in this situation. The rationale is that zero is the closest permissible value.

7.4   SEMIPARAMETRIC ESTIMATION: SIMPLIFYING THE ESTIMATION OF THE PARAMETERS OF THE MODEL OF SECTION 7.3

In some practical applications of the model of Section 7.3, the basic assumptions lead to a simplification in the estimation process. For example, if we are interested in the number of claims, we might assume that the random variable for the number of claims attributed to policyholder i during policy year j, denoted $m_{ij}X_{ij}$, has a Poisson distribution with mean $m_{ij}\Theta_i$, given that $\Theta_i = \theta_i$. Then

$$E\left[m_{ij}X_{ij} \mid \Theta_i\right] = Var(m_{ij}X_{ij} \mid \Theta_i) = m_{ij}\Theta_i,$$

and therefore $\mu(\Theta_i) = v(\Theta_i) = \Theta_i$, so that $\mu = v$. Hence, rather than use both Estimators (7.3) and (7.4) to estimate μ and v, respectively, we could just use $\bar{X}..$ as our estimator for both μ and v. The following example illustrates this concept.

EXAMPLE 7.5

The number of claims arising from 300 insureds over a single period of observation has the following distribution:

Number of Claims:	0	1	2	3	4	5
Number of Insureds:	123	97	49	21	8	2

The number of claims for each insured is assumed to follow a (conditional) Poisson distribution, but the mean of each such distribution may be different for individual insureds. For each insured, obtain a credibility estimate for the number of claims during the next period of observation.

SOLUTION

We have the values (i) $r = 300$ insureds, (ii) $n_i = 1$ year of experience on each insured, for $i = 1, 2, ..., 300$, and (iii) $m_{i1} = 1$ exposure unit for each policyholder during our one period of observation.

For policyholder i, we assume that $X_{i1} | \Theta_i = \theta_i$ has a Poisson distribution with mean θ_i. Consequently, $\mu(\Theta_i) = v(\Theta_i) = \Theta_i$ and $\mu = v$. As in Example 6.6, the sample mean is $\bar{x}_{\cdot1} = 1.0$. Then, applying Theorem 5.2, we obtain

$$Var(X_{i1}) = Var\big(E[X_{i1} | \Theta]\big) + E\big[Var\big(X_{i1} | \Theta_i\big)\big]$$
$$= Var\big[\mu(\Theta_i)\big] + E\big[v(\Theta_i)\big]$$
$$= a + v = a + \mu.$$

We have just shown that the variance of X_{i1} is an unbiased estimator of $a + \mu$, so we can use the difference (sample variance minus sample mean) as an estimate of the parameter a. In our example, the sample variance is

$$\sum_{i=1}^{300} \frac{(x_{i1} - \bar{x}_{\cdot1})^2}{300}$$

$$= \frac{123(0-1)^2 + 97(1-1)^2 + 49(2-1)^2 + 21(3-1)^2 + 8(4-1)^2 + 2(5-1)^2}{300}$$

$$= 1.20$$

Hence our estimate of a is $1.20 - 1.0 = .20$, and our estimates of k and Z are

$$k = \frac{\hat{v}}{\hat{a}} = \frac{1.0}{.20} = 5.00$$

and

$$\hat{Z} = \frac{n_i}{n_i + k} = \frac{1}{1+5.00} = .167,$$

respectively. The estimated number of claims for each insured (according to the modeling scheme) is

$$\hat{Z}x_{i1} + (1 - \hat{Z})\bar{x}_{i\cdot} = .167x_{i1} + .833(1.00),$$

where x_{i1} is equal to 0, 1, 2, 3, 4 or 5, depending on the experience of the insured during the first observation period. The results are summarized in Table 7.3.

TABLE 7.3

Claims Observed in First Period x_{i1}	Claims Predicted for Second Period $.167x_{i1} + .833(1.00)$
0	.833
1	1.000
2	1.167
3	1.334
4	1.501
5	1.668

❑

Note that in Example 7.5, $v = \mu$, so that in order to carry out the requisite estimation procedure only one year of experience is required for each policyholder. Note also that we have used the biased form of the estimator for the variance of $\overline{X}._1$, both here and in Section 6.6.4. The unbiased version of the estimator would use 299 in the denominator, rather than 300. The result, accurate to two decimals, would still be 1.20.

EXAMPLE 7.6

Suppose we are interested in the number of individual members of various group health insurance policies who file insurance claims. We assume that the probability of a claim varies among the groups, but is constant among the individual members of each group. We further assume that this probability is constant from one policy year to the next. We let $m_{ij}X_{ij}$ denote the random variable for the number of the m_{ij} insureds of the ith group policy who file claims during the jth policy year. We wish to investigate the existence of any relationships among μ, v, and a which may simplify the estimation of these three parameters of the credibility model.

SOLUTION

We let Θ_i denote the random variable representing the probability of at least one claim during the policy year for the members of the ith group. A reasonable additional assumption is that $m_{ij}X_{ij}$ has a binomial distribution with parameters m_{ij} and Θ_i. Then we obtain

$$E\left[m_{ij}X_{ij} \mid \Theta_i\right] = m_{ij}\Theta_i$$

and

$$Var\left(m_{ij}X_{ij} \mid \Theta_i\right) = m_{ij}\Theta_i\left(1-\Theta_i\right).$$

Consequently, $\mu(\Theta_i) = \Theta_i$ and $v(\Theta_i) = \Theta_i(1-\Theta_i)$, and therefore

$$\mu = E[\Theta_i],$$

$$v = \mu - E[\Theta_i^2],$$

and

$$a = Var(\Theta_i) = E[\Theta_i^2] - \mu^2 = \mu - v - \mu^2.$$

Therefore, if we have estimates of μ and v, for example, we can obtain an estimate of a by using the equation $a = \mu - v - \mu^2$. ❏

7.5 EXERCISES

7.1 Introduction

7-1 Which of the following statements best expresses the main advantage of the Bühlmann-Straub model over the Bühlmann model?

I. The Bühlmann-Straub model allows different numbers of exposure units across past policy years.

II. The Bühlmann-Straub model allows a wider variety of statistical loss functions.

III. The Bühlmann-Straub model is less mathematically complex, so the required computational sophistication is lower.

7.2 Model for One Policyholder with Known Underlying Probability Distributions

7-2 Which of the following statements are true for the Bühlmann-Straub model of Section 7.2?

I. This model generalizes that of Section 6.6.1 by allowing different numbers of exposure units by policy year.

II. This model is more restrictive than that of Section 6.6.1, because this model requires that a number of probability distributions be known.

7-3 How are the following quantities interrelated, based on the notation of the Bühlmann-Straub model of Section 7.2?

(a) μ

(b) $E_\Theta\left[\mu(\Theta)\right]$

(c) $E_\Theta\left[\mu(\Theta)\,|\,X_1\right]$

(d) $E[X_2]$

(e) $E[X_2\,|\,X_1]$

7-4 Consider Example 6.8, which dealt with the four urns. Suppose that, during the first observation period, we drew four balls of which exactly three were marked 1. If seven balls are to be drawn during the second period of observation, what is the best estimate under the Bühlmann-Straub model for one policyholder of the number of balls marked 1 drawn during that period?

7-5 Let the conditions be as in Exercise 7-4, except that we have now observed $X_2 = \frac{2}{7}$. If seven balls are to be drawn during the third period of observation, what is the best estimate under the Bühlmann-Straub model for one policyholder of the number of balls marked 1 drawn during that period?

7.3 Model for Two or More Policyholders

7-6 Compute the estimated aggregate claim amount to be observed during the fourth policy year on each of the three groups whose first three years of experience data are presented in the following table. The aggregate claim amounts are in millions of dollars. Assume no inflation.

Group Policyholder		Policy Year			
		1	2	3	4
1	Aggregate Claim Amount	8,000	11,000	15,000	–
	Size of Group	40	50	70	75
2	Aggregate Claim Amount	20,000	24,000	18,000	–
	Size of Group	100	120	120	95
3	Aggregate Claim Amount	10,000	15,000	13,500	–
	Size of Group	50	60	60	60

7-7 Which of the following statements are true for the Bühlmann-Straub model of Section 7.3?

I. This model generalizes that of Section 6.6.1 by allowing different numbers of exposure units by policy year and/or policyholder.

II. This model generalizes that of Section 7.2 by dropping the requirement that all relevant probability distributions be known.

7.4 Semiparametric Estimation

7-8   The number of claims arising from 200 insureds over a single period of observation has the following distribution:

Number of Claims: 0   1   2   3
Number of Insureds: 125 40 20 15

The number of claims for each insured is assumed to follow a (conditional) Poisson distribution, but the mean of each such distribution may be different for individual insureds. For each insured, obtain a credibility estimate for the number of claims during the next period of observation.

7-9   Using the notation and methodology presented in Example 7.6, calculate the estimated value of a, given the values $\mu = .30$ and $v = .10$.

CHAPTER 8

CREDIBILITY AND BAYESIAN INFERENCE

8.1 INTRODUCTION

In Section 10.3 we will show that the Bühlmann credibility estimate is the best linear approximation to the Bayesian estimate of the pure premium. In this chapter, following Ericson [1970] and Jewell [1974], we present (without proof) a theorem showing that the Bühlmann credibility estimate is equal to the Bayesian estimate of the pure premium for a large class of problems. We use the Bernoulli, Poisson, and normal distributions to illustrate these results. We begin with some definitions.

8.2 CONJUGATE PRIOR DISTRIBUTIONS

Suppose that H is the event that some hypothesis is true and that B is another event. Then we can use $P[H]$ to denote our initial (or prior) degree of belief in H. We call $P[H]$ the **prior probability of H**. According to the definition of conditional probability, we can consider $P[B|H]$ to represent the conditional probability of event B, given hypothesis H is true. However, when considered as a function of H, the expression $P[B|H]$ is called the **likelihood of H** on B, and is a crucial element of Bayesian analysis. Finally, $P[H|B]$ is called the **posterior probability of H given B**.

EXAMPLE 8.1

The results of ten independent Bernoulli trials with (constant) probability of success, Θ, are: SSSFSFSFSF. In other words, we have a sequence of ten trials in which we observed six successes and four failures. So, the likelihood function is

$$L(\Theta = \theta) = \theta^6 (1-\theta)^4,$$

Here the likelihood, L, is a function of Θ and represents the probability of the observed sequence given $\Theta = \theta$.

It is useful at this point to reconsider Bayes' theorem, stated in the notation of this chapter as

$$P[H \mid B] = \frac{P[B \mid H] \cdot P[H]}{P[B]}, \qquad (8.1)$$

provided $P[B] > 0$. Ignoring $P[B]$, which may be considered a constant since it does not depend on H, we can interpret Equation (8.1) as the following function of H:

The posterior probability of H is proportional to the product of (a) the prior probability of H, $P[H]$, and (b) the likelihood of H on B, $P[B|H]$.

In Section 4.2 we constructed various discrete prior, posterior, and predictive probability distributions. At this time we will introduce several formal definitions.

Definition 8.1

A distribution of prior probabilities (i.e., a prior distribution) is said to be a **conjugate prior distribution for a given likelihood** (i.e., the conditional distribution of the current observations) if both the prior distribution and the resulting posterior distribution are from the same family of probability distributions. (For example, in the proof of Theorem 8.1, the prior beta distribution, $\beta(a,b)$, is shown to have posterior beta distribution $\beta(a+r, b+n-r)$. Thus, both the prior and posterior distributions are from the same family (the beta) of probability distributions, with different parameter values.) So $\beta(a,b)$ is the conjugate prior in this case.

A major advantage of using conjugate prior distributions is that the posterior distribution for one period (e.g., year) can be used as the prior distribution for the next period. Since no new functional forms are required, the computational complexity of the procedure is considerably reduced.

We illustrate the concept of conjugate prior distributions with the examples presented in the following three subsections.

8.2.1 BERNOULLI EXAMPLE

We assume that we have a sequence of n Bernoulli random variables, $N_1, N_2, ..., N_n$, each with constant probability of success Θ. We assume that these n random variables are conditionally independent, given $\Theta = \theta$. We discuss the inferences that can be made about Θ. We first note that for $a > 0$ and $b > 0$,

$$g(\theta \mid a, b) = \begin{cases} \dfrac{\Gamma(a+b)}{\Gamma(a) \cdot \Gamma(b)} \theta^{a-1}(1-\theta)^{b-1} & 0 \leq \theta \leq 1 \\ 0 & \text{otherwise} \end{cases} \tag{8.2}$$

is the density function of a random variable having a beta distribution with parameters a and b. We use $\beta(a,b)$ to denote such a distribution. We use $B(n,\Theta)$ to denote a binomial distribution with parameters n and Θ, where n is the number of independent trials and Θ is the probability of success on an individual trial. Given $B(n,\Theta)$, the probability of r successes in n independent Bernoulli trials is given by

$$\binom{n}{r} \Theta^r (1-\Theta)^{n-r}, \tag{8.3}$$

for $r = 0,1,...,n$. We are now ready to present the main result of this section.

Theorem 8.1

If (a) n conditionally independent Bernoulli random variables, denoted $N_1, N_2, ..., N_n$, have constant[1] probability of success (b) the conditional density function of N_i given $\Theta = \theta$, is

$$f(n_i \mid \theta) = \begin{cases} \theta & n_i = 1 \\ 1-\theta & n_i = 0 \end{cases},$$

n_i is the realization of the random variable N_i, where n_i is the realization of the random variable N_i and (c) the prior distribution of Θ is $\beta(a,b)$, then the posterior distribution of Θ is $\beta(a+r, b+n-r)$, where $r = \sum_{}^{n} n_i$ is the number of successes observed in the n Bernoulli trials. (Cont.)

---

[1] By "constant" we mean that Θ does not change over time, so that it is constant from one Bernoulli trial to another. Nevertheless, Θ is assumed to be a random variable having $\beta(a,b)$ as its prior distribution.

Proof
From Equation (8.2), we note that the prior beta density of Θ is

$$\frac{\Gamma(a+b)}{\Gamma(a)\cdot\Gamma(b)}\theta^{a-1}(1-\theta)^{b-1}, \qquad (8.2)$$

for $0 \le \theta \le,...,n$. By the conditional independence assumption, the joint likelihood , $f(n_1,n_2,...,n_n \mid \theta)$, can be rewritten as the product of the n likelihoods, $\prod\limits^{n} f(n_i \mid \theta)$. The product of the likelihoods is proportional to

$$\theta^r(1-\theta)^{n-r}. \qquad (8.4)$$

Since the posterior density is proportional to the product of Expressions (8.2) and (8.4), the posterior density is proportional to

$$\theta^{a+r-1}(1-\theta)^{b+n-r-1}, \qquad (8.5)$$

which establishes the result.[2]

8.2.2 POISSON EXAMPLE

We assume that we have a sequence of m random variables, denoted $N_1,N_2,...,N_m$, having a Poisson distribution with constant mean Θ. The random variables $N_1,N_2,...,N_m$ are assumed to be conditionally independent, given $\Theta = \theta$. The Poisson conditional density function given $\Theta = \theta$ is

$$f(n \mid \theta) = \begin{cases} \frac{e^{-\theta}\theta^n}{n!} & n = 0,1,... \\ 0 & \text{otherwise} \end{cases}. \qquad (8.6)$$

We also note that for $\alpha > 0$ and $\beta > 0$,

$$g(\theta \mid \alpha,\beta) = \begin{cases} \frac{e^{-\beta\theta}\beta^\alpha\theta^{\alpha-1}}{\Gamma(\alpha)} & \theta \ge 0 \\ 0 & \text{otherwise} \end{cases} \qquad (8.7)$$

is the density function of a random variable having a gamma distribution with parameters α and β. We use $G(\alpha,\beta)$ to denote such a distribution.

---

[2] See Exercise 8-2(a) for more details.

Theorem 8.2
Computational Issues

If (a) m conditionally independent Poisson random variables, denoted $N_1, N_2, ..., N_m$, have constant mean Θ, (b) the conditional density function of N_i given $\Theta = \theta$ is $f(n_i \mid \Theta)$ and (c) the prior distribution of Θ is $G(\alpha, \beta)$, then the posterior distribution of Θ is $G(\alpha + m\bar{n}, \beta + m)$, where n_i is the realization of the random variable N_i and $m\bar{n} = \sum\limits_{i=1}^{m} n_i$.

Proof

From Equation (8.7), we note that the prior density of Θ is

$$\frac{e^{-\beta\theta}\beta^{\alpha}\theta^{\alpha-1}}{\Gamma(\alpha)}, \tag{8.8}$$

for $\theta > 0$, and zero otherwise. By the conditional independence assumption, the joint likelihood $f(n_1, n_2, ..., n_m \mid \theta)$ can be rewritten as the product of the m likelihoods, $\prod\limits_{i=1}^{m} f(n_i \mid \theta)$. The product of the likelihoods is, from Equation (8.6), proportional to

$$(e^{-\theta}\theta^{n_1})(e^{-\theta}\theta^{n_2}) \cdots (e^{-\theta}\theta^{n_m}) = e^{-m\theta} \cdot \theta^{\left(\sum\limits_{i=1}^{m} n_i\right)} = e^{-m\theta}\theta^{m\bar{n}}. \tag{8.9}$$

The posterior density is proportional to the product of (8.8) and (8.9), so it is proportional to $e^{-(\beta+m)\theta}\theta^{\alpha+m\bar{n}-1}$, which establishes the result.[3]

For insurance ratemaking, the posterior distribution for one year is the prior distribution for the next year. The use of conjugate prior distributions enables the actuary to continue using distributions of the same form, thereby substantially reducing the required amount of computation. Of course, with modern computers and sophisticated statistical software packages such as WinBUGS, it is not difficult to solve such problems using more precise priors and thereby obtain better answers without expending much additional effort. For an example of this see Chapter 13. For a less sophisticated alternative approach, see Chapter 11.

---

[3] See Exercise 8-2(b) for more details.

8.2.3 NORMAL EXAMPLE

We assume that we have a sequence of n random variables, denoted $X_1, X_2, ..., X_n$, from a normal distribution with mean Θ and variance σ_1^2. The random variables $X_1, X_2, ..., X_n$ are assumed to be conditionally independent, given Θ. Then for $\Theta = \theta$, the conditional probability density function for each of the X_i's is

$$f(x \mid \theta) = \frac{1}{\sigma_1 \cdot \sqrt{2\pi}} \exp\left[-\frac{(x-\theta)^2}{2\sigma_1^2} \right] \tag{8.10}$$

and the probability density function of Θ is

$$g(\theta) = \frac{1}{\sigma_2 \cdot \sqrt{2\pi}} \exp\left[-\frac{(x-\mu)^2}{2\sigma_2^2} \right]. \tag{8.11}$$

Note that both f and g are normal probability density functions. We are now ready to present the main result of this section.

Theorem 8.3

If (a) n conditionally independent normal random variables, denoted $X_1, X_2, ..., X_n$, have constant mean and known constant variance σ_1^2, (b) the conditional density function of X_i given $\Theta = \theta$ is $f(x_i \mid \theta)$, and (c) the prior density function of Θ is the normal density, $g(\theta)$ with known constant mean μ and known constant variance σ_2^2, then the posterior probability density function of Θ is normal with mean

$$\tilde{\mu} = \frac{\mu \sigma_1^2 + \sigma_2^2 n \bar{x}}{\sigma_1^2 + n \sigma_2^2} \tag{8.12}$$

and variance

$$\tilde{\sigma}^2 = \frac{\sigma_1^2 \sigma_2^2}{\sigma_1^2 + n \sigma_2^2}, \tag{8.13}$$

where $\bar{x} = \dfrac{1}{n} \sum_{i=1}^{n} x_i$ is the average of the realizations of the n random variables $X_1, X_2, ..., X_n$.

(Cont.)

Proof

The posterior density function of Θ is proportional to the product of the prior density function of Θ and the joint likelihood of Θ on $X_1 = x_1$, $X_2 = x_2, ..., X_n = x_n$, namely

$$\exp\left[-\frac{(\theta-\mu)^2}{2\sigma_2^2}\right] \cdot f(x_1, x_2, ..., x_n \mid \theta). \qquad (8.14)$$

Due to the conditional independence of the X_i's, Expression (8.14) can be rewritten as

$$\exp\left[-\frac{(\theta-\mu)^2}{2\sigma_2^2}\right] \cdot \left[\prod_{i=1}^{n} f(x_i \mid \theta)\right]$$

$$= \exp\left[-\frac{(\theta-\mu)^2}{2\sigma_2^2}\right] \cdot \left[\prod_{i=1}^{n} \exp\left[-\frac{(x_i-\theta)^2}{2\sigma_1^2}\right]\right]. \qquad (8.15)$$

Deleting terms not involving θ, the right side of Equation (8.15) is found to be proportional to

$$\exp\left[\frac{\theta n\overline{x}}{\sigma_1^2} - \frac{n\theta^2}{2\sigma_1^2} - \frac{\theta^2}{2\sigma_2^2} + \frac{(\theta-\mu)^2}{2\sigma_2^2}\right]. \qquad (8.16)$$

Completing the square inside the brackets, and deleting terms not involving θ, we find Expression (8.16) to be proportional to

$$\exp\left\{-\frac{\sigma_1^2 + n\sigma_2^2}{2\sigma_1^2\sigma_2^2}\left[\theta - \frac{\mu\sigma_1^2 + \sigma_2^2 n\overline{x}}{\sigma_1^2 + n\sigma_2^2}\right]^2\right\}.$$

Thus we have shown that the posterior density function of Θ, given $X_1 = x_1, X_2 = x_2, ..., X_n = x_n$, is normal with mean $\tilde{\mu}$ and variance $\tilde{\sigma}^2$, as given by Equations (8.12) and (8.13), respectively.

8.3 CREDIBILITY AND CONJUGATE DISTRIBUTIONS

Mayerson [1964] showed that for each of three pairs of conjugate priors and their likelihoods, namely, beta-binomial, gamma-Poisson, and normal-normal (with known variance), the Bühlmann credibility estimates are equal to the corresponding Bayesian estimate of the pure premium. The results for the beta-binomial and gamma-Poisson pairs had been demonstrated earlier by Bailey [1950]. The result also holds for the gamma-exponential and geometric-beta pairs. We will now illustrate this result for the Bernoulli, Poisson, and normal examples considered in Section 8.2.

The following theorem shows that the mean of the posterior distribution of Θ is equal to the mean of the predictive distribution of X_{n+1}, provided

$$E\left[X_i \,|\, \Theta\right] = \mu(\Theta) \tag{8.17}$$

for $i = 1, 2, \dots$.

Theorem 8.4

Let $X_1, X_2, \dots$ be random variables with mean such that (a) Equation (8.17) holds for $i = 1, 2, \dots$, and (b) the X_i's are conditionally independent given Θ. Then, for $n = 1, 2, \dots$,

$$E[X_{n+1} \,|\, X_1 = x_1, X_2 = x_2, \dots, X_n = x_n]$$
$$= E_\Theta\left[\mu(\Theta) \,|\, X_1 = x_1, X_2 = x_2, \dots, X_n = x_n\right]. \tag{8.18}$$

Proof

$$E[X_{n+1} \,|\, X_1 = x_1, X_2 = x_2, \dots, X_n = x_n]$$
$$= E_\Theta\left[E\left[X_{n+1} \,|\, X_1 = x_1, X_2 = x_2, \dots, X_n = x_n, \Theta\right]\right]$$
$$= E_\Theta\left[E\left[X_{n+1} \,|\, \Theta\right] X_1 = x_1, X_2 = x_2, \dots, X_n = x_n\right]$$
$$= E_\Theta\left[\mu(\Theta) \,|\, X_1 = x_1, X_2 = x_2, \dots, X_n = x_n\right],$$

where the second equality is a result of the conditional independence assumption and the third equality results from the application of Equation (8.17).

> ## Corollary 8.1
> Under the conditions of Theorem 8.4, if $\mu(\Theta) = \Theta$, then
>
> $$E[X_{n+1} \mid X_1 = x_1, X_2 = x_2, ..., X_n = x_n]$$
> $$= E_\Theta[\Theta \mid X_1 = x_1, X_2 = x_2, ..., X_n = x_n].$$
>
> **Proof**
> Simply replace $\mu(\Theta)$ by Θ in the proof of Theorem 8.4.

8.3.1 BERNOULLI EXAMPLE REVISITED

Let I denote the indicator random variable representing the result of a single Bernoulli trial. We assume that I has probability Θ of success, where Θ has a beta distribution denoted by $\beta(a,b)$. Since the mean[4] and variance of a random variable with distribution $\beta(a,b)$ are $\frac{a}{a+b}$ and $\frac{ab}{(a+b+1)(a+b)^2}$, respectively, the value of k is

$$
\begin{aligned}
k &= \frac{E_\Theta\left[Var_I\left(I \mid \Theta\right)\right]}{Var_\Theta\left(E_I\left[I \mid \Theta\right]\right)} = \frac{E_\Theta\left[\Theta(1-\Theta)\right]}{Var_\Theta(\Theta)} \\[2mm]
&= \frac{E_\Theta[\Theta] - E_\Theta[\Theta^2]}{Var_\Theta(\Theta)} \\[2mm]
&= \frac{E_\Theta(\Theta) - \left(Var_\Theta(\Theta) + (E_\Theta[\Theta])^2\right)}{Var_\Theta(\Theta)} \\[2mm]
&= \frac{\frac{a}{a+b} - \left\{\frac{ab}{(a+b+1)(a+b)^2} + \left(\frac{a}{a+b}\right)^2\right\}}{\frac{ab}{(a+b+1)(a+b)^2}} \\[2mm]
&= \frac{1 - \left\{\frac{b+(a+b+1)(a)}{(a+b+1)(a+b)}\right\}}{\frac{b}{(a+b+1),(a+b)}} \\[2mm]
&= \frac{\frac{(a+b+1)(a+b)-b-(a+b+1)(a)}{(a+b+1)(a+b)}}{\frac{b}{(a+b+1)(a+b)}} \\[2mm]
&= \frac{(a+b+1)(b) - b}{b} = (a+b+1) - 1 = a+b. \quad (8.19)
\end{aligned}
$$

---

[4] See Exercise 8-8(a)(i).

Since $k = a + b$, then

$$Z = \frac{n}{n+k} = \frac{n}{n+a+b}. \qquad (8.20)$$

For the Bernoulli example of Section 8.2.1, the posterior distribution of Θ is $\beta(a+r, b+n-r)$, and the mean of this posterior distribution of Θ is $\frac{a+r}{a+b+n}$. We can rewrite this mean as

$$\frac{a}{a+b+n} + \frac{r}{a+b+n} = \frac{a}{a+b+n}\left(\frac{a+b}{a+b}\right) + \frac{r}{a+b+n}\left(\frac{n}{n}\right)$$

$$= \left(\frac{a+b}{a+b+n}\right)\left(\frac{a}{a+b}\right) + \left(\frac{n}{a+b+n}\right)\left(\frac{r}{n}\right). \qquad (8.21)$$

Since $Z = \frac{n}{a+b+n}$ and $(1-Z) = \frac{a+b}{a+b+n}$, we can rewrite the right side of Equation (8.21) as

$$(1-Z)\left(\frac{a}{a+b}\right) + Z\left(\frac{r}{n}\right). \qquad (8.22a)$$

Descriptively, (8.22a) can be interpreted as

$$(1-Z)(mean\ of\ prior) + Z(mean\ of\ observed\ data), \qquad (8.22b)$$

since (a) the mean of the prior beta distribution is $\frac{a}{a+b}$, and (b) the proportion of successes observed in n trials, which is the mean of the observed data, is $\frac{r}{n}$.

Thus we have shown that if (a) the data can be assumed to have a binomial distribution (the result of n independent Bernoulli trials), and (b) a beta distribution is employed as the prior distribution, then the mean of the posterior distribution is equal to the corresponding Bühlmann credibility estimate. Moreover, the mean of the posterior distribution is equal to the mean of the predictive distribution of the next observation (i.e., Bernoulli trial). The mean of the predictive distribution of the next observation is the Bayesian estimate of the frequency component of the pure premium, assuming a squared error loss function.

Assumptions (a) and (b) are employed in Exercises 8-14 and 8-15, and in numerical examples presented in Chapter 11.

8.3.2 POISSON EXAMPLE REVISITED

Let N be a random variable having a Poisson distribution with mean Θ. In turn, let the mean of the Poisson distribution, Θ, have a gamma distribution, $G(\alpha, \beta)$, whose density function is defined by Equation (8.7). Since the mean and variance of $G(\alpha, \beta)$ are $\frac{\alpha}{\beta}$ and $\frac{\alpha}{\beta^2}$, respectively, the value of k is

$$k = \frac{E_\Theta\left[Var_N\left(N\,|\Theta\,\right)\right]}{Var_\Theta\left(E_N\left[N\,|\Theta\,\right]\right)} = \frac{E_\Theta[\Theta]}{Var_\Theta(\Theta)} = \frac{\frac{\alpha}{\beta}}{\frac{\alpha}{\beta^2}} = \beta. \qquad (8.23)$$

Since $k = \beta$, then for m independent trials (or periods of observation)

$$Z = \frac{m}{m+k} = \frac{m}{m+\beta}. \qquad (8.24)$$

For the Poisson distribution example of Section 8.2.2, the posterior distribution of Θ is $G(\alpha + m\bar{n}, \beta + m)$ and the mean of the posterior distribution of Θ is $\frac{\alpha + m\bar{n}}{m+\beta}$.[5] We can rewrite this mean as

$$\frac{\alpha}{m+\beta} + \frac{m\bar{n}}{m+\beta} = \frac{\beta}{m+\beta}\left(\frac{\alpha}{\beta}\right) + \frac{m}{m+\beta}(\bar{n}).$$

Since $Z = \frac{m}{m+\beta}$ and $1-Z = \frac{\beta}{m+\beta}$, we can rewrite the posterior mean as

$$(1-Z)\left(\frac{\alpha}{\beta}\right) + Z(\bar{n}). \qquad (8.25a)$$

Descriptively, (8.25a) can be stated as

$$(1-Z)(mean\ of\ prior) + Z(mean\ of\ observed\ data), \qquad (8.25b)$$

since the mean of the prior gamma distribution is $\frac{\alpha}{\beta}$.

---

[5] See Exercise 8-8(b)(ii).

In Section 9.3 we show that the corresponding predictive distribution is a negative binomial distribution.

In summary, we have shown that if (a) the data can be assumed to have a Poisson distribution, with parameter (mean) Θ, and (b) a gamma distribution is employed as the prior distribution of Θ, then the mean of the posterior distribution is equal to the corresponding Bühlmann credibility estimate. Exercises 8-9, 8-10, 8-11, and 8-15 illustrate the application of this approach.

8.3.3 NORMAL EXAMPLE REVISITED

As in Section 8.2.3, let X be a random variable having a normal distribution with mean Θ and variance σ_1^2. In turn, let Θ have the normal distribution $N(\mu, \sigma_2^2)$, whose density function is defined by Equation (8.11). Under these assumptions, the value of k is

$$k = \frac{E_\Theta\left[Var_X\left(X\,|\Theta\right)\right]}{Var_\Theta\left(E_X\left[X\,|\Theta\right]\right)} = \frac{E_\Theta\left[\sigma_1^2\right]}{Var_\Theta(\Theta)} = \frac{\sigma_1^2}{\sigma_2^2}. \qquad (8.26)$$

Then for n conditionally independent trials (or periods of observation) we have

$$Z = \frac{n}{n+k} = \frac{n}{n+\left(\dfrac{\sigma_1^2}{\sigma_2^2}\right)}. \qquad (8.27)$$

We can rewrite the mean of the posterior distribution of Θ as

$$E\left[\Theta\,|\,X_1 = x_1, X_2 = x_2, \ldots, X_n = x_n\right]$$

$$= \frac{\mu\sigma_1^2 + \sigma_2^2 n\bar{x}}{\sigma_1^2 + n\sigma_2^2}$$

$$= \frac{\sigma_1^2}{\sigma_1^2 + n\sigma_2^2}\cdot\mu + \frac{n\sigma_2^2}{\sigma_1^2 + n\sigma_2^2}\cdot\bar{x} = (1-Z)H + ZR \qquad (8.28)$$

where $H = \mu, R = \bar{x}$, and

$$Z = \frac{n\sigma_2^2}{\sigma_1^2 + n\sigma_2^2} = \frac{n}{n + \left(\frac{\sigma_1^2}{\sigma_2^2}\right)},$$

as already established in Equation (8.27), above. Descriptively, Equation (8.28) can be stated as

$$(1-Z)(mean\ of\ prior) + Z(mean\ of\ observed\ data),$$

since the mean of the prior normal distribution of Θ is μ.

In summary, we have shown that if (a) the data are assumed to have a normal distribution with mean Θ and variance σ_1^2, and (b) a normal distribution with mean and variance σ_2^2 is employed as the prior distribution of Θ, then the mean of the posterior distribution is equal to the corresponding Bühlmann credibility estimate. Again, since the conditions of Theorem 8.4 are satisfied, the mean of the posterior distribution is also equal to the mean of the predictive distribution of the next observation (i.e., normal trial). Also, the mean of the posterior distribution of Θ is the Bayesian point estimate of Θ, assuming a squared error loss function.

Note that the estimate, $(1-Z)\mu + Z\bar{x}$, is a linear function of the realizations $x_1, x_2, ..., x_n$ of the corresponding random variables $X_1, X_2, ..., X_n$, because $\bar{x}$ is a linear function of $x_1, x_2, ..., x_n$. Finally, replacing the realizations of the X_i's by the corresponding random variables, we obtain $(1-Z)\mu + Z\bar{X}$, as the estimator of Θ, where $\bar{X} = \frac{1}{n}\sum_{i=1}^{n} X_i$. (See Exercise 8-17 for an application of this method.)

8.4 CREDIBILITY AND EXPONENTIAL FAMILIES

8.4.1 EXPONENTIAL FAMILIES

We begin this section by defining exponential families of distributions, and presenting a few examples thereof. We then state, without proof, an important general result.

Definition 8.2

Consider a family $\{f(x\,|\,\Theta);\Theta\,\varepsilon\,\Omega\}$ of probability density functions, where Ω is the interval set $\Omega = \{\Theta : c < \Theta < d\}$ and c and d are known constants.

(a) A probability density function of the form

$$f(x\,|\,\Theta) = \begin{cases} \exp\left[p(\Theta) \cdot A(x) + B(x) + q(\Theta)\right] & a < x < b \\ 0 & \text{otherwise} \end{cases}$$

is said to be a member of the **exponential family of probability density functions of the continuous type**.

(b) A probability density function of the form

$$f(x\,|\,\Theta) = \begin{cases} \exp\left[p(\Theta) \cdot A(x) + B(x) + q(\Theta)\right] & x = x_1, x_2, \dots \\ 0 & \text{otherwise} \end{cases}$$

is said to a member of the **exponential family of probability density functions of the discrete type**.

Definition 8.3

An exponential family for which $A(x) = x$ is said to be a **linear exponential family**.

To illustrate, let the random variable X have a binomial density function of the form given by Equation (8.3). For $x = 0,1,\dots,n$, we can rewrite the right side of Equation (8.3) as

$$\binom{n}{x}\left(\frac{\Theta}{1-\Theta}\right)^x (1-\Theta)^n, \tag{8.29}$$

with r replaced by x. We let $y = \left(\frac{\Theta}{1-\Theta}\right)^x$ and take the natural logarithm of both sides of the equation, yielding

$$\ln y = x \cdot \ln\left(\frac{\Theta}{1-\Theta}\right),$$

or

$$y = \exp(\ln y) = \exp\left\{x \cdot \ln\left(\frac{\Theta}{1-\Theta}\right)\right\}.$$

Thus we can rewrite Expression (8.29) as

$$\binom{n}{x} \cdot \exp\left\{x \cdot \ln\left(\frac{\Theta}{1-\Theta}\right)\right\} \cdot (1-\Theta)^n.$$

Since $\binom{n}{x}$ and $(1-\Theta)^n$ can be written as $\exp[B(x)]$ and $\exp[q(\Theta)]$, respectively, and we can let $A(x) = x$ and $p(\Theta) = \ln\left(\frac{\Theta}{1-\Theta}\right)$, the binomial density function is indeed an example of a linear exponential family of the discrete type.

The Poisson, exponential, and normal (with known variance) distributions are also examples of linear exponential families.

8.4.2 CONDITIONS FOR THE EQUALITY OF THE BÜHLMANN AND BAYESIAN ESTIMATORS

Ericson [1970] and Jewell [1974] have shown that the class of prior-likelihood families for which the Bühlmann credibility estimator of the pure premium is equal to the corresponding Bayesian estimator can be extended beyond the four prior-likelihood families discussed in Section 8.3. Specifically Ericson [1970] shows the result stated in the following theorem.

Theorem 8.5

If (a) the conjugate prior distribution is used as the prior distribution, and (b) the likelihood density is a member of a linear exponential family, then the Bühlmann credibility estimator of the pure premium is equal to the corresponding Bayesian estimator assuming a squared error loss function.[6]

---

[6] This was defined in Chapter 3.

8.4.3 AN ALTERNATE PROCEDURE FOR OBTAINING BÜHLMANN AND BAYESIAN ESTIMATES

Gerber [1995] proposed an alternative (but closely related) procedure for obtaining the Bühlmann/Bayesian estimate of the pure premium for the five pairs of conjugate priors and their likelihoods listed in the first paragraph of Section 8.3. Gerber stated that the advantage of his procedure is that it avoids a preliminary reparameterization of the parameters such as that described in Section 8.4.1 for the binomial density function.

8.5 SUMMARY OF KEY RESULTS OF THE BAYESIAN PARADIGM

8.5.1 PARAMETERS

Both the prior distribution and the posterior distribution involve one or more parameters. To be specific, we consider the case of a vector of parameters, Θ, which may consist of one or more components.

The posterior distribution of Θ is obtained by applying Bayes' Theorem to the prior distribution of Θ and the likelihood of Θ on the observation(s). The posterior distribution of Θ is an updated version of the prior distribution, given the results of one or more periods of observation. In the example of Chapter 4, we updated the joint prior distribution of the die-spinner parameters A and B, based on the observation $X_1 = x_1$, to obtain the posterior distribution specified by $P[A = a_i, B = b_j \mid X_1 = x_1]$, for $i = 1, 2$ and $j = 1, 2$.

8.5.2 RANDOM VARIABLES

The conditional distribution of the random variable X_2, given the value of the random variable X_1, is called the predictive distribution of X_2 given the value of X_1. This is similar to the posterior distribution of a parameter.

The predictive distribution is obtained by summing or integrating the product of the likelihood and the posterior distribution over the prior parameter space. For example, in Chapter 4 the predictive distribution (see Table 4.6) is obtained by summing the products of the (joint) posterior probabilities of A and B given $X_1 = k$ (see Table 4.5) and the conditional probabilities (i.e., the likelihood) of $X_1 = k$ given A and B (see Table 4.4).

Let X_i denote the random variable for the aggregate amount of insurance claims during the ith period of observation, for $i = 1, 2, \ldots$. Then the predictive distribution of X_{n+1}, given $X_1 = x_1, X_2 = x_2, \ldots, X_n = x_n$, is the relevant distribution for risk management and decision making because it incorporates both the experience of the n observation periods and the uncertainty inherent in estimating the parameters of the model.

8.5.3 PURE PREMIUM ESTIMATES (EXPECTED VALUES)

The initial pure premium estimate, before any observations are made, is $E[X_1]$. The revised pure premium estimate, after the first observation, is the conditional expectation $E[X_2 \mid X_1]$. This is simply the mean of the predictive distribution of the random variable X_2, given the outcome of the random variable X_1. More generally, the revised pure premium estimate is $E[X_{n+1} \mid X_1 X_2, \ldots, X_n]$ for the $(n+1)^{st}$ period of observation.

8.5.4 EXAMPLE 6.1 REVISITED

In the following example we recompute the estimate of Example 6.1, using the Bayesian paradigm instead of Bühlmann's model. The point we wish to make is that if the prior distribution of the parameter of interest is not a conjugate prior distribution, then the Bayesian estimate may be different from the Bühlmann estimate.

EXAMPLE 8.2

The number of claims, N_i, during the ith policy year $(i = 1, 2)$ for an individual insured has a Poisson distribution with parameter Θ. The prior distribution of Θ is the uniform distribution over the interval $(0,1)$. An individual insured has exactly one claim during the first policy year. Use the Bayesian paradigm to estimate the insured's expected number of claims during the second policy year.

SOLUTION

We seek the exact value of $E[N_2 \mid N_1 = 1]$, under the assumptions listed above. By Corollary 8.1, it is sufficient to calculate $E[\Theta \mid N_1 = 1]$, the posterior mean of Θ given $N_1 = 1$. The prior density function of Θ is

$$f(\theta) = \begin{cases} 1 & 0 < \theta < 1 \\ 0 & \text{elsewhere} \end{cases}.$$

The likelihood of Θ on $N_1 = 1$ is $e^{-\theta}\theta^1$. Then, for $0 < \theta < 1$, the posterior density function of Θ given $N_1 = 1$ is proportional to the product of the prior density and the likelihood, specifically

$$f(\theta) \cdot (e^{-\theta}\theta^1) = (1)(e^{-\theta}\theta^1) = \theta \cdot e^{-\theta}$$

for $0 < \theta < 1$. The posterior density of Θ is

$$j(\theta \mid N_1 = 1) = c \cdot \theta \cdot e^{-\theta}$$

where c is the constant that satisfies

$$\int_0^\infty c \cdot \theta \cdot e^{-\theta} \, d\theta = 1.$$

We can determine c by evaluating the above integral using integration by parts and solving for c. The result is

$$c = \frac{1}{1 - 2e^{-1}}.$$

This implies that $f(\theta \mid N_1 = 1) = c \cdot \theta \cdot e^{-\theta} = \frac{\theta \cdot e^{-\theta}}{1 - 2e^{-1}}$.

Finally, the posterior mean of Θ is

$$\int_0^1 \theta \cdot f(\theta \mid N_1 = 1) \, d\theta = \int_0^1 \theta \cdot \frac{\theta \cdot e^{-\theta}}{1 - 2e^{-1}} \, d\theta$$

$$= \int_0^1 \frac{\theta^2 \cdot e^{-\theta}}{1 - 2e^{-1}} \, d\theta = \frac{2 - 5e^{-1}}{1 - 2e^{-1}} = .608.$$

Thus we have shown that the Bayesian estimate (given $N_1 = 1$) of the expected number of claims during the second policy year is .608, which differs from the corresponding Bühlmann estimate of .571 calculated in Example 6.1. ❑

8.6 EXERCISES

8.1 Introduction
8.2 Conjugate Prior Distributions

8-1 Given the occurrence of an event, B, the posterior probability of a hypothesis, H, is proportional to the product of what two factors?

8-2 By definition, if f is a (continuous) probability density function, then $\int_{-\infty}^{\infty} f(x)\, dx = 1$.

(a) In particular, if f is the density function of a beta distribution, $\beta(a,b)$ with $a > 0$ and $b > 0$, then Equation (8.2) leads to

$$\int_{-\infty}^{\infty} f(x)\, dx \;=\; \int_{0}^{1} \frac{\Gamma(a+b)}{\Gamma(a)\cdot\Gamma(b)}\, x^{a-1}(1-x)^{b-1}\, dx \;=\; 1.$$

This implies that $\int_{0}^{1} x^{a-1}(1-x)^{b-1}\, dx = \frac{\Gamma(a)\cdot\Gamma(b)}{\Gamma(a+b)}$. Use the last equation to show that

$$\int_{0}^{1} \theta^{a+r-1}(1-\theta)^{b+n-r-1}\, d\theta \;=\; \frac{\Gamma(a+r)\cdot\Gamma(b+n-r)}{\Gamma(a+b-n)},$$

thereby completing the proof of Theorem 8.1.

(b) Next, let g be the density function of a gamma distribution, $G(\alpha,\beta)$. Then using Equation (8.7) with x replaced by θ, we obtain

$$\int_{-\infty}^{\infty} g(\theta)\, d\theta \;=\; \int_{0}^{\infty} \frac{e^{-\beta\theta}\theta^{\alpha-1}}{\Gamma(\alpha)}\, d\theta \;=\; 1,$$

This implies that $\int_0^\infty e^{-\beta\theta}\theta^{\alpha-1}\,d\theta = \beta^{-\alpha}\cdot\Gamma(\alpha)$. Use the last equation to show that

$$\int_0^\infty e^{-(\beta+m)\theta}\theta^{\alpha+m\bar{n}-1}\,d\theta \;=\; (\beta+m)^{-(\alpha+m\bar{n})}\cdot\Gamma(\alpha+m\bar{n}),$$

thereby completing the proof of Theorem 8.2.

8-3   The number of claims, R, for an individual risk in one year has a binomial distribution with parameter $n = 5$ and probability of claim Q. Q, in turn, has a prior density function given by $f(q) = 60q^3(1-q)^2$, $0 \le q \le 1$. Given that no claims occurred in the first year, the posterior density of Q is proportional to $q^n(1-q)^m$. What are the values of n and m?

8-4   You are given (i) an individual risk has exactly one claim each year, (ii) the severity of each claim has the exponential density function $f(x)\,|\,T{=}t) = te^{-tx}$, $x > 0$, (iii) the parameter, T, has probability density function $h(t) = te^{-t}, t > 0$, and (iv) a claim of \$5 is observed during the first year. Determine the posterior density function of T.

8-5   Assume that the number of insurance claims, R, filed by an individual in a single policy year has a binomial distribution with parameters $n = 3$ and Θ. Assume further that the parameter Θ has probability density function $g(\theta) = 6(\theta-\theta^2)$, for $0 < \theta < 1$. Given that a single claim is filed by the individual during that policy year, find the posterior density function of Θ.

8-6   The number of claims, N_i, during the ith policy year for an individual risk has a Poisson distribution with parameter Θ. In turn, Θ has a prior gamma distribution with density function $g(\theta) = \theta\cdot e^{-\theta}$, for $0 < \theta < \infty$. Find the posterior density of Θ, given that $N_1 = 1$.

8-7   The number of claims, N, during the first policy year for an individual insured has a Poisson distribution with parameter Θ. The prior distribution of Θ is the uniform distribution over the interval $(1,3)$. Determine the unconditional prior probability $P[N=0]$.

8.3 Credibility and Conjugate Distributions

8-8   (a) Use the information in Exercise 8-2(a) and Theorem 8.1 to show the following:

   (i) The mean of the prior distribution, $\beta(a,b)$, is $\frac{a}{a+b}$.

   (ii) The mean of the posterior distribution, $\beta(a+r,b+n-r)$, is $\frac{a+m\bar{n}}{\beta+m}$.

   (b) Use the information in Exercise 8-2(b) and Theorem 8.2 to show the following:

   (i) The mean of the prior distribution, $G(\alpha,\beta)$, is $\frac{\alpha}{\beta}$.

   (ii) The mean of the posterior distribution, $G(\alpha+m\bar{n}, \beta+m)$, is $\frac{\alpha+r}{a+b+n}$.

8-9   You are given that,

   (i) the number of claims follows a Poisson distribution with mean Θ,

   (ii) prior to the first year of coverage, Θ is assumed to have the gamma density function

$$f(\theta) = \frac{1000^{150}}{\Gamma(150)}\theta^{149}e^{-1000\theta}, \ \theta > 0,$$

   (iii) during the first year of coverage, 300 claims are observed on 1500 exposure units, and

   (iv)   during the second year of coverage, 525 claims are observed on 2500 exposure units.

   What is the mean of the posterior distribution of Θ, given the results of the first two years of coverage?

8-10 You are given that,

(i) the number of claims per risk in a homogeneous collection of 20 risks follows a Poisson distribution with mean Θ,

(ii) Θ has a gamma distribution with mean .10 and variance .0025, and

(iii) during the first year of observation, 6 claims are incurred by the 20 risks.

Find the variance of the posterior distribution of Θ.

8-11 You are given that,

(i) the number of claims, N, for a single insured follows a Poisson distribution with mean Θ,

(ii) Θ has a gamma distribution with mean .10 and variance .0003,

(iii) 150 claims occurred during the last three-year period, and

(iv) 200 policies were in force during each of the last three years.

Find the mean of the posterior distribution of Θ.

8-12 For each of the following distributions, give the corresponding conjugate prior distribution:

(a) Binomial
(b) Normal (with known variance)
(c) Poisson

8-13 Which of the following statements are true?

I. Posterior distributions are of model parameters, whereas predictive distributions focus on actual phenomena.

II. A senior decision maker or manager would usually find a predictive distribution more useful than a posterior distribution.

III. The main advantage of conjugate prior distributions is the simplified computational process.

8-14 The prior distribution of a random variable, H, is given by $P[H=.25]=.8$ and $P[H=.50]=.2$. The result of a single experiment, D_1, is distributed according to

$$P[D_1 = d_1 \mid H = h] = h^{d_1}(1-h)^{(1-d_1)},$$

for $d_1 = 0,1$.

(a) If $D_1 = 1$, what is the posterior distribution of H?
(b) If $D_1 = 1$, what is the predictive distribution of the result of the next experiment, D_2?

8-15 Let N_i be the random variable denoting the number of claims during the ith policy year. N_i has a Poisson distribution with parameter Θ, and Θ, in turn, has probability density function $g(\theta) = e^{-\theta}, \theta > 0$.

(a) What is the unconditional probability $P[N_1 = 2]$? (Hint: Note that the quantity to be integrated is a gamma density function.)

(b) Using the result of part (a), determine the predictive distribution $P[N_2 = d\}N_1 = 2]$, for $d = 0,1,...$.

(c) Which of the quantities N_1, N_2, and Θ, defined in parts (a) and (b), can be observed?

8-16 Which of the following statements are true?

I.   One major advantage of conjugate prior distributions is that the prior distribution for one year can become the posterior distribution for the next year.

II. If n independent Bernoulli trials are performed with constant probability of success Θ, and the prior distribution of Θ is a beta distribution, then the posterior distribution of Θ is also a beta distribution.

8-17 Let $X_1, X_2, ..., X_n$ be random variables representing the net profit (or loss) under each of n workers' compensation policies in force during a particular calendar year. The following assumptions are made:

(i) $X_1, X_2, ..., X_n$ are identically distributed normal random variables with mean Θ and variance 1.

(ii) $X_1, X_2, ..., X_n$ are conditionally independent, given Θ.

(iii) The prior density of Θ is a normal density, with mean 6 and variance 5.

Given the values $n = 4$, $X_1 = -3$, $X_2 = 0$, $X_3 = 7$, $X_4 = 4$, determine (a) the mean of the posterior normal distribution of Θ, (b) the variance of the posterior normal distribution of Θ, and (c) the predictive distribution of X_5.

8-18 Use the notation of Exercise 8-17 and make the following assumptions:

(i) $E[X_5 \mid X_1 = 5, X_2 = 3, X_3 = 8, X_4 = 4] = 5$

(ii) $\sigma_1^2 = 64$

(iii) $\sigma_2^2 = 9$

Determine the mean of the prior distribution of Θ.

8.4 Credibility and Exponential Families

8-19 Consider the following information:

(i)   The distribution of claims is binomial with parameters n and Θ, $0 \le \Theta \le 1$.

(ii) The prior density of Θ is the beta density

$$f(\theta) = \frac{\Gamma(4+5) \cdot \theta^3 \cdot (1-\theta)^4}{\Gamma(4) \cdot \Gamma(5)}, \ 0 \le \theta \le 1,$$

with mean $\frac{4}{4+5}$ and variance $\frac{20}{(3+4+2)^2 \cdot (3+4+3)}$.

(iii) Two claims are observed in three trials.

Determine the mean of the posterior distribution of Θ.

8-20 Each of X_1 and X_2 is a random variable representing the result of a single observation. Both X_1 and X_2 have the (conditional) probability density function $f(x \,|\, \Theta)$, which is a member of a linear exponential family. The prior density function of Θ, $g(\theta)$, is a conjugate prior density for $f(x \,|\, \Theta)$. It is known that

(i) $E[X_1] = E[X_2] = 1$,

(ii) a single trial results in the observation $X_1 = 4$,

(iii) $E[X_2 \,|\, X_1 = 4] = 2$, and

(iv) the expected value of the process variance is

$$E_\Theta[Var(X \,|\, \Theta)] = 3.$$

Determine $Var_\Theta\big(E[X \,|\, \Theta]\big)$, the variance of the hypothetical means.

8.5 Summary of Key Results of the Bayesian Paradigm

8-21 Tim and Jim are identical twins. Both observe that 100 consecutive tosses of a two-sided coin all result in "heads." Tim thinks that the probability is still 0.50 that the result of the next toss will be a "head" while Jim thinks that this probability is much closer to 1. Briefly describe their philosophical differences in the context of the Bayesian paradigm.

CHAPTER 9

FREQUENCY-SEVERITY INSURANCE MODEL WITH CONTINUOUS SEVERITY COMPONENT

9.1 INTRODUCTION

In this chapter we present another two-stage model of an insurance operation. The frequency component is based on a Poisson distribution, and the severity component is based on an exponential distribution. In order to describe this two-stage model, we need to return to the concept of a predictive distribution, which we discussed in Section 4.2. We assume here that the number of claims is independent of the severity or amount of the individual claim losses.

9.2 PREDICTIVE DISTRIBUTIONS

We begin by defining S_i as the random variable representing the amount of aggregate claims during the ith policy year (or, equivalently, the ith period of observation). Our goal is to calculate the predictive (or probability) distribution of S_{m+1}, given $S_1, S_2, ..., S_m$. We assume that given a parameter Θ, the random variables $S_1, S_2, ..., S_{m+1}$ are independent and identically distributed with conditional probability density function p. We use f to denote the density function of Θ. Thus we can write the conditional density of S_{m+1}, given $S_1 = s_1, S_2 = s_2, ..., S_m = s_m$, as

$$\frac{\int p(s_{m+1} \mid \theta) \cdot \prod_{i=1}^{m} p(s_i \mid \theta) \cdot f(\theta) \, d\theta}{\int \prod_{i=1}^{m} p(s_i \mid \theta) \cdot f(\theta) \, d\theta},$$

where

$$\frac{\prod\limits_{i=1}^{m} p(s_i \mid \theta) \cdot f(\theta)}{\int \prod\limits_{i=1}^{m} p(s_i \mid \theta) \cdot f(\theta) \, d\theta}$$

is the posterior density of Θ, given $S_1 = s_1, S_2 = s_2, ..., S_m = s_m$.

9.3 FREQUENCY COMPONENT

For $i = 1, 2, ...$, let N_i be the random variable representing the number of claims during the ith period of observation, with a Poisson distribution with parameter (mean) Λ. Here we assume that Λ is a random variable with distribution function $G(\alpha, \beta)$. Given m observations $n_1, n_2, ..., n_m$, the posterior distribution of Λ is $G(\alpha + m\bar{n}, \beta + m)$, as shown in Section 8.2.2. The parameters α and β determine the prior gamma distribution. The data are summarized by the parameters m and $m\bar{n} = \sum\limits_{i=1}^{m} n_i$. We let $g(\lambda)$ denote the density function of $G(\alpha + m\bar{n}, \beta + m)$. Thus we are able to write the conditional probability of $N_{m+1} = n$, given $N_1 = n_1, N_2 = n_2, ..., N_m = n_m$, as

$$\frac{\int_0^\infty \frac{e^{-\lambda}\lambda^n}{n!} \cdot g(\lambda) \, d\lambda}{\int_0^\infty g(\lambda) \, d\lambda} = \frac{\int_0^\infty \frac{e^{-\lambda}\lambda^n}{n!} \cdot e^{-(\beta+m)\lambda} \lambda^{\alpha+m\bar{n}-1} \, d\lambda}{\int_0^\infty e^{-(\beta+m)\lambda} \lambda^{\alpha+m\bar{n}-1} \, d\lambda}$$

$$= \frac{\frac{1}{n!}\int_0^\infty e^{-(\beta+m+1)\lambda} \lambda^{\alpha+m\bar{n}-1+n} \, d\lambda}{\Gamma(\alpha+m\bar{n}) \cdot (\beta+m)^{-(\alpha+m\bar{n})}}$$

$$= \frac{\Gamma(\alpha+m\bar{n}+n) \cdot (\beta+m+1)^{-(\alpha+m\bar{n}+n)}}{n! \cdot \Gamma(\alpha+m\bar{n}) \cdot (\beta+m)^{-(\alpha+m\bar{n})}}$$

$$= \binom{\alpha+m\bar{n}+n-1}{n}\left(\frac{1}{\beta+m+1}\right)^n \left(\frac{\beta+m}{\beta+m+1}\right)^{\alpha+m\bar{n}},$$

$$\tag{9.1}$$

for $n = 0, 1, ...$, which is in the form of a negative binomial density function. The mean of this negative binomial density function is $\frac{\alpha + m\bar{n}}{\beta + m}$, which was shown in Section 8.3.2 to equal the Bühlmann credibility estimate of the frequency of claims. The negative binomial density also represents the predictive density function of the number of claims in the $(m+1)^{st}$ period of observation, given $N_1 = n_1, N_2 = n_2, ..., N_m = n_m$. Here $n = n_{m+1}$ takes on the values $0, 1, ...$.

This predictive density function provides (estimated) probabilities of each of the possible number of claims, so it provides much more information than is provided by only its (estimated) mean. The following example illustrates an important application of the predictive density function. The results of this application should be of great use to certain parties.

EXAMPLE 9.1

Using the assumptions of this section, find

$$P[N_5 \geq 6 \mid N_1 = 1, N_2 = 6, N_3 = 8, N_4 = 2]$$

the conditional probability that at least 6 claims are observed during the 5th period of observation.

SOLUTION

We have $m = 4$ and $m\bar{n} = \sum_{i=1}^{4} n_i = 1+6+8+2 = 17$. Then using the negative binomial conditional probabilities given by Equation (9.1), we find the desired probability to be

$$\sum_{n=6}^{\infty} \binom{\alpha + 17 + n - 1}{n} \left(\frac{1}{\beta + 4 + 1}\right)^n \left(\frac{\beta + 4}{\beta + 4 + 1}\right)^{\alpha + 17}$$

$$= \sum_{n=6}^{\infty} \binom{\alpha + n + 16}{n} \left(\frac{1}{\beta + 5}\right)^n \left(\frac{\beta + 4}{\beta + 5}\right)^{\alpha + 17}$$

$$= 1 - \sum_{n=0}^{5} \binom{\alpha + n + 16}{n} \left(\frac{1}{\beta + 5}\right)^n \left(\frac{\beta + 4}{\beta + 5}\right)^{\alpha + 17}.$$ ❑

9.4 SEVERITY COMPONENT

We assume that the amount of each individual claim, X, has an exponential distribution with mean Δ and probability density function given by

$$p(x \mid \Delta) = \frac{e^{-x/\Delta}}{\Delta}, \tag{9.2}$$

for $x > 0$ and $\Delta > 0$.[1] The moments of X are $E_X[X \mid \Delta] = \Delta$ and $Var_X(X \mid \Delta) = \Delta^2$. The mean claim amount, Δ, has a conjugate prior distribution whose probability density function, $f(\delta \mid m', y')$, is proportional to $\frac{e^{-y'/\delta}}{\delta m'}$, for $y' > 0, m' > 3$, and $\delta > 0$. Such a density function is called an **inverse gamma density function** and has mean $\frac{y'}{m'-2}$, as shown in Exercise 9-1(b). The insurance process is observed for m periods of observation with n_i claims occurring during period i. The total aggregate claim amount over the m periods of observation is

$$y = \sum_{i=1}^{m\bar{n}} x_i. \tag{9.3}$$

Then the posterior density function of Δ, $f(\delta \mid m', y', m\bar{n}, y)$ is proportional to

$$\left(\prod_{i=1}^{m\bar{n}} \frac{e^{-x_i/\delta}}{\delta} \right) \left(\frac{e^{-y'/\delta}}{\delta^{m'}} \right) = \frac{e^{-\frac{y'+y}{\delta}}}{\sigma^{m'} + m\bar{n}},$$

which is also an inverse gamma density function. The mean of the posterior distribution of Δ (see Exercise 9-1(b)) is given by

$$\frac{y' + y}{m' + m\bar{n} - 2} = \left(\frac{m'-2}{m'+m\bar{n}-2} \right)\left(\frac{y'}{m'-2} \right) + \left(\frac{m\bar{n}}{m'+m\bar{n}-2} \right)\left(\frac{y}{m\bar{n}} \right)$$

$$= (1-Z)(mean\ of\ prior) + Z(mean\ of\ observed\ data),$$

---

[1] The exponential distribution was chosen primarily to keep the mathematical sophistication relatively simple. Other probability distributions, such as the log-normal distribution, frequently provide a more accurate representation of the actual distribution of losses. See Hewitt [1970] for a discussion of a two-stage Bayesian credibility model in which the loss distribution is assumed to be log-normal. Other references on loss distributions are Hewitt [1967] and Klugman, Panjer and Willmot [2008].

where Z is determined in Exercise 9-5. Since $E[X|\Delta]=\Delta$, it follows that the mean of the predictive distribution of X is equal to the mean of the posterior distribution of Δ.

The predictive density function of X, which reflects the uncertainty in the estimation of the parameter values as well as in the random nature of the claim amounts, is given by

$$p(x|m',y',m\bar{n},y) = \int_0^\infty p(x|\delta) \cdot f(\delta|m',y',m\bar{n},y)\, d\delta$$

$$= C\int_0^\infty \left(\frac{e^{-x/\delta}}{\delta}\right)\left(\frac{e^{-\frac{y'+y}{\delta}}}{\delta^{m'+m\bar{n}}}\right) d\delta, \qquad (9.4)$$

where

$$C = \frac{(y'+y)^{m'+m\bar{n}-1}}{\Gamma(m'+m\bar{n}-1)}. \qquad (9.5)$$

The normalizing constant C can be determined using the results of Exercise 9-1(a). Equation (9.4) can be rewritten as

$$p\left(x|m',y',m\bar{n},y\right) = C\int_0^\infty e^{-\frac{x+y'+y}{\delta}} \delta^{-m'-m\bar{n}-1}\, d\delta. \qquad (9.6)$$

Making the change of variable $w = \frac{x+y'+y}{\delta}$, and noting that $d\delta = -\frac{x+y'+y}{w^2}\, dw$, we can rewrite Equation (9.6) as

$$p\left(x|m',y',m\bar{n},y\right) = \left(\frac{(y'+y)^{m'+m\bar{n}-1}}{\Gamma(m'+m\bar{n}-1)}\right)\left(\frac{\int_0^\infty w^{m'+m\bar{n}-1}e^{-w}\, dw}{(x+y'+y)^{m'+m\bar{n}}}\right)$$

$$= \left(\frac{(y'+y)^{m'+m\bar{n}-1}}{\Gamma(m'+m\bar{n}-1)}\right)\left(\frac{\Gamma(m'+m\bar{n})}{(x+y'+y)^{m'+m\bar{n}}}\right)$$

$$= \frac{(y'+y)^{-1}(m'+m\bar{n}-1)}{\left(1+\frac{x}{y'+y}\right)^{m'+m\bar{n}}}, \qquad (9.7)$$

which is a member of the Pareto family of density functions

In practice, the predictive distribution corresponding to the density function of Equation (9.7) should be used to predict the amounts of the claims, if any, occurring during the $(m+1)^{st}$ period of observation. When there is substantial uncertainty about the value of the parameter Δ the relatively tame exponential distribution gets transformed into the heavy-tailed Pareto distribution. The following example illustrates an important application of the predictive distribution of claim amounts.

EXAMPLE 9.2

Suppose 17 claims are observed during the first four periods of observation, with total aggregate claim amount of $1,000,000. Using the assumptions of this section, find

$$P\left[X_{18} \geq 100,000 \middle| \sum_{i=1}^{17} X_i = 1,000,000\right].$$

SOLUTION

We have $m = 4, m\bar{n} = \sum_{i=1}^{m} n_i = 17$, and $y = \sum_{i=1}^{m\bar{n}} X_i = 1,000,000.$

Using the Pareto density function given by Equation (9.7), we find the desired probability to be

$$\int_{100,000}^{\infty} \frac{(y+y')^{-1}(m'+m\bar{n}-1)}{\left(1+\frac{x}{y+y'}\right)^{m'+m\bar{n}}} dx = -\left(1+\frac{x}{y+y'}\right)^{-m'-m\bar{n}+1}\Bigg|_{100,000}^{\infty}$$

$$= \left(1+\frac{100,000}{1,000,000+y'}\right)^{-m'-16}. \qquad \square$$

Thus, the desired probability is just a function of the two parameters – y' and m' of the prior distribution. These parameters must be specified by the actuary.

9.5 THE TWO-STAGE MODEL

In Sections 9.3 and 9.4 we presented the predictive distributions of the number of claims and the amount of the individual claim losses, respectively. We assumed that the random variables corresponding to the two distributions are independent. Ideally, we would like to use the two predictive distributions to construct a simple, closed-form expression for the predictive distribution of aggregate claim amounts. In other words, we seek a predictive distribution of the random sum of random variables

$$S_{m+1} = \sum_{i=1}^{N} X_{i,m+1}, \tag{9.8}$$

where $X_{i,m+1}$ is the amount of the ith loss during the $(m+1)^{st}$ period of observation. The predictive distribution of the sum can be used to give the probabilities that losses will exceed various amounts and thereby serves as an excellent management tool. Unfortunately, in most situations it is not possible to determine a closed-form expression for the predictive distribution. One approach is to simulate the predictive distribution by using stochastic simulation methods to construct an empirical version of the predictive distribution of aggregate claims.

One illustration of the use of stochastic simulation to construct an empirical distribution is found in Herzog [1983].[2] More practical applications of the simulation of a two-stage model in a Bayesian context are found in Herzog and Rubin [1983] and DeVinti and Herzog [1991].

An alternative procedure is described by Heckman and Meyers [1983]. They present an algorithm for determining the aggregate loss distribution by inverting a characteristic function. This entails approximating the claim severity distribution function by a piece-wise linear cumulative distribution function. As long as the given severity distribution does not have any mass points, the Heckman-Meyers procedure produces exact results and generally requires less computer time than does a stochastic simulation approach.

A third procedure is the recursive approach described by Panjer and Willmot [1992]. This procedure works, without additional modification, even if the given severity distribution has mass points.

---

[2] See Example 1.

9.6 PURE PREMIUM ESTIMATOR

Theorem 5.1 showed that if S_{m+1} is a random variable representing the total aggregate claims during the $(m+1)^{st}$ period of observation, and if the claims frequency and claims severity processes may be assumed to be independent, then

$$
\begin{aligned}
&E[S_{m+1} \mid N_1{=}n_1,...,N_m{=}n_m, X_1{=}x_1,...,X_{m\bar{n}}{=}x_{m\bar{n}}] \\
&= E[N_{m+1} \mid N_1{=}n_1,...,N_m{=}n_m] \cdot E[X \mid X_1{=}x_1,...,X_{m\bar{n}}{=}x_{m\bar{n}}]. \quad (9.9)
\end{aligned}
$$

In Equation (9.9) N_{m+1} is the random variable representing the number of claims during the $(m+1)^{st}$ period of observation, and X is the random variable representing the claim amount of an individual claim. $E[S_{m+1} \mid N_1 = n_1,..., N_m = n_m, X_1{=}x_1,..., X_{m\bar{n}} = x_{m\bar{n}}]$, the expected aggregate claim amount, is also called the pure premium for period $m+1$.

If (a) N_{m+1} has a negative binomial distribution as discussed in Section 9.3, (b) X has a Pareto distribution as discussed in Section 9.4, and (c) N_{m+1} and X are assumed to be conditionally independent, then

$$
\begin{aligned}
&E[N_{m+1} \mid N_1 = n_1,..., N_m = n_m] \cdot E[X \mid X_1 = x_1,..., X_{m\bar{n}} = x_{m\bar{n}}] \\
&\qquad\qquad = \left(\frac{\alpha + m\bar{n}}{\beta + m} \right)\left(\frac{y' + y}{m' + m\bar{n} - 2} \right). \quad (9.10)
\end{aligned}
$$

The first term is the mean of the predictive distribution of N_{m+1}, as discussed in Section 9.3. The second term is the mean of the predictive distribution of X, as discussed in Section 9.4.

9.7 ALTERNATIVE PURE PREMIUM ESTIMATOR USING BÜHLMANN'S MODEL

Alternatively, we could estimate the pure premium by using a Bühlmann credibility model in which only the aggregate claim amounts of each insured are considered; in other words, the frequency and severity components are not considered separately. The number of claims, N, is assumed to have a Poisson distribution with mean $E[N|\Lambda] = \Lambda$. Moreover, $Var(N|\Lambda,) = \Lambda$, and Λ is assumed to have the gamma distribution, $G(\alpha, \beta)$. Then we have

$$E[\Lambda] = \frac{\alpha}{\beta}, \tag{9.11a}$$

$$E[\Lambda^2] = \frac{\alpha(\alpha+1)}{\beta^2}, \tag{9.11b}$$

and

$$Var(\Lambda) = \frac{\alpha}{\beta^2}. \tag{9.11c}$$

The amount of an individual claim, X, is assumed to have an exponential distribution with mean Δ and variance Δ^2. Finally, Δ has the inverse gamma distribution, $IG(y', m')$, presented in Section 9.4, so that

$$E[\Delta] = \frac{y'}{m'-2}, \tag{9.12a}$$

$$E[\Delta^2] = \frac{(y')^2}{(m'-2)(m'-3)}, \tag{9.12b}$$

and

$$Var(\Delta) = \frac{(y')^2}{(m'-2)^2(m'-3)}. \tag{9.12c}$$

Given (Λ, Δ), the ordered pair of (independent) random variables representing the means of the Poisson and exponential distributions, respectively, the hypothetical mean of the pure premium is

$$E\left[\sum_{i=1}^{N} X_i \,|\, \Lambda, \Delta\right] = E[N|\Lambda] \cdot E[X|\Delta] = \Lambda\Delta, \tag{9.13}$$

and the variance of the hypothetical means is

$$
\begin{aligned}
Var(\Lambda\Delta) &= E[\Lambda^2\Delta^2] - \left([E[\Lambda\Delta]\right)^2 \\
&= E[\Lambda^2]\cdot E[\Delta^2] - \left(E[\Lambda]\right)^2 \cdot \left(E[\Delta]\right)^2 \\
&= \left(\frac{\alpha(\alpha+1)}{\beta^2}\right)\left(\frac{(y')^2}{(m'-2)(m'-3)}\right) - \left(\frac{\alpha^2}{\beta^2}\right)\left(\frac{(y')^2}{(m'-2)^2}\right) \\
&= \frac{\alpha(y')^2(\alpha+m'-2)}{\beta^2(m'-2)^2(m'-3)}.
\end{aligned} \tag{9.14}
$$

Given (Λ, Δ), the process variance of the pure premium is calculated, using Theorem 5.3, to be

$$
\begin{aligned}
Var\left(\sum_{i=1}^{N} X_i \mid \Lambda,\Delta\right) &= E[N]\cdot Var(X) + Var(N)\cdot\left(E[X]\right)^2 \\
&= \Lambda\Delta^2 + \Lambda\Delta^2 = 2\Lambda\Delta^2,
\end{aligned} \tag{9.15}
$$

and the expected process variance is

$$
E[2\Lambda\Delta^2] = 2\cdot E[\Lambda]\cdot E[\Delta^2] = \frac{2\alpha(y')^2}{\beta(m'-2)(m'-3)}. \tag{9.16}
$$

Then, substituting from Equations (9.14) and (9.16) and simplifying, we have

$$
k = \frac{E[2\Lambda\Delta^2]}{Var(\Lambda\Delta)} = \frac{2\beta(m'-2)}{\alpha+m'-2}. \tag{9.17}
$$

The prior mean is

$$
E[\Lambda\Delta] = E[\Lambda]\cdot E[\Delta] = \left(\frac{\alpha}{\beta}\right)\left(\frac{y'}{m'-2}\right) = \frac{\alpha y'}{\beta(m'-2)}. \tag{9.18}
$$

We observe m years of data, so $Z = \frac{m}{m+k}$, $1-Z = \frac{k}{m+k}$, and the mean of the data is $\frac{y}{m}$. Then the credibility estimate is

$$C = (1-Z)(mean\ of\ prior) + Z(mean\ of\ ovserved\ data)$$
$$= \left(\frac{k}{m+k}\right)\left(\frac{\alpha y'}{\beta(m'-2)}\right) + \left(\frac{m}{m+k}\right)\left(\frac{y}{m}\right). \tag{9.19a}$$

Substituting for k from Equation (9.17) and simplifying, we obtain the credibility estimate

$$C = \frac{2\alpha y' + (\alpha+m'-2)y}{2\beta(m'-2) + (\alpha+m'-2)m} \tag{9.19b}$$

which can be compared with the prior mean of Equation (9.18).

In comparing the alternative estimate of the pure premium, given by Equation (9.19b), with the original estimate, given by Equation (9.10), note that $m\bar{n}$, the total number of claims during the m years, is not needed for the alternative Bühlmann estimate. Finally, we note that the pure premium estimator of Section 9.6 has a smaller mean squared error than does the Bühlmann estimator of this section.

9.8 SUMMARY OF CHAPTERS 8 AND 9

In Table 9.1, which is similar to one given by Morgan [1983],[3] we summarize much of the material of Chapters 8 and 9. For example, the second column summarizes the results of Sections 8.2.1 and 8.3.1. Here we assume that the data are from a Bernoulli random variable and the prior distribution of the probability of success, Θ, has a beta distribution. This implies that the hypothetical mean and process variance are Θ and $\Theta(1-\Theta)$, respectively. These lead to a k value of $a+b$ and a predictive density having the form of the Bernoulli density function. The third column summarizes the results of Sections 8.2.2, 8.3.2, and 9.3. The

---

[3] See page 13.

fourth column summarizes the results of Section 9.4. Finally, the last column summarizes the results of Sections 8.2.3 and 8.3.3.

TABLE 9.1

Characteristics of Simple Exponential Families				
Likelihood	Bernoulli	Poisson	Exponential	Normal
Prior	Beta: $\beta(a,b)$	Gamma: $G(\alpha,\beta)$	Inverse Gamma: $IG(x',m')$	Normal: $N(\mu,\sigma_2^2)$
Hypothetical Mean	Θ	Θ	Δ	Θ
Process Variance	$\Theta(1-\Theta)$	Θ	Δ^2	σ_1^2
Variance of the Hypothetical Mean	$\dfrac{ab}{(a+b+1)(a+b)^2}$	$\dfrac{\alpha}{\beta^2}$	$\dfrac{(y')^2}{(m'-2)(m'-3)}$	σ_2^2
Expected Process Variance	$\dfrac{ab}{(a+b+1)(a+b)}$	$\dfrac{\alpha}{\beta}$	$\dfrac{(y')^2}{(m'-2)(m'-3)}$	σ_1^2
k	$a+b$	β	$m'-2$	σ_1^2/σ_2^2
Predictive Density	Bernoulli	Negative Binomial	Pareto	Normal

9.9 ADVANTAGES AND DISADVANTAGES OF THE BÜHLMANN AND BAYESIAN APPROACHES

The main advantages of Bühlmann's approach, compared to the Bayesian approach, are the following:

(1) It usually requires fewer computational resources.

(2) It usually requires less mathematical skills.

(3) It is usually easier to explain to laymen.

(4) It does not require the choice of a prior distribution, which can sometimes be difficult.

The main advantages of the Bayesian approach, compared to Bühlmann's approach, are the following:

(1) It gets the correct answer (see Example 2.1).

(2) The end result is an entire probability distribution of values rather than just a single point estimate.

(3) It does a better job of forcing the analyst to make explicit assumptions.

(4) It provides a more unified, rather than an ad hoc, framework for incorporating subjective notions into the stochastic modeling process.

(5) Under Bühlmann's approach it is theoretically possible for estimated variances to be negative. Negative estimated variances are of no practical use.

9.10 BÜHLMANN VIEW

Bühlmann expressed strong support for the Bayesian paradigm of statistics, but felt that whenever possible the prior should be based on experience data rather than on subjective judgment. To quote Bühlmann, as reported in Hickman and Heacox [1999]:

"Whereas early Bayesian statisticians used the prior distribution of risk parameters as a means to express judgment (which in insurance we would call underwriting judgment), [I] think of the probability distribution of the risk parameters as having an objective meaning. Hence, it needs to be extracted from the data gathered about the collective. (Only in the case of a lack of such data might one accept the subjective view *faute de mieux*.) For this reason, I have always insisted on speaking about the structural distribution of risk parameters, avoiding the standard Bayesian terminology, 'prior distribution'."

9.11 EXERCISES

9.1 Introduction
9.2 Predictive Distributions

9-1 (a) Find the constant C such that $\int_0^\infty C \cdot \delta^{-n} e^{-s/\delta} \, d\delta = 1$, where $n > 3$.

(b) Show that for the value of C determined in part (a),

$$C \int_0^\infty \delta^{-n+1} e^{s/\delta} \, d\delta = \frac{s}{n-2}.$$

Hint: Let $\Delta = \frac{s}{\delta}$ and note that we have a gamma density function.

9.3 Frequency Component

9-2 Using the assumptions of Section 9.3, find the value of $P[N_4 \leq 5 \mid N_1 = 2, N_2 = 8, N_3 = 5]$, the conditional probability that no more than five claims are observed during the fourth period of observation.

9-3 Let N be a random variable representing the result of a single Bernoulli trial, and let Θ be the probability of success. Assume, as established by Theorem 8.1, that the posterior distribution of Θ is $\beta(a+r, b+n-r)$, where r is the number of successes observed in the first n (independent) Bernoulli trials. By mimicking the analysis of Section 9.3, determine the predictive distribution of the result of the $(n+1)^{st}$ trial, N_{n+1}. In other words, show that

$$P[N_{n+1} = 1] = \frac{a+r}{a+b+n}$$

and

$$P[N_{n+1} = 0] = \frac{b+n-r}{a+b+n}.$$

9-4 Which of the following statements are true?

I. If the likelihood function is a member of the Bernoulli family of distribution functions, and the prior is a beta distribution, then the predictive distribution is also a Bernoulli distribution.

II. If the likelihood function is a member of the Poisson family of distribution functions, and the prior is a gamma distribution, then the predictive distribution is also a Poisson distribution.

9.4 Severity Component

9-5 For the exponential density function of Section 9.4, show each of the following.

(a) The expected value of the process variance is

$$E_\Delta \left[Var_X (X \mid \Delta) \right] = E_\Delta [\Delta^2] = \frac{(y')^2}{(m'-2)(m'-3)}.$$

(b) The variance of the hypothetical means is

$$Var_\Delta \left(E_X [X \mid \Delta] \right) = Var_\Delta (\Delta) = \frac{(y')^2}{(m'-2)^2 (m'-3)}.$$

(c) The credibility factor is $Z = \frac{m}{m+k} = \frac{m}{m+m'-2}$, since there are m observation periods and $k = m'-2$, where k is obtained by dividing the result of part (a) by that of part (b).

Hint: The required integration for parts (a) and (b) is similar to that of Exercise 8-2.

9-6   The conditional claim severity distribution of X is exponential with density function

$$p(x \mid M) = \frac{1}{M} \cdot e^{-x/M}, \quad x > 0, \; M > 0,$$

where, in turn, the parameter M has density function

$$f(m) = \frac{400}{m^3} \cdot e^{-20/m}, \quad m > 0.$$

Determine the mean of the claim severity distribution.

9-7   The amount of an individual claim, X, has an exponential distribution with parameter (mean) M, and M has an inverted gamma distribution with density function

$$p(m) = \frac{4e^{-2/m}}{m^4}, \quad m > 0.$$

The conditional mean and variance of X given M are given by $E[X \mid M=m] = m$ and $Var(X \mid M=m) = m^2$, respectively. Determine $f(3)$, the value of the unconditional density function at $X = 3$.

9-8   Nine claims are observed during the first two periods of observation with total aggregate claims of \$2,000,000. Using the assumptions of Section 9.4, find

$$P\left[X_{10} \geq 300,000 \middle| \sum_{i=1}^{9} X_i = 2,000,000 \right].$$

9.5 The Two-Stage Model

9-9   Which of the following statements are true?

   I.   It is usually possible, in realistic applications, to obtain closed-form solutions to the predictive distribution of aggregate claim amounts.

II. Stochastic simulation can be used to estimate the predictive distribution of aggregate claims.

III. Heckman and Meyers have developed an algorithm for obtaining the exact predictive distribution of aggregate claims, a procedure which entails the inversion of characteristic functions.

9.6 The Pure Premium
9.7 Alternative Pure Premium Estimate Using Bühlmann's Model

9-10 The following information is available:

Class	Frequency of Claims Mean	Variance	Severity of Claims Mean	Variance
A	.1667	.1389	4	20
B	.8333	.1389	2	5

Classes A and B have equal number of risks. A risk is randomly selected, with equal probability, from one of the two classes and four observations are made of that risk. Let R_1 denote the random variable for the aggregate loss of the risk. The value $R_1 = .25$ has been observed.

(a) Calculate the associated credibility factor.
(b) Calculate the Bühlmann estimate of $E[R_2 \mid R_1 = .25]$, the conditional mean of the next observation.

9-11 Two risks have the following severity distribution:

Amount of Claim	Probability of Claim Amount Risk 1	Risk 2
100	.50	.70
1,000	.30	.20
20,000	.20	.10

Risk 1 is twice as likely to be selected as Risk 2. A risk is selected and a claim of size 100 is observed, but the underlying risk is unknown. Determine the Bühlmann credibility estimate of the expected value of the second claim amount from the selected risk.

9-12 The claim frequency distributions F_1 and F_2 and the claim severity distributions G_1 and G_2 are defined as follows:

Number of Claims	Probability of Claim Number		Amount of Claim	Probability of Claim Amount	
	F_1	F_2		G_1	G_2
0	.80	.60	100	.40	.80
1	.20	.40	200	.60	.20

A frequency distribution and a severity distribution are each selected with probability $\frac{1}{2}$, and a claim of amount 100 is observed. Utilizing only aggregate claim amounts, determine the Bühlmann credibility estimate for the next observation from the same pair of distributions.

9.8 Summary of Chapters 8 and 9
9.9 Advantages and Disadvantages of the Bühlmann and Bayesian Approaches

9-13 Which of the following statements are true for the Bayesian approach to credibility?

I.   It always produces the optimum estimate.

II. The estimate is always within the range of the hypotheses.

III. It always produces an estimate on or between the observation and the prior hypothesis (mean).

IV. It produces the best least-squares fit to the optimum estimate.

IV. It requires a separate mechanism for handling partial credibility.

V.   It relates to the concept of confidence intervals.

VI. The estimate is a linear approximation to the Bühlmann estimate.

VII. It does a better job than Bühlmann's approach in forcing the analyst to make explicit assumptions.

9-14 Which of the following statements are true for Bühlmann's approach to credibility?

I.   It always produces the optimum estimate.

II.   The estimate is always within the range of the hypotheses.

III.   It always produces an estimate on or between the observation and the prior hypothesis (mean).

IV.   It produces the best least-squares fit to the optimum estimate.

V.   It requires a separate mechanism for handling partial credibility.

VI.   It is related to the concept of confidence intervals.

VII.   The estimate is a linear approximation to the Bayesian estimate using a squared loss function.

9-15 Provide the predictive distribution corresponding to the pairs of likelihood functions and conjugate priors listed below.

Likelihood Function	Conjugate Prior	Predictive Distribution
Bernoulli	Beta	(a)
Poisson	Gamma	(b)
Exponential	Inverse Gamma	(c)

CHAPTER 10

CREDIBILITY AND LEAST SQUARES

10.1 INTRODUCTION

In Section 10.3, we show that the credibility estimates produced by the Bühlmann model are the best linear approximations to the corresponding Bayesian estimates. We begin this chapter with a numerical example comparing Bayesian estimates to those obtained using Bühlmann's model.

Suppose the actuary has decided to use $E[X_2 \mid X_1 = k]$, the mean of the predictive distribution (see Table 4.7), as an updated estimate of the pure premium. Further, suppose the actuary is unwilling to assume a particular family of distributions for either (a) the process generating the claims, or (b) the prior distribution of the parameters of the claims process. Recall that such distributions are required in order to do a Bayesian analysis and thereby produce a predictive distribution. The actuary is willing, however, to use a linear approximation of the mean of the predictive distribution as the (estimate of the) pure premium.

For the above situation, Bühlmann [1967] and [1970] has shown that the credibility estimates of Section 6.2 are the best linear approximations to the Bayesian estimates of the pure premium. By "best" we mean that the weighted sum (i.e., expected value) of the squared differences between the linear approximations and the Bayesian estimates is minimized. This result is illustrated in the following section.

10.2 LINEAR APPROXIMATION EXAMPLE

Let the possible outcomes of a single trial be denoted by the vector $\mathbf{R} = (R_1, R_2, R_2) = (1, 2, 14)$. Let the Bayesian premium estimates which

183

correspond to these outcomes be denoted by the vector $\mathbf{P} = (P_1, P_2, P_3) = \left(\frac{42}{24}, \frac{55}{24}, \frac{70}{24}\right)$, as shown in Table 4.7, and let the initial or prior probabilities of the results be denoted by the vector $\mathbf{w} = (w_1, w_2, w_3) = \left(\frac{6}{9}, \frac{2}{9}, \frac{1}{9}\right)$, as given in Table 4.1. For this example, we define the "best" linear approximation to $\mathbf{P}$ as that obtained by determining the values of a and b that minimize

$$SS = \sum_{i=1}^{3} w_i (a + bR_i - P_i)^2, \tag{10.1}$$

which is the usual weighted least squares approach. (See, for example, Draper and Smith [1998].) The desired estimates of a and b, denoted $\hat{a}$ and $\hat{b}$, are $\frac{22}{12}$ and $\frac{1}{12}$, respectively. Then we see that each component of the least squares linear approximation of the premium estimate, given by

$$\hat{a} + \hat{b}\mathbf{R} = \frac{22}{12} + \frac{1}{12}\mathbf{R} = \left(\frac{11}{6}, 2, 3\right), \tag{10.2}$$

is identical to the corresponding Bühlmann credibility estimate of Table 6.2.

We summarize the results of this example by presenting the revised pure premium estimates, given the result of a single trial, for both the Bayesian and Bühlmann credibility models in the following table.

TABLE 10.1

Pure Premium Estimates		
Outcome of First Trial $\mathbf{R}$	Bühlmann Estimate $\hat{a} + \hat{b}\mathbf{R}$	Bayesian Estimate $\mathbf{P}$
0	44/24	42/24
2	48/24	55/24
14	72/24	70/24

Both the Bühlmann and the Bayesian pure premium estimates are shown in Figure 10.1, which is an extension of Figure 6.6. As already seen in Chapter 6, the Bühlmann estimates, represented by the dots, lie on a straight line. The Bayesian estimates are represented by the stars. The Bühlmann estimates are the best linear approximation to the Bayesian estimates under a squared error loss function.

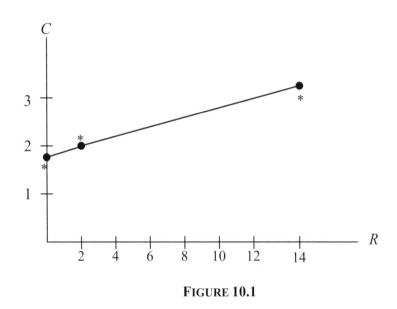

FIGURE 10.1

10.3 LINEAR APPROXIMATION THEORY[1]

In this section, we present a proof that the Bühlmann credibility estimates are the best linear approximations to the Bayesian estimates of the pure premium (i.e., the mean of the predictive distribution). The proof is based on Gerber [1979], Section 6.3.

We begin by assuming that the random variables $X_1, X_2,...,X_n$, which represent aggregate claim amounts for observation periods $1,2,...,n$, respectively, are identically distributed. Further, we assume that their common distribution, $F(x_i \mid \Theta)$, has mean $\mu(\Theta)$ and standard deviation

---

[1] The material in this section and its accompanying exercises is presented at a more advanced level than that of the rest of the text.

$\sigma(\Theta)$, where Θ represents an unknown parameter value which must be described via a prior distribution. We let μ denote $E_\Theta[\mu(\theta)]$. Moreover the X_i's are assumed to be conditionally independent, given Θ. (In Exercise 10-7 we show that the X_i's are *not* (unconditionally) independent, given Θ.) We let $\mathbf{X} = (X_1, X_2, ..., X_n)$ denote the vector of these random variables. We let $P_i = E[X_i]$ denote the pure premium for period $i, i = 1, 2, ..., n+1$.

We restrict the discussion to estimators of the pure premium that are linear functions of the data, so that they are of the form

$$\hat{P}_{n+1} = a_0 + \sum_{i=1}^{n} a_i X_i. \tag{10.3}$$

The coefficients $a_0, a_1, ..., a_n$ are determined by the requirement that they minimize

$$E\left[\left(\hat{P}_{n+1} - E[X_{n+1} \mid X_1, X_2, ..., X_n]\right)^2\right], \tag{10.4}$$

or, equivalently,

$$E\left[\left(a_0 + \sum_{i=1}^{n} a_i X_i - E[X_{n+1} \mid X_1, X_2, ..., X_n]\right)^2\right]. \tag{10.5}$$

In other words, the coefficients are determined so as to minimize the squared loss function. Taking the partial derivative of Expression (10.5) with respect to a_0 and setting it to zero, we obtain

$$a_0 + \sum_{i=1}^{n} a_i \cdot E[X_i] = E[X_{n+1}]. \tag{10.6}$$

Taking the partial derivative of Expression (10.5) with respect to a_j and setting it to zero, we obtain

$$a_0 \cdot E[X_j] + \sum_{i=1}^{n} a_i \cdot E[X_i X_j] = E[X_j X_{n+1}], \tag{10.7}$$

for $j = 1, 2, ..., n$. The system of equations given by Equations (10.6) and (10.7) is transformed by multiplying Equation (10.6) by $E[X_j]$ and subtracting the result term-by-term from Equation (10.7), obtaining

$$\sum_{i=1}^{n} a_i \cdot Cov(X_i, X_j) = Cov(X_j, X_{n+1}), \tag{10.8}$$

for $j = 1, 2, ..., n$. (In most applications the covariance matrix of the observations is nonsingular.) For $i \neq j$,

$$Cov(X_i, X_j) = Cov\big(E[X_i \mid \Theta], E[X_j \mid \Theta]\big) + E\big[Cov(X_i, X_j \mid \Theta)\big]$$

$$= Cov\big(\mu(\Theta), \mu(\Theta)\big) + 0$$

$$= Var\big(\mu(\Theta)\big),$$

since, by the conditional independence assumption,

$$E\big[Cov(X_i, X_j \mid \Theta)\big] = 0,$$

for $i \neq j$. Hence, for $i \neq j$, we have shown that

$$Cov(X_i, X_j) = Var\big(\mu(\theta)\big)$$
$$= w, \tag{10.9}$$

where w does not depend on i or j. Letting $w + v$ denote $Var(X_i)$ for $i = 1, 2, ..., n$, we can rewrite Equation (10.8) in matrix form as

$$\begin{pmatrix} w+v & w & w & w & \cdots & w \\ w & w+v & w & w & \cdots & w \\ w & w & w+v & w & \cdots & w \\ w & w & w & w+v & \cdots & w \\ \vdots & \vdots & \vdots & \vdots & \cdots & \vdots \\ \vdots & \vdots & \vdots & \vdots & \cdots & \vdots \\ \vdots & \vdots & \vdots & \vdots & \cdots & \vdots \\ w & w & w & w & \cdots & w+v \end{pmatrix} \begin{pmatrix} a_1 \\ a_2 \\ a_3 \\ a_4 \\ \vdots \\ \vdots \\ \vdots \\ a_n \end{pmatrix} = \begin{pmatrix} w \\ w \\ w \\ w \\ \vdots \\ \vdots \\ \vdots \\ w \end{pmatrix}$$

For $1 = 1, 2, \ldots, n$ we have

$$\begin{aligned} a_i &= \frac{w}{(w+v) + w + w + \cdots + w} \\ &= \frac{w}{nw + v} \\ &= \frac{Var\big(\mu(\Theta)\big)}{n \cdot Var\big(\mu(\Theta)\big) + E\big[\sigma^2(\Theta)\big]}. \end{aligned} \qquad (10.10)$$

since, by Theorem 5.2,

$$\begin{aligned} w + v = Var(X_1) &= E\big[Var\big(X_1 \mid \Theta\big)\big] + Var\big(E[X_1 \mid \Theta]\big) \\ &= E\big[\sigma^2(\Theta)\big] + Var\big(\mu(\Theta)\big) \\ &= E\big[\sigma^2(\Theta)\big] + w, \end{aligned}$$

which implies that $v = E[\sigma^2(\theta)]$.

Next we note from Equation (10.10) that

$$na_i = \frac{n \cdot Var\big(\mu(\Theta)\big)}{n \cdot Var\big(\mu(\Theta)\big) + E\big[\sigma^2(\Theta)\big]} = \frac{n}{n + \dfrac{E[\sigma^2(\theta)]}{Var(\mu(\Theta))}} = \frac{n}{n+k} = Z.$$

Hence, for $i = 1, 2, \ldots, n$, we have shown that $na_i = Z$, or

$$a_i = \frac{Z}{n}. \qquad (10.11)$$

From Equation (10.6), we obtain

$$a_0 = E[X_{n+1}] - \sum_{i=1}^{n} a_i \cdot E[X_i],$$

or

$$a_0 = \mu - \sum_{i=1}^{n} a_i \mu, \qquad (10.12)$$

Since

$$E[X_i] = E_\Theta \big[E[X_i \mid \Theta] \big] = E_\Theta \big[\mu(\Theta) \big] = \mu.$$

Rewriting Equation (10.12), we obtain

$$a_0 = \mu - \sum_{i=1}^{n} a_i \mu = \mu - \sum_{i=1}^{n} \left(\frac{Z}{n} \right) \mu - Z\mu = (1-\mu),$$

that is,

$$a_0 = (1-Z)\mu. \qquad (10.13)$$

Finally, substituting the value of a_0 given by Equation (10.13) and the values of a_i given by Equation (10.11) into Equation (10.3), we obtain

$$\hat{P}_{n+1} = (1-Z)\mu + \sum_{i=1}^{n} \frac{Z}{n} \cdot X_i = (1-Z)\mu + Z \sum_{i=1}^{n} \frac{X_i}{n} = (1-Z)\mu + Z\bar{X},$$

where $\bar{X} = \sum_{i=1}^{n} \frac{X_i}{n}$. In other words, we have established the desired result of $\hat{P}_{n+1} = (1-Z)\mu + Z\bar{X}$, where $Z = \frac{n}{n+k}$. The estimator $\hat{P}_{n+1}$ is a linear function of the X_i's, since P_{n+1} is a linear function of $\bar{X}$, which, in turn, is a linear function of the X_i's.

Finally, in Exercise 10-9 we show that the minimization of Expression (10.4) with X_{n+1} replaced by any one of $E[X_{n+1} \mid \mathbf{X}], \mu(\Theta)$, or $E[\mu(\Theta) \mid \mathbf{X}]$, yields the same answer.

10.4 EXERCISES

10.1 Introduction
10.2 Linear Approximation Example

10-1   Use the pure premium estimates of Table 10.1 to show that

$$\sum_i W_i(a+bR_i) = \sum_i W_i P_i.$$

This shows that the weighted sum of the Bühlmann estimates of the pure premium is equal to the weighted sum of the Bayesian estimates, where the weights are the prior probabilities for the possible values of the pure premium.

10-2   Find the least squares estimates of a and b that minimize the sum of squares given by Equation (10.1).

10-3   Redefine the three vectors of Section 10.2 as follows:

$$\mathbf{W} = (1,1,1) \qquad \mathbf{R} = (1,2,3) \qquad \mathbf{P} = (1,4,9)$$

Find the least squares estimates of a and b that minimize Equation (10.1).

10-4   For $i=1,2$, let X_i denote the outcome of a single trial for which the following values apply:

Outcome r	Prior Probability $P[X_1 = r]$	Bayesian Estimate $E[X_2 \mid X_1 = r]$
0	1/3	1
3	1/3	6
12	1/3	8

What are the Bühlmann credibility estimates for each of the three possible outcomes?

10-5 For $i = 1, 2$, let X_i denote the outcome of a single trial for which the following values apply:

Outcome r	Prior Probability $P[X_1 = r]$	Bühlmann Estimate	Bayesian Estimate $E[X_2 \mid X_1 = r]$
1	1/3	2.626	2.6
8	1/3	7.729	7.8
12	1/3	10.645	—

Determine the Bayesian estimate $E[X_2 \mid X_1 = 12]$.

10.3 Linear Approximation Theory

10-6 True or false: The Bühlmann model produces the best linear least squares fit to the optimal estimate.

10-7 A necessary condition for two random variables X_1 and X_2 to be pairwise independent is that $E[X_1, X_2] = E[X_1] \cdot E[X_2]$ (i.e., X_1 and X_2 are uncorrelated). Let X_1 and X_2 be as defined in Section 10.3 with $Var(\mu(\Theta)) > 0$.

(a) Show that $E[X_1 X_2] = \mu^2 + Var(\mu(\Theta))$.

(b) Show that $E[X_1] = \mu = E[X_2]$.

(c) Use parts (a) and (b) to show that X_1 and X_2 are not pairwise independent.

10-8 Let U, V, and W, be mutually independent random variables for which $Var(W) > 0$. Let $X = U + W$ and $Y = V + W$.

(a) Show that X and Y are conditionally independent, given $W = w$.

(b) Show that X and Y are *not* unconditionally independent.

10-9 Show that the minimization of Expression (10.4) with X_{n+1} replaced by any one of

(i) $E[X_{n+1} | \mathbf{X}]$,

(ii) $\mu(\Theta)$, or

(iii) $E_\Theta[\mu(\Theta) | \mathbf{X}]$

yields the same answer, $\hat{P}_{n+1}$.

CHAPTER 11

CASE STUDY: CLINICAL TRIALS – AN APPLICATION OF BAYESIAN INFERENCE ABOUT BINOMIAL PROPORTIONS

11.1 INTRODUCTION

The focus of this chapter is a Bayesian approach to testing the statistical hypothesis that the proportions of success of two treatments are equal. This approach has a number of advantages over the classical or frequentist approach to such hypothesis testing. One advantage is that it obviates the need for the question of "How much data are needed for our results to be fully credible?"

Before beginning our discussion, we present an alternative approach to that presented in Section 8.2.1 where we considered a sequence of n independent Bernoulli trials and the probability of success, Θ, on such trials. Here, rather than assuming as we did in Section 8.2.1 that Θ has a prior beta distribution, we assume that Θ takes on positive probability only at a finite number of points on the interval $(0,1)$. We illustrate this approach in the following example. This type of problem is the single-treatment analog of the two-treatment problem that is the main focus of this chapter.

EXAMPLE 11.1

We observe a sequence consisting of six successes in ten independent Bernoulli trials with constant probability of success, Θ. Find the posterior distribution for Θ given that its prior distribution is the one summarized in Table 11.1.

TABLE 11.1

Prior Probability Distribution of Θ	
θ	$P[\Theta = \theta]$
.40	.30
.50	.40
.60	.30

SOLUTION

The likelihood function for this example is

$$L(\Theta) = \Theta^6(1-\Theta)^4$$

because there were 6 successes and 4 failures in the 10 trials. The posterior probabilities are proportional to the product of the likelihood and the corresponding prior probability. We summarize our calculations in Table 11.2.

TABLE 11.2

Values of Likelihood Function			
θ	$P[\Theta = \theta]$	$L(\theta) = \theta^6(1-\theta)^4$	$P[\Theta = \theta] \cdot L(\theta)$
.40	.30	$(.4)^6(.6)^4 = .00053$	$(.3)(.00053) = .000159$
.50	.40	$(.5)^6(.5)^4 = .00098$	$(.4)(.00098) = .000392$
.60	.30	$(.6)^6(.4)^4 = .00119$	$(.3)(.00119) = .000357$
Total	1.0	.00270	.00908

A normalizing factor must be applied to the entries of the last column of Table 11.2 to make their sum equal to one. The normalizing factor is the reciprocal of the sum of the entries in the last column of Table 11.2, namely,

$$\frac{1}{\sum_{\theta} P[\Theta = \theta] \cdot L(\theta)} = \frac{1}{.00908} = 110.13.$$

The posterior probabilities are those given in Table 11.3.

TABLE 11.3

Posterior Probability Distribution of Θ	
θ	$\left(P[\Theta = \theta] \cdot L(\theta)\right) \cdot \left(\dfrac{1}{\sum_{\theta} P[\Theta = \theta] \cdot L(\theta)}\right)$
.40	$(.000159) \cdot (110.13) = .175$
.50	$(.000392) \cdot (110.13) = .432$
.60	$(.000357) \cdot (110.13) = .393$

11.2 BACKGROUND

In clinical trial studies, the issue is typically to compare the efficacy of two or more different treatments or, less typically, to compare the side effects of such treatments. Both issues lead to statistical inference questions in which the task is to compare the proportion of successes/failures of the treatments. Over the years, there have been a number of clinical trial studies that have generated controversy.

One such study was conducted by Merck during 2000 to compare the side effects of its non-steroidal anti-inflammatory drug, Vioxx, to those of naproxen – the generic name of a competing non-steroidal anti-inflammatory drug produced under a variety of brand names such as Aleve. In this study, as reported in Ziliak and McCloskey [2008], eight of the people treated with Vioxx suffered heart attacks during the study versus only one of the people in the control group treated with naproxen. Ziliak and McCloskey [2008] castigated Merck for claiming that because of "the lack of statistical significance at the 5 percent level, there was no difference in the *effects* of the two" drugs.

Another controversial study was one conducted during the 1980s at two Harvard university hospitals and reported in Ware [1989]. The purpose of this study was to compare two treatments for persistent pulmonary hypertension (severe respiratory problems) in newborns. A new extracorporeal pulmonary oxygenation treatment (ECMO) was compared to a conventional medical therapy (CMT). Berry [1989] criticized the Harvard researchers for withholding the ECMO treatment from some of their patients: "there was a substantial amount of historical data that, in my view, carry more weight than the Ware study, but suggest that randomizing patients to non-ECMO therapy as in the Ware study was unethical."

11.3 HARVARD STUDY DATA AND ANALYSIS

In this chapter, we consider the Harvard study whose data are found in Ware [1989]. We present a Bayesian analysis of these data based on Albert [1995]. We believe that this is the type of analysis that Ziliak and McCloskey would have preferred for the clinical trial for Vioxx that Merck conducted during 2000. The methodological approach of this chapter allows the actuary to keep the computational sophistication low yet to employ prior distributions other than the conjugate priors discussed in Chapter 8.

The Harvard study consisted of two phases. In Phase 1, nine patients received the ECMO treatment and ten patients received CMT. All of the ECMO patients survived, while only six of the ten CMT patients survived. Because both prior studies and the results of Phase 1 indicated that ECMO was the superior approach, the Harvard researchers gave all twenty new patients in Phase 2 the ECMO treatment. All but one of these twenty survived.

11.4 ANALYSIS USING A UNIFORM PRIOR DISTRIBUTION

In his analysis, Albert began by combining the data of Phases 1 and 2 of the Harvard study. Under this scheme, 29 patients received the ECMO treatment and one died, while four of the ten who received the CMT died. Albert then posed two questions. First, was there a difference in the efficacy of the two treatments? Second, what was the magnitude of the benefit of the ECMO treatment compared to the CMT?

At this point, we introduce some notation. We let (1) P_E denote a random variable representing the proportion of infants with this respiratory condition who would survive if given the ECMO treatment and (2) P_C denote a random variable representing the proportion of infants with this respiratory condition who would survive if given the CMT. We can now restate the two questions. The first is a test of the hypothesis that the two proportions are equal. The second is to estimate the magnitude of the difference $P_E - P_C$.

Albert's approach was to assume that the proportions could only take on a limited number of discrete values with positive probability. This enabled him to summarize the ensemble of such prior probabilities in a two-way table as follows:

TABLE 11.4

						P_E					
Prior Probabilities of P_C and P_E											
P_C	0	.10	.20	.30	.40	.50	.60	.70	.80	.90	1
0	.0444	.0051	.0051	.0051	.0051	.0051	.0051	.0051	.0051	.0051	.0051
.10	.0051	.0444	.0051	.0051	.0051	.0051	.0051	.0051	.0051	.0051	.0051
.20	.0051	.0051	.0444	.0051	.0051	.0051	.0051	.0051	.0051	.0051	.0051
.30	.0051	.0051	.0051	.0444	.0051	.0051	.0051	.0051	.0051	.0051	.0051
.40	.0051	.0051	.0051	.0051	.0444	.0051	.0051	.0051	.0051	.0051	.0051
.50	.0051	.0051	.0051	.0051	.0051	.0444	.0051	.0051	.0051	.0051	.0051
.60	.0051	.0051	.0051	.0051	.0051	.0051	.0444	.0051	.0051	.0051	.0051
.70	.0051	.0051	.0051	.0051	.0051	.0051	.0051	.0444	.0051	.0051	.0051
.80	.0051	.0051	.0051	.0051	.0051	.0051	.0051	.0051	.0444	.0051	.0051
.90	.0051	.0051	.0051	.0051	.0051	.0051	.0051	.0051	.0051	.0444	.0051
1	.0051	.0051	.0051	.0051	.0051	.0051	.0051	.0051	.0051	.0051	.0444

The entries in the above table are shown to four decimal places. Each of the entries on the main diagonal is in fact equal to $\frac{1}{22}$ and each of the other terms is equal to $\frac{1}{220}$. The sum of the entries on the main diagonal is .50. This is the prior probability of the hypothesis that $P_C = P_E$. Albert considered this distribution of prior probabilities to be both non-informative and uniform.

The likelihood function for this problem is

$$L(P_C, P_E) = P_C{}^6 \cdot (1-P_C)^4 \cdot P_E{}^{28} \cdot (1-P_E)^1$$

because 28 of the 29 patients given the ECMO therapy survived and 6 of the 10 given CMT survived. The posterior probabilities are proportional to the product of the likelihood and the associated prior probability. The results must then be normalized to obtain the actual posterior probabilities displayed in Table 11.5. As is typical in a Bayesian analysis, these posterior probabilities can be considered to be revised estimates of the prior probabilities of Table 11.4.

TABLE 11.5

P_C	P_E										
	0	.10	.20	.30	.40	.50	.60	.70	.80	.90	1
0	0	0	0	0	0	0	0	0	0	0	0
.10	0	0	0	0	0	0	0	0	.00001	.00012	0
.20	0	0	0	0	0	0	0	.00001	.00036	.00482	0
.30	0	0	0	0	0	0	0	.00008	.00238	.03217	0
.40	0	0	0	0	0	0	0	.00026	.00721	.09756	0
.50	0	0	0	0	0	0	.00001	.00047	.01327	.17947	0
.60	0	0	0	0	0	0	.00010	.00058	.01623	.21950	0
.70	0	0	0	0	0	0	.00001	.00462	.01295	.17513	0
.80	0	0	0	0	0	0	0	.00020	.05698	.07708	0
.90	0	0	0	0	0	0	0	.00003	.00072	.09767	0
1	0	0	0	0	0	0	0	0	0	0	0

Posterior Probabilities of P_C and P_E

From Table 11.5 we note the following:

- Our results replicate those of Albert.

- The posterior probability is 15.9 percent that the two proportions are equal. (We note that this number is obtained by summing the terms on the main diagonal of the matrix of Table 11.5.)

- The posterior probability that P_C is greater than P_E is less than 0.1 percent. (We note that this number is obtained by summing all of the terms below the main diagonal of the matrix of Table 11.5.)

- The posterior probability that P_E is greater than P_C is 84.0 percent. (We note that this number is obtained by summing all of the terms above the main diagonal of the matrix of Table 11.5.)

- When either P_E or P_C is equal to either zero or one, then the likelihood is zero.

- The last point raises the issue of how sensitive the results are to the choice of the endpoints of the vectors of the proportions. We can test this by adding .01 to zero and subtracting .01 from one and redoing our calculations. As can be seen from Table 11.6, this slight change does have a substantial impact on the results.

TABLE 11.6

P_C	\multicolumn{11}{c}{P_E}
	.01	.10	.20	.30	.40	.50	.60	.70	.80	.90	.99
.01	0	0	0	0	0	0	0	0	0	0	0
.10	0	0	0	0	0	0	0	0	.00000	.00006	.00008
.20	0	0	0	0	0	0	0	.00001	.00017	.00224	.00324
.30	0	0	0	0	0	0	0	.00004	.00111	.01498	.02160
.40	0	0	0	0	0	0	0	.00012	.00336	.04543	.06552
.50	0	0	0	0	0	0	.00005	.00022	.00618	.08358	.12053
.60	0	0	0	0	0	0	0	.00027	.00756	.10222	.14741
.70	0	0	0	0	0	0	0	.00215	.00603	.08156	.11761
.80	0	0	0	0	0	0	0	.00009	.02653	.03590	.05177
.90	0	0	0	0	0	0	0	.00001	.00034	.04348	.00656
.99	0	0	0	0	0	0	0	0	0	0	.00001

Revised Posterior Probabilities of P_C and P_E

In particular, from Table 11.6 we note the following:

- These results should be preferred to those obtained initially even though this tact was not one pursued by Albert [1995].

- The posterior probability is 7.1 percent that the two proportions are equal. (We note that this number is obtained by summing the terms on the main diagonal of the matrix of Table 11.6 and is a substantial decline from the original result.) This is less than the prior probability of .5 and casts some doubt that the proportions are equal.

- The posterior probability that P_C is greater than P_E is again less than 0.1 percent. (We note that this number is obtained by summing all of the terms below the main diagonal of the matrix of Table 11.6.)

- The posterior probability that P_E is greater than P_C is 92.8 percent.

- The posterior probability is 94.7 percent that P_E is either 0.9 or 0.99.

- In order to estimate the magnitude of the $P_E - P_C$, we summarize its posterior distribution as:

TABLE 11.7

Revised Posterior Probability Distribution of $P_E - P_C$										
$P_E - P_C$										
−.10	0	.10	.20	.30	.40	.50	.60	.70	.80	.90
.04%	7.1%	4.9%	14.1%	22.6%	23.4%	16.7%	8.1%	2.4%	0.3%	.01%

11.5 ANALYSIS USING A MORE-INFORMATIVE PRIOR DISTRIBUTION

Next, Albert constructed an alternative prior distribution that was not uniform but was instead based on the results of some earlier studies. Albert observed that "based on historical experience … the conventional therapy has an approximate 20% survival rate." This lead Albert to the following prior for P_C :

TABLE 11.8

Prior Probability Distribution of P_C										
0	.10	.20	.30	.40	.50	.60	.70	.8-	.90	1
0	28%	30%	21%	12%	6%	3%	0	0	0	0

This prior has a total of 79% of its probability at the three points .10, .20, and .30.

Albert then cited a University of Michigan study, conducted before the Harvard study, in which "all 11 infants assigned to the ECMO therapy survived, and the one assigned to the CMT therapy died." Because the University of Michigan study suggests that ECMO may be a much better treatment, Albert used the following prior probability distribution for P_E :

TABLE 11.9

Prior Probability Distribution of P_E										
0	.10	.20	.30	.40	.50	.60	.70	.80	.90	1
0	18%	18%	17%	14%	12%	9%	6%	4%	2%	0

Albert wanted the prior for P_E to be more diffuse because it was based only on a single study having a limited number of patients. Albert assumed that P_C and P_E were independent so that their joint prior distribution could be obtained by multiplying their marginal prior distributions. The results are shown in Table 11.10.

TABLE 11.10

					P_E						
P_C	0	.10	.20	.30	.40	.50	.60	70	.80	.90	1
0	0	0	0	0	0	0	0	0	0	0	0
.1	0	.0504	.0504	.0476	.0392	.0336	.0252	.0168	.0112	.0056	0
.2	0	.0540	.0540	.0510	.0420	.0360	.0270	.0180	.0120	.0060	0
.3	0	.0378	.0378	.0357	.0294	.0252	.0189	.0126	.0084	.0042	0
.4	0	.0216	.0216	.0204	.0168	.0144	.0108	.0072	.0048	.0024	0
.5	0	.0108	.0108	.0102	.0084	.0072	.0054	.0036	.0024	.0012	0
.6	0	.0054	.0054	.0051	.0042	.0036	.0027	.0018	.0012	.0006	0
.7	0	0	0	0	0	0	0	0	0	0	0
.8	0	0	0	0	0	0	0	0	0	0	0
.9	0	0	0	0	0	0	0	0	0	0	0
1	0	0	0	0	0	0	0	0	0	0	0

The header spans: **Prior Probabilities of P_C and P_E**

We note that Albert assumed that there would be no probability mass at either 0 or 1, thereby obviating the problem with those choices noted earlier.

If we next multiply the prior above by the likelihood considered earlier and then normalize the results, we obtain the following posterior joint distribution:

Table 11.11

							P_E				
						Posterior Probabilities of P_C and P_E Under Subjective Prior Distribution					
P_C	0	.10	.20	.30	.40	.50	.60	70	.80	.90	1
0	0	0	0	0	0	0	0	0	0	0	0
.10	0	0	0	0	0	0	0	.00001	.00012	.00078	0
.20	0	0	0	0	0	0	.00001	.00027	.00496	.03352	0
.30	0	0	0	0	0	0	.00003	.00124	.02317	.15669	0
.40	0	0	0	0	0	0	.00006	.00215	.04015	.27155	0
.50	0	0	0	0	0	0	.00005	.00198	.03693	.24978	0
.60	0	0	0	0	0	0	.00003	.00121	.02258	.15275	0
.70	0	0	0	0	0	0	0	0	0	0	0
.80	0	0	0	0	0	0	0	0	0	0	0
.90	0	0	0	0	0	0	0	0	0	0	0
1	0	0	0	0	0	0	0	0	0	0	0

From Table 11.11, we note the following:

- The posterior probability that P_E is greater than P_C is almost 100 percent.

- The posterior probability is 99.3 percent that P_E is either 0.8 or 0.9. This is a high probability of success for the ECMO treatment. It might be interesting to redo these calculations with additional prior probability given to a value of P_E above .9. We leave this to the reader.

- The posterior probability distribution of the difference $P_E - P_C$ is:

Table 11.12

					$P_E - P_C$					
Posterior Probability Distribution of $P_E - P_C$										
$-.10$	0	.10	.20	.30	.40	.50	.60	.70	.80	.90
0	0	.10%	2.50%	19.20%	29.10%	29.50%	16.20%	3.40%	0.10%	0

11.6 CONCLUSIONS AND GENERAL OBSERVATIONS

The Bayesian approach presented here obviates the need to consider the question of "How much data do we need for our results to be credible." In fact, with even a small sample, we can still use this type of Bayesian approach to obtain revised probability estimates. Of course, the more observations we have, the more reliable such estimates will be.

The Bayesian approach gets us away from classical statistics and the yes/no question of whether our results are statistically significant at the 5 percent level. Instead, we obtain an (estimated) posterior probability of the validity of the null hypothesis. This is a better way to do statistical inference.

Finally, the approach considered here is computationally straightforward. If desired, a finer grid could be used.

11.7 EXERCISES

11-1 Suppose that we are given the following prior probabilities:

  • $P[\theta = .10] = .25$ and   • $P[\theta = .20] = .35$.

Suppose that we are also given the following values of the likelihood for Θ.

  • $L[\theta = .10] = .04$.   • $L[\theta = .20] = .06$.

Compute the quotient of the posterior probabilities: $\dfrac{P[\theta=.20 \,|\, data]}{P[\theta=.10 \,|\, data]}$.

11-2 Suppose that we are given the following prior probabilities:

  • $P[\theta = .40] = .30$ and   • $P[\theta = .50] = .40$.

Suppose that we are also given the following values of the likelihood for Θ.

  • $L[\theta = .40] = .08$ and   • $L[\theta = .50] = .06$.

Compute the quotient of the posterior probabilities: $\dfrac{P[\theta = .50 \,|\, data]}{P[\theta=.40 \,|\, data]}$.

204 ◆ CHAPTER 11

11-3 What is the main disadvantage of the yes/no question of statistical tests of significance compared to the Bayesian approach?

11-4 How can the problems considered here be structured as missing data problems?

11-5 Given the following prior distributions for P_C and P_E, which are assumed to be independent,

Prior Probability Distribution of P_C		
.10	.20	.30
30%	40%	30%

Prior Probability Distribution of P_E		
.70	.80	.90
30%	30%	40%

and given the combined observational data of the Harvard study described in the first paragraph of Section 11.3, calculate:

(a) the joint prior distribution,

(b) the likelihood function,

(c) the product of the likelihood and the prior distribution,

(d) the normalization factor, and

(e) the posterior distribution.

11-6 According to Table 11.11, we computed the posterior probability $P[P_E=.90\,|\,data] = .86508$. What is the corresponding prior probability $P[P_E=.90)]$?

CHAPTER 12

CASE STUDY:
APPLICATION OF CREDIBILITY
TO GROUP HEALTH INSURANCE

12.1 INTRODUCTION

In this chapter we generalize the Bühlmann credibility model of Chapter 6, following Fuhrer [1988], and use this generalized model to estimate future claims under group health insurance.

Fuhrer [1988] presents a variety of credibility formulas applicable to group insurance, with a focus on group health insurance. In this chapter, we examine an application of the non-linear credibility formulas discussed in Section V of Fuhrer [1988]. In performing **experience** *rating*, some insurance companies impose an upper limit on the amount incurred by an individual group member. This limit is called the **pooling limit**. The application of pooling limits makes experience rating less sensitive to the effects of a small number of unusually large claims. Our application uses a generalization of the Bühlmann credibility model of Chapter 6 of this text to compute an optimal pooling point. The model is constructed using an approach similar to the least-squares approach of Section 10.3 of this text.

Background and preliminary material are presented in Sections 12.2 and 12.3. These involve the development of a linear model from which the non-linear model will be derived. The non-linear model itself is described in Section 12.4. A more general model is suggested in Section 12.5. Section 12.6 consists of a summary and some concluding remarks.

12.2 General Approach

Here, we use the notation of Section 10.3 rather than that of Fuhrer [1988]. The basic idea is that we are interested in predicting the amount of aggregate losses for year $n+1$. Fuhrer's approach is to produce a point estimate of the expected aggregate losses for year $n+1$ conditional on the results (i.e., the actual aggregate losses) for each of the prior n years. Symbolically, Fuhrer's approach is to use the conditional expectation $E[X_{n+1} \mid X_1 = x_1, X_2 = x_2, \ldots, X_n = x_n]$ as an improvement over the initial (or prior) estimate, $E[X_{n+1}]$. Fuhrer begins by describing a linear model which can be used to obtain the desired point estimate. This approach is a way to approximate the result one would obtain using a full Bayesian approach which, as discussed in Section 9.2, also uses the results of the first n years. The end result of the full Bayesian analysis is an entire predictive distribution. Fuhrer's preliminary approach is similar to the Bühlmann approach of Chapter 6 of this text.[1] Moreover, both methods implicitly assume that squared error loss is the appropriate loss function (see Chapter 2) for obtaining a point estimate from a predictive distribution.

In order to estimate

$$E[X_{n+1} \mid X_1, \ldots, X_n] \tag{12.1}$$

Fuhrer uses the estimator

$$a_0 + \sum_{i=1}^{n} a_i \cdot X_i. \tag{12.2}$$

Fuhrer's assumptions are identical to those of Section 10.3 except that he drops the conditional independence assumption. In this case, as in Section 10.3, the basic idea is to find the parameters $a_0, a_1, \ldots, a_n$ that minimize the expected squared error

$$E\left[a_0 + \sum_{i=1}^{n} a_i \cdot X_i - E\left[X_{n=1} \mid X_1, \ldots, X_n\right]\right]^2 \tag{12.3}$$

---

[1] The interested reader may want to review Section 9.9 – "Advantages and Disadvantages of the Bühlmann and Bayesian approaches."

between the Bühlmann estimator and the conditional expectation we are trying to estimate/approximate.

At this point, we suggest the reader review Section 10.3. Of particular note is that X_i represents the aggregate claim amount during the ith period of observation or policy year.

Proceeding as in Section 10.3, for each value of $j = 0, 1, \ldots, n$, we differentiate Expression (12.3) with respect to a_j, obtaining (1) the set of n linear equations

$$\sum_i^n a_i \cdot Cov(X_i, X_j) = Cov(X_{n+1}, X_j) \qquad (12.4)$$

where $j = 1, 2, \ldots, n$, and (2) the additional equation

$$a_0 = E[X_{n+1}] - \sum_{i=1}^n a_i \cdot E[X_i]. \qquad (12.5)$$

This result is valid as long as the moments exist and there is a unique set of a_i's that satisfy the system of equations (12.4) and (12.5).

12.2.1 GENERAL APPROACH WHEN $n = 1$

In the specific case in which $n = 1$, the system of Equation (12.4) simplifies to

$$a_1 \cdot Cov(X_1, X_1) = Cov(X_2, X_1) \qquad (12.6)$$

so that

$$a_1 = \frac{Cov(X_2, X_1)}{Cov(X_1, X_1)} = \frac{Cov(X_1, X_2)}{Var(X_1)} \qquad (12.7)$$

and from Equations (12.2) and (12.5) the (linear) credibility estimator of $E[X_2 \mid X_1]$ is found to be

$$E[X_2] - a_1 \cdot E[X_1] + a_1 \cdot X_1. \qquad (12.8)$$

If we further assume that $\mu = E[X_1] = E[X_2]$ and replace a_1 in Equation (12.8) by Z, then the (linear) credibility estimator of $E[X_2 | X_1]$ becomes

$$\mu - Z\mu + ZX_1$$

which we can rewrite in the usual form of

$$ZX_1 + (1-Z)\mu \qquad (12.9)$$

where, from Equation (12.7),

$$Z = a_1 = \frac{Cov(X_1, X_2)}{Var(X_1)}. \qquad (12.10)$$

12.2.2 GENERAL APPROACH WHEN $n > 1$

In this more general approach we use two or more years of prior experience data. While this is more complex than the approach of Section 12.2.1 that only involved one year of prior experience data, it is not difficult to treat in practice. We illustrate this via the following example.

EXAMPLE 12.1

Using the notation above, we assume that

- $n = 3$,
- $Var(X_i) = 0.90$, and
- $Cov(X_i, X_j) = .40 - (.05) \cdot |i - j|$.

What are the values of the parameters $a_1, a_2,$ and a_3?

SOLUTION
The system of equations of (12.4) becomes

$$a_1 \cdot Cov(X_1, X_1) + a_2 \cdot Cov(X_2, X_1) + a_3 \cdot Cov(X_3, X_1) = Cov(X_4, X_1)$$
$$a_1 \cdot Cov(X_1, X_2) + a_2 \cdot Cov(X_2, X_2) + a_3 \cdot Cov(X_3, X_2) = Cov(X_4, X_2)$$
$$a_1 \cdot Cov(X_1, X_3) + a_2 \cdot Cov(X_2, X_3) + a_3 \cdot Cov(X_3, X_3) = Cov(X_4, X_3).$$

Replacing the covariances by their numeric values, we obtain

$$a_1 \cdot (.90) + a_2 \cdot (.35) + a_3 \cdot (.30) \; = \; .25$$
$$a_1 \cdot (.35) + a_2 \cdot (.90) + a_3 \cdot (.35) \; = \; .30$$
$$a_1 \cdot (.30) + a_2 \cdot (.35) + a_3 \cdot (.90) \; = \; .35.$$

We can rewrite the last system of equations in matrix notation as

$$[a_1 \; a_2 \; a_3] \cdot \begin{bmatrix} .90 & .35 & .30 \\ .35 & .90 & .35 \\ .30 & .35 & .90 \end{bmatrix} = [.25 \; .30 \; .35]$$

or

$$[a_1 \; a_2 \; a_3] = [.25 \; .30 \; .35] \cdot \begin{bmatrix} .90 & .35 & .30 \\ .35 & .90 & .35 \\ .30 & .35 & .90 \end{bmatrix}^{-1}$$

Using standard matrix inversion methods, we obtain the solution $a_1 = .114$, $a_2 = .180$, and $a_3 = .281$.

EXAMPLE 12.2

Using the results of the last example and assuming further that $E[X_i] = 7$ for all i, compute the Bühlmann estimate/approximation to $E[X_4 | X_1 = 8, X_2 = 5, X_3 = 11]$. This is the conditional expectation of aggregate losses for year 4 given the specified results for years 1, 2, and 3.

SOLUTION

We first compute a_0. By Equation (12.5), we have

$$a_0 = E[X_4] - \sum_{i=1}^{3} a_i \cdot E[X_i]$$
$$= 7 - (.114)(7) - (.180)(7) - (.281)(7) = 2.975.$$

Then, using (1) the results of Example 12.1 and (2) Expression (12.2), we obtain the Bühlmann estimate/approximation to the conditional expectation $E[X_4 | X_1 = 8, X_2 = 5, X_3 = 11]$:

$$a_0 + \sum_{i=1}^{3} a_i \cdot x_i \;=\; 2.975 + (.114)(8)$$

$$+ (.180)(5)$$

$$+ (.281)(11)$$

$$=\; 7.878.$$

The result is an increase over the unconditional or prior expectation $E[X_4] = 7$.

12.3 CREDIBILITY FOR GROUP INSURANCE

We next consider a group insurance policy consisting of m risks. In this scenario, the risks would be the employees and dependent units of a group insurance policyholder – in other words, a company with a group health insurance plan for its employees and their dependents. The goal is to estimate the aggregate claims for the group for some insurance coverage during a particular year.

12.3.1 NOTATION

We first let X_{it} denote the claim amount of the ith risk during year t, where $i = 1, 2, \ldots, m$ and $t = 1, 2, \ldots$. We then define the average claim amount for the group during year t by:

$$\overline{X}_{\cdot t} = \frac{1}{m} \sum_{i=1}^{m} X_{it}.$$

12.3.2 CREDIBILITY MODEL FOR $E[X_{\cdot 2} \mid \overline{X}_{\cdot 1} = \overline{x}_{\cdot 1}]$

Here Fuhrer [1988; Section III] suggests using the model

$$Z\overline{X}_{\cdot 1} + (1-Z)\mu$$

to estimate/approximate $E[\overline{X}_{\cdot 2} \mid \overline{X}_{\cdot 1} = \overline{x}_{\cdot 1}]$ where (i) $n = 1$, (ii) the prior mean is $\mu = E[X_1] = E[X_2]$

and (iii)

$$Z = \frac{Cov[\bar{X}_{.1}, \bar{X}_{.2}]}{Var[\bar{X}_{.1}]}$$

$$= \frac{Cov\left[\frac{1}{m}\sum_{i=1}^{m} X_{i1}, \frac{1}{m}\sum_{i=1}^{m} X_{i2}\right]}{Var\left[\frac{1}{m}\sum_{i=1}^{m} X_{i1}\right]} = \frac{Cov\left[\sum_{i=1}^{m} X_{i1}, \sum_{i=1}^{m} X_{i2}\right]}{Var\left[\sum_{i=1}^{m} X_{i1}\right]} \qquad (12.11)$$

EXAMPLE 12.3

Suppose that we have two independent risks each of which is insured for two years. (So, $m = 2$ and $n = 1$.) Moreover, suppose that the random variables X_{i1} and X_{i2} representing the claim amount of risk i during years one and two, respectively, have joint probability distribution specified by the following table:

TABLE 12.1

Joint Distribution of X_{i1} and X_{i2}			
	X_{i2}		
X_{i1}	2.0	6.0	All
2.0	0.3	0.2	0.5
6.0	0.2	0.3	0.5
All	0.5	0.5	1.0

Use Equation (12.11) to obtain Z.

SOLUTION

From Equation (12.11) with $m = 2$ we need to evaluate

$$Z = \frac{Cov\left[\sum_{i=1}^{2} X_{i1}, \sum_{i=1}^{2} X_{i2}\right]}{Var\left[\sum_{i=1}^{2} X_{i1}\right]}. \qquad (12.12)$$

To do this, we first compute the individual means:

$$E[X_{i1}] = E[X_{i2}] = (.50)(2) + (.50)(6) = 4.$$

The denominator of Equation (12.12) is

$$Var\left[\sum_{i=1}^{2} X_{i1}\right] = 2Var[X_{i1}]$$

$$= 2E\left[(X_{11}-E[X_{11}])^2\right]$$

$$= 2E\left[(X_{11}-4)^2\right] = 2\left[(.50)(2-4)^2 + (.50)(6-4)^2\right] = 8.$$

The numerator of Equation (12.12) is

$$Cov\left[\sum_{i=1}^{2} X_{i1}, \sum_{i=1}^{2} X_{i2}\right] = E\left[(X_{11}+X_{21}-E[X_{11}]-E[X_{21}])\right.$$

$$\left. \cdot (X_{12}+X_{22}-E[X_{12}]-E[X_{22}])\right]$$

$$= E\left[((X_{11}-E[X_{11}])+(X_{21}-E[X_{21}]))\right.$$

$$\left. \cdot ((X_{12}-E[X_{12}])+(X_{22}-E[X_{22}]))\right]$$

$$= E\left[(X_{11}-E[X_{11}])\cdot(X_{12}-E[X_{12}])+(X_{21}-E[X_{21}])\right.$$

$$\left. \cdot (X_{22}-E[X_{22}])\right]$$

$$= 2\cdot E\left[(X_{11}-E[X_{11}])\cdot(X_{12}-E[X_{12}])\right]$$

$$= 2\cdot\{(.30)\cdot(2-4)(2-4)+(.20)(2-4)(6-4)$$

$$+(.20)(6-4)(2-4)+(.30)(4-2)(6-4)\} = 1.60.$$

Hence,

$$Z = \frac{Cov\left[\sum_{i=1}^{2} X_{i1}, \sum_{i=1}^{2} X_{i2}\right]}{Var\left[\sum_{i=1}^{2} X_{i1}\right]} = \frac{1.60}{8} = .20.$$

12.4 SPECIFIC APPROACH TO OBTAINING AN OPTIMAL POOLING LEVEL

We begin, following the discussion of Section V of Fuhrer [1988], by defining

$$X_{i1}(v) = \min(X_{i1}, v) \tag{12.13}$$

where v is the pooling point, currently unknown, and m is the number of employees within the group. Thus, $X_{i1}(v)$ caps the maximum value at v. We correspondingly define

$$\bar{X}_{\cdot 1}(v) = \frac{1}{m} \sum_{i=1}^{m} X_{i1}(v).$$

The basic approach is to approximate

$$E\left[\bar{X}_{\cdot 2} \mid \bar{X}_{\cdot 1}(v) = \bar{x}_{\cdot 1}(v)\right]$$

by the estimator

$$a_0(v) + Z(v) \cdot \bar{X}_{\cdot 1}(v) \tag{12.14}$$

where $a_0(v)$ and $Z(v)$ are parameters to be estimated. This estimator is better than the one given by Expression (12.2) whenever

$$E\left[E[\bar{X}_{\cdot 2} \mid \bar{X}_{\cdot 1}] - \left(a_0(v) + Z(v) \cdot \bar{X}_{\cdot 1}(v)\right)\right]^2$$
$$< E\left[E[\bar{X}_{\cdot 2} \mid \bar{X}_{\cdot 1} - (a_0 + Z \cdot \bar{X}_{\cdot 1})\right]^2.$$

When the last inequality is true, the computation of the best estimator involves maximizing the quantity

$$R(v) = \frac{\left[Cov[\bar{X}_{\cdot 1}(v), \bar{X}_{\cdot 2}]\right]^2}{Var\left[\bar{X}_{\cdot 1}(v)\right]}$$

$$= \frac{\left\{Cov\left[\frac{1}{m}\sum_{i=1}^{m} X_{i1}(v), \frac{1}{m}\sum_{i=1}^{m} X_{i2}\right]\right\}^2}{Var\left[\frac{1}{m}\sum_{i=1}^{m} X_{i1}(v)\right]} = \frac{\left\{Cov\left[\sum_{i=1}^{m} X_{i1}(v), \sum_{i=1}^{m} X_{i2}\right]\right\}^2}{m^2 \cdot Var\left[\sum_{i=1}^{m} X_{i1}(v)\right]}$$

$$\tag{12.15}$$

with respect to v. One simple way to determine the optimal choice of v is to examine every possibility and require at least two years of experience data. While this may be computationally intensive, for most practical problems it should only take a modern computer a short time to accomplish.

Given , the parameters $Z(v)$ and $a_0(v)$ are, respectively,

$$Z(v) = \frac{Cov\left[\bar{X}_{\cdot 1}(v), \bar{X}_{\cdot 2}\right]}{Var\left[\bar{X}_{\cdot 1}(v)\right]} = \frac{Cov\left[\sum_{i=1}^{m} X_{i1}(v), \sum_{i=1}^{m} X_{i2}\right]}{Var\left[\sum_{i=1}^{m} X_{i1}(v)\right]} \quad (12.16)$$

and

$$a_0(v) = E\left[\bar{X}_{\cdot 2}\right] - Z(v) \cdot E\left[\bar{X}_{\cdot 1}(v)\right]. \quad (12.17)$$

We illustrate the approach of this section in the following, admittedly oversimplified examples.

EXAMPLE 12.4

We assume (1) no inflation and (2) that the group of employees/insureds does not change over time.

Suppose that we have two independent risks each of which is insured for two years. (So $m = 2$.) Moreover, suppose that the random variables X_{i1} and X_{i2} representing the risks for the two years have joint probability distribution specified by Table 12.2:

TABLE 12.2

Joint Distribution of X_{i1} and X_{i2}				
	X_{i2}			
X_{i1}	2	7	9	All
2	0.30	0.10	0.10	0.50
7	0.10	0.10	0.05	0.25
9	0.10	0.05	0.10	0.25
All	0.50	0.25	0.25	1.00

Use these data and Equation (12.15) to determine

$$R(6) = \frac{\left\{Cov\left[\sum_{i=1}^{2} X_{i1}(6), \sum_{i=1}^{2} X_{i2}\right]\right\}^2}{m^2 \cdot Var\left[\sum_{i=1}^{2} X_{i1}(6)\right]}. \tag{12.18}$$

SOLUTION

We begin by replacing the values of X_{i1} that exceed "6" by "6" in Table 12.2:

TABLE 12.3

Joint Distribution of $X_{i1}(6)$ and X_{i2}				
	X_{i2}			
$X_{i1}(6)$	2	7	9	All
2	0.30	0.10	0.10	0.50
6	0.10	0.10	0.05	0.25
6	0.10	0.05	0.10	0.25
All	0.50	0.25	0.25	1.00

We then consolidate the entries of Table 12.3 into Table 12.4:

TABLE 12.4

Joint Distribution of $X_{i1}(6)$ and X_{i2}				
	X_{i2}			
$X_{i1}(6)$	2	7	9	All
2	0.30	0.10	0.10	0.50
6	0.20	0.15	0.15	0.50
All	0.50	0.25	0.25	1.00

Now, the variance of $X_{i1}(6)$ in this example is identical to the variance of X_{i1} in Example 12.3, namely 8. The numerator is computed in a manner similar to that used in Example 12.3. We omit the details here. The result is

$$Cov\left[\sum_{i=1}^{2} X_{i1}(6), \sum_{i=1}^{2} X_{i2}\right] = 2.40.$$

So,

$$R(6) = \frac{\left\{Cov\left[\sum_{i=1}^{2} X_{i1}(6), \sum_{i=1}^{2} X_{i2}\right]\right\}^{2}}{m^{2} \cdot Var\left[\sum_{i=1}^{2} X_{i1}(6)\right]} = \frac{(2.4)^{2}}{4 \cdot 8} = .18.$$

EXAMPLE 12.5

Using the earlier results from this section, what is the value of the parameter $Z(6)$?

SOLUTION

From Expression (12.16), we have

$$Z(6) = \frac{Cov\left[\sum_{i=1}^{2} X_{i1}(6), \sum_{i=1}^{2} X_{i2}\right]}{Var\left[\sum_{i=1}^{2} X_{i1}(6)\right]} = \frac{2.4}{8} = .30.$$

EXAMPLE 12.6

Using the earlier results from this section, what is the value of the parameter $a_0(6)$?

SOLUTION

From Expression (12.17), we have

$$a_0(6) = E[\bar{X}_{.2}] - Z(6) \cdot E[\bar{X}_{.1}(6)] = 5 - (.30) \cdot (4) = 3.80.$$

EXAMPLE 12.7

Using the earlier results from this section, use the estimator $a_0(6) + Z(6) \cdot \bar{X}_{.1}(6)$ to determine all possible estimates of

$$E\left[\bar{X}_{.2} \mid \bar{X}_{.1}(6) = \bar{x}_{.1}(6)\right].$$

SOLUTION
We summarize our calculations in Table 12.5:

TABLE 12.5

$x_{11}(6)$	$x_{21}(6)$	$\bar{x}_{.1}(6)$	$a_0(6) + Z(6) \cdot \bar{x}_{.1}(6)$
2	2	2	$3.8 + (.3) \cdot (2) = 4.4$
2	6	4	$3.8 + (.3) \cdot (4) = 5.0$
6	2	4	$3.8 + (.3) \cdot (4) = 5.0$
6	6	6	$3.8 + (.3) \cdot (6) = 5.6$

We note that the estimator of this section $a_0(v) + Z(v) \cdot \bar{X}_{.1}(v)$ can be rewritten as

$$
\begin{aligned}
a_0(v) + Z(v) \cdot \bar{X}_{.1}(v) &= E[\bar{X}_{.2}] - Z(v) \cdot E[\bar{X}_{.1}(v)] \\
&\quad + Z(v) \cdot \bar{X}_{.1}(v) \\
&= E[\bar{X}_{.2}] + Z(v) \cdot \left\{ \bar{X}_{.1}(v) - E\left[\bar{X}_{.1}(v)\right] \right\}.
\end{aligned}
$$
(12.19)

In this form, we see that the effect of the pooling is to reduce the influence of "extreme values" on the conditional (i.e., posterior) estimate of the mean aggregate loss amount during the second policy year.

12.5 A MORE GENERAL MODEL

Fuhrer [1988; Section II] also considers a more general form for the average claim amount for the group during year t:

$$
\bar{X}_{.t} = \frac{\sum_{i=1}^{m} X_{it} P_i}{\sum_{i=1}^{m} P_i}
$$

where P_i is the manual premium[2] for risk i. When the manual premium is constant over all of the risks (i.e., $P_i = P$ for all i), then the expression for the average claim amount simplifies to

$$\overline{X}_{\cdot t} = \frac{1}{m} \sum_{i=1}^{m} X_{it}.$$

12.6 SUMMARY AND CONCLUSION

In this chapter we have provided a number of simple examples that illustrate the pooling-limit approach of Fuhrer [1988]. We have also described the mathematics of that approach and showed how this approach relates to some of the earlier chapters of this text. After reading this chapter, the interested reader should be better able to gain additional insight into Fuhrer [1988] 's important paper.

12.7 EXERCISES

12-1 Verify Equations (12.4) and (12.5) for the case $n = 1$. Specifically, show that for $n = 1$

$$a_0 = E[X_2] - E[X_1] \cdot \frac{Cov[X_1, X_2]}{Var[X_1]} \text{ and } a_1 = \frac{Cov[X_1, X_2]}{Var[X_1]}.$$

12-2 Using the notation of this chapter, we assume that

- $n = 4$,
- $Var(X_i) = .80$, and
- $Cov(X_i, X_j) = .60 - (.10) \cdot |i - j|$.

What are the values of the parameters a_1, a_2, a_3 and a_4 ?

---

[2] The manual premium is defined as the premium for a group developed from the insurer's standard rate tables.

12-3 Using the results of Exercise 12-2 and assuming further that $E[X_i] = 7$ for all i, compute the Bühlmann estimate/approximation to $E[X_5 \mid X_1 = 8, X_2 = 5, X_3 = 11, X_4 = 10]$. This is the conditional expectation of aggregate losses for year five given the specified results for years 1, 2, 3 and 4.

12-4 Use Equation (12.15) to determine $R(8)$, given

- $m = 2$,
- $E[\overline{X}_{\cdot i}] = 7$ for $i = 1, 2$,
- $E[\overline{X}_{\cdot i}(8)] = 5$ for $i = 1, 2$,
- $Cov\left[\sum\limits_{i=1}^{2} X_{i1}(8), \sum\limits_{i=1}^{2} X_{i2}(8)\right] = 2.0$,
- $Cov\left[\sum\limits_{i=1}^{2} X_{i1}(8), \sum\limits_{i=1}^{2} X_{i2}\right] = 2.5$,
- $Var\left[\sum\limits_{i=1}^{2} X_{i1}\right] = 4$, and
- $Var\left[\sum\limits_{i=1}^{2} X_{i1}(8)\right] = 3$.

12-5 Using the assumptions of Exercise 12-4, employ Equation (12.16) to determine $Z(8)$.

12-6 Using the assumptions of Exercise 12-4, employ Equation (12.17) to determine $a_0(8)$.

12-7 Determine $E[\overline{X}_{\cdot 1}(8)]$ given that

- $n = 1$,
- $E[\overline{X}_{\cdot 1}] = 5$ for $i = 1, 2$,
- $a_0(8) = 4$,
- $Z(8) = .40$.

12-8 Given $a_0(8) = 4$ and $Z(8) = .50$ compute

    (a) $E[\overline{X}_{\cdot2}] \mid \overline{X}_{\cdot1}(8) = 1]$,

    (b) $E[\overline{X}_{\cdot2}] \mid \overline{X}_{\cdot1}(8) = 4]$, and

    (c) $E[\overline{X}_{\cdot2}] \mid \overline{X}_{\cdot1}(8) = 7]$,

CHAPTER 13

A CASE STUDY IN BAYESIAN ANALYSIS: THE IMPACT OF NEWBORN SCREENING ON CYSTIC FIBROSIS HOSPITALIZATION COSTS

13.1 INTRODUCTION

In this chapter, we consider an application in which the goal is to predict future health care costs for a chronic disease producing many high-cost episodes. This application is based on Rosenberg and Farrell [2008] – a copy of which constitutes Appendix A of this text. A second, similar application of credibility methods to a medical insurance cost problem is presented in Fellingham, Tolley, and Herzog [2006]. A copy of this paper constitutes Appendix B.

13.1.1 PURPOSE

The purpose of the work of Rosenberg and Farrell [2008] was to analyze data from a clinical trial study in order to investigate the impact of newborn screening on reducing the number and cost of hospitalizations of children with cystic fibrosis. In addition, the authors hoped that the study would suggest that early diagnosis of cystic fibrosis through neonatal screening would be medically beneficial as well as free of major risks. This work entailed predicting the frequency and severity of hospitalization costs for a group of children with cystic fibrosis.

13.1.2 DATA

The data consist of observations on 77 children who participated in a clinical trial study in Wisconsin. The data for 13 full calendar years of the study (1990-2002) are summarized in Table 13.1. All costs were adjusted to 2001 dollars on a monthly basis using the medical care component of the U.S. Bureau of Labor Statistic's Consumer Price Index (http://data.bls.gov). This clinical trial study used both (1) physician costs and (2) costs related to the care within the hospital, such as nursing,

221

pharmacy, and laboratory. These cost data were collected using an intricate cost-accounting process at the University of Wisconsin-Madison Hospitals and Clinics.

TABLE 13.1

Basic Data				
Calendar Year	Number of Children in Study	Number of Exposure Years	Number of Hospi-talizations	Average Cost Per Hospitalization
1990	46	45.50	37	$15,462
1991	48	47.10	40	11,094
1992	57	56.60	22	9,543
1993	66	65.30	19	9,386
1994	69	67.60	21	9,954
1995	65	62.80	14	5,355
1996	61	60.00	23	10,143
1997	59	59.00	15	8,660
1998	59	57.90	15	12,164
1999	57	56.30	11	12,107
2000	55	55.00	6	14,042
2001	55	54.40	9	18,287
2002	53	53.00	12	19,244

Table 13.2 shows the average annual frequency of hospitalization by child.

Table 13.2

Average Annual Frequency of Hospital Visits by Child	
Rate of Hospitalization	Number of Children
0.00	30
0.10	15
0.20	10
0.30	4
0.40	2
0.50	4
0.60	3
0.70	1
0.80	0
0.90	1
1.00	0
1.10	0
1.20	0
1.30	3
1.40	0
1.50	0
1.60	0
1.70	1
1.80	0
1.90	1
2.00	0
2.10	0
2.20	1
2.30	0
2.40	0
2.50	0
2.60	1

Eight children who had many hospitalizations were categorized as "high utilizers."

Table 13.3 shows the distribution of the cost of the 259 hospital visits experienced in this study. The cost of these visits ranged from a low of $1,000 to a high of $74,100.

TABLE 13.3

Cost of Hospitalization	Number of Visits
<$5,000	76
$5,000 - $10,000	47
$10,000 - $15,000	59
$15,000 - $20,000	37
$20,000 - $25,000	19
$25,000 - $30,000	8
$30,000 - $35,000	7
$35,000 - $40,000	3
$40,000 - $45,000	0
$45,000 - $50,000	1
$50,000 - $55,000	0
$55,000 - $60,000	0
$60,000 - $65,000	0
$65,000 - $70,000	1
$70,000 - $75,000	1

13.1.3   THE MODEL

As in the two-stage model of Chapter 9, a two-stage model is used here in which the first stage predicts the number of hospital visits and the second stage predicts the cost of each visit.

13.1.4   METHOD USED TO ESTIMATE MODEL PARAMETERS

Rosenberg and Farrell used the Markov chain Monte Carlo method to obtain the estimated posterior and predictive distributions required for their study. The Monte Carlo part of the method is a simulation technique that when combined with Markov chain concepts creates simulated draws from the posterior distribution of the parameters. For more details on Markov chain Monte Carlo methods, the reader may refer to any of three sources: 1) Section 13.3 of this chapter, 2) Gelman, Carlin, Stern and Rubin [2004], or 3) Gilks, Richardson, and Spielgelhalter [1996].

13.1.5   WINBUGS SOFTWARE PACKAGE

Rosenberg and Farrell used version 1.4 of WinBUGS – a software package developed to implement Bayesian models – to perform all of their calculations. For a tutorial on WinBUGS the reader should refer to Scollnik [2001].

13.1.6 FREQUENCY STAGE

Rosenberg and Farrell [2008] employed a Poisson distribution with mean, $e_{ij} \cdot \mu_{ij}$. Here, e_{ij} represents the number of exposure units for child i, during his/her j^{th} year of age; while μ_{ij} represents the corresponding expected number of hospital visits. Rosenberg and Farrell estimated $\log(\mu_{ij})$ via a multiple linear regression model. The logarithm was used to ensure that the estimated mean of the Poisson distribution would be positive. The coefficients of the model were all assumed to have normal distributions with mean zero and very large variance. A random effect term was included to reflect individual variation. This term was assumed to have a normal distribution with mean zero and constant variance, σ_a^2. Finally, σ_a^2 was assumed to have a non-informative inverse gamma distribution. Such a distribution has a density function of the form

$$h(x) = \frac{\beta^\alpha}{\Gamma(\alpha)} \left(\frac{1}{x}\right)^{\alpha+1} \exp\left(\frac{-\beta}{x}\right) \quad \text{for} \quad x > 0.$$

13.1.7 SEVERITY STAGE

The severity costs were modeled by two separate components. The input data for this model were restricted to those children who had at least one hospital visit during this study. One component estimated physician charges while the other estimated facility costs such as those for nursing, pharmacy, and laboratory. Both component models had similar forms. In both cases the cost of the jth hospital visit for the ith child, X_{ij}, was assumed to have a gamma distribution, $G(\alpha_i, \theta_i)$ where the corresponding density function is

$$g(x \mid \alpha_i, \theta_i) = \frac{\exp\left(-\frac{x}{\theta_i}\right) \cdot (\theta_i)^{-\alpha_i} \cdot x^{\alpha_i - 1}}{\Gamma(\alpha_i)} \quad \text{for} \quad x > 0.$$

Here, α_i is the shape parameter and θ_i is the scale parameter. The gamma distribution was chosen based on the shape of the data plotted in Figure 2 of Rosenberg and Farrell [2008]. Under this form of the gamma density, the mean is equal to $\alpha_i \cdot \theta_i$. Rosenberg and Farrell chose this particular form of the gamma density, so that as the scale parameter increases so does the average hospitalization cost. In addition, Rosenberg and Farrell assumed that α_i had a gamma distribution (1) whose prior shape parameter was 5.0 and (2) whose prior scale parameter was 2.0, so that

$$E[\alpha_i] = (5.0) \cdot (2.0) = 10 \quad \text{and} \quad Var[\alpha_i] = (5.0) \cdot (2.0)^2 = 20.$$

As for μ_{ij} in the frequency stage, θ_i was modeled via multiple linear regression. Only the data on the 47 children hospitalized during this study were used to construct this model. The coefficients of the models were all assumed to have normal distributions with mean zero and very large variance. Again, a random effect term was included in each component model to reflect individual variation. This term was assumed to have a normal distribution whose mean was zero and whose variance had a non-informative inverse gamma distribution.

For those children who had no hospitalizations during this study, composite severity models (averaged over all the studies' hospitalizations) were used to predict future hospitalization costs in the simulation portion of the study but may have had a *simulated* hospitalization.

13.1.8 PREDICTOR VARIABLES

There were six predictor variables used in both multiple linear regression models.

Two of these predictors were numeric age variables:

- Age at diagnosis ($AgeDx$)
- Age at hospitalization (j)

The remaining predictors were indicator variables. One of these identified the gender of the child as female.

The data were obtained from a randomized clinical trial study conducted in Wisconsin. Babies born in Wisconsin between April, 1985 and June, 1994 were screened at birth for cystic fibrosis and then randomly assigned to either a control group or a screened group. Parents of those in the screened group were told their children had cystic fibrosis immediately after diagnosis. Some of the newborns with cystic fibrosis who were assigned to the control group were diagnosed prior to their fourth birthday through traditional means, such as signs, symptoms, or family history. At the child's fourth birthday the neonatal screening results were disclosed to the parents of all of the children. This was done for ethical reasons. A second indicator variable (Screened) was then used to identify the children assigned to the screened group.

Finally, two additional indicator variables were used to partition the children into three groups depending on the nature or their illness. One indicator variable (MI) identified children with *meconium ileus* – an obstruction of the intestine (*ileus*) caused by a deficiency of *trypsin* and other digestive enzymes from the pancreas. This accounted for 21% of the children. The other (Sev) identified those who did not have *meconium ileus* but did have a severe form of cystic fibrosis as indicated by their genotype. This accounted for an additional 51% of the children, leaving 28% of the children in the third group. The intent of this partition was to construct homogeneous groups in order to facilitate the modeling of the cost of hospitalization.

13.1.9 REGRESSION MODEL FOR FREQUENCY COMPONENT

Having defined the predictor variables, we can specify the regression model used for the frequency component as

$$\log(e_{ij} \cdot \mu_{ij}) = a_0 + a_{fem} Female_i + a_{scr} Screened_i$$
$$+ a_j j + a_{dx} AgeDx_i + a_{mi} MI_i + a_{sev} Sev_i + \varepsilon_i$$

where ε_i is a random effects term used to incorporate the variation around the mean of the number of hospital visits of the ith child.

13.1.10 REGRESSION MODEL FOR FACILITY COSTS

The regression model for the facility costs for the children who had one or more hospital visits during the study is as follows:

$$\log(\theta_i) = b_0 + b_{fem} Female_i$$
$$+ b_{scr} Screened_i$$
$$+ b_{midx1} \left(\frac{MI_i}{\sqrt{AgeDx_i}} \right)$$
$$+ b_{mxDx2} MI_i \cdot \sqrt{AgeDx_i}$$
$$+ b_{sev} Sev_i \cdot \sqrt{AgeDx_i} + \varepsilon_i$$

13.1.11 REGRESSION MODEL FOR PHYSICIAN COSTS

The regression model for the physician costs for the children who had one or more hospital visits during the study is:

$$\log(\gamma_i) = c_0 + c_{scr} Screened_i + c_{midx1} MI_i \cdot \left(\frac{1}{AgeDx_i} \right)$$
$$+ c_{midx2} MI_i \cdot AgeDx_i + \varepsilon_i$$

13.1.12 INCORPORATING THE VARIABILITY OF THE ESTIMATES OF THE PARAMETERS OF THE REGRESSION MODEL

Rosenberg and Farrell used the Markov chain Monte Carlo method to estimate the posterior distribution of the parameters, μ_{ij}, θ_i, and, γ_i. For each of these parameters, the estimation process entailed simulating the parameters of a regression model, thereby incorporating the variability of the parameter estimates into that model. A failure to account for this variability would cause the variance of the predictions to be under-estimated.

13.2 RESULTS

The experience during the first year of life was simulated for two of the children in the study. One child, B, was in the "high utilizer" group; the other, child A, was not in that group. For child A, the average simulated aggregate cost during the year was $2,218 with a standard deviation of $3,330. The largest aggregate cost resulting from the simulation of child A was $38,123. In contrast, child B had an average simulated aggregate cost of \$46,404 for the year, with a standard deviation of \$27,871. The 95th percentile of the aggregate cost for child B was \$98,460 while the maximum simulated aggregate cost was \$241,568. These results show that the two long-tailed distributions – one for claim frequency and the other for claim severity – have caused the simulated aggregate cost of hospitalization for child B to be widely dispersed.

Four years of experience – 1990, 1992, 1996, and 1999 – were simulated for the group consisting of all of the children in the study during those years. These results are summarized in Tables 2-5 of Rosenberg and Farrell [2008]. These tables also include separate results for the "high-utilizer" group and for the "remainder" group.

In order to provide more insight into the calculations performed by Rosenberg and Farrell, we consider the calculations they performed to simulate the results of child B during its first year of life. Specifically, we summarize the process used to obtain the predictive distributions for (1) the number of hospitalizations and (2) the cost of hospitalization.

13.2.1 PREDICTIVE DISTRIBUTION FOR THE NUMBER OF HOSPITAL VISITS OF CHILD B DURING ITS FIRST YEAR OF LIFE

If child B was in the study for the entire year of age, Rosenberg and Farrell set its exposure, $e_{ij} = e_{B,0} = 1$. In order to simulate the number of hospital visits from a Poisson distribution with mean, $e_{B,0} \cdot \mu_{B,0} = 1 \cdot \mu_{B,0} = \mu_{B,0}$, one needs to draw values of $\mu_{B,0}$ from its regression model. The first step in this process is to simulate the posterior distribution of the parameters of the regression model for $\log(\mu_{B,0})$ and to draw values from the distribution of its random effect term. This scheme yields a simulated posterior distribution (see Figure 13.1 on the following page) of the mean of the number of hospitalizations at age 0. A predictive distribution for the number of hospitalizations for child B at age zero can then be obtained by drawing values, $(\mu_{B,0}^{*})$, from this posterior distribution and then drawing values from a Poisson distribution with mean, $\mu_{B,0}^{*}$. Rosenberg and Farrell [2008] summarized the resulting predictive distribution in Figure 13.2 (Figure 8 of their paper).

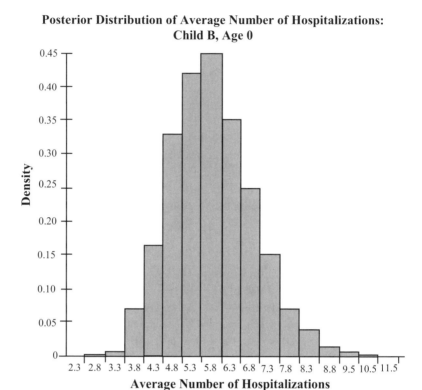

Posterior Distribution of Average Number of Hospitalizations: Child B, Age 0

Figure 13.1

13.2.2 Predictive Distribution for the Cost of Each Hospitalization of Child B during its First Year of Life

To simulate the facility cost component of the hospitalization cost, (X_B), of each hospital visit, Rosenberg and Farrell needed to draw a value from the gamma distribution, $G(\alpha_B, \theta_B)$. In order to do this, they first drew a value of α_B^* from the posterior (gamma) distribution of α_B. The next step in this process was to obtain a simulated value, θ_B^*, of θ_B. This was accomplished by simulating the posterior distribution of each of the parameters of the regression model for $\log(\theta_B)$, computing the mean of the resulting regression model, and drawing a value from the distribution of the random effects term. Rosenberg and Farrell then had the parameter values they needed to draw a simulated value of X_B from $G(\alpha_B^*, \theta_B^*)$. Repeated application of this simulation process produced the desired predictive distribution for the facility cost component.

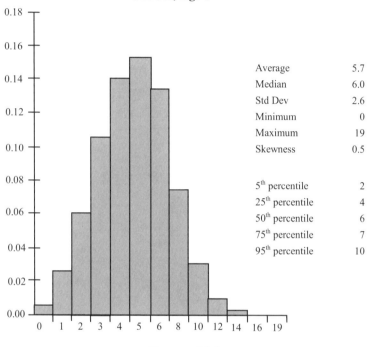

FIGURE 13.2

A similar procedure was used to obtain a predictive distribution for the physician cost component of the cost of hospitalization.

These two components could then be combined to form a predictive distribution of the (total) cost of each hospitalization.

13.2.3 PREDICTIVE DISTRIBUTION FOR THE COST OF HOSPITALIZATION OF CHILD B DURING ITS FIRST YEAR OF LIFE

Using (1) the predictive model for the number of hospital visits of child B during its first year of life together with (2) the predictive distribution for the cost of each hospital visit of child B during its first year of life, Rosenberg and Farrell were able to obtain the predictive distribution for the cost of hospitalization for child B during its first year of life. This predictive distribution is shown in Figure 13.3 which is Figure 10 of Rosenberg and Farrell's paper.

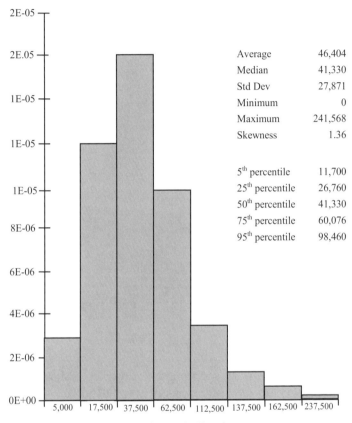

Predictive Distribution of Number of Hospitalizations: Child B, Age 0

Average	46,404
Median	41,330
Std Dev	27,871
Minimum	0
Maximum	241,568
Skewness	1.36
5th percentile	11,700
25th percentile	26,760
50th percentile	41,330
75th percentile	60,076
95th percentile	98,460

Yearly Cost of Hospitalizations

FIGURE 13.3

13.3 MARKOV-CHAIN MONTE CARLO TECHNIQUES[1]

The key idea involves generating a sample from a distribution that can't be simulated directly. Using ideas from Markov chain theory, we find an equilibrium distribution from which we simulate random draws. In this situation, the equilibrium distribution is the posterior distribution.

---

[1] This section closely follows the Appendix to Farrell and Rosenberg [2008].

To create the posterior distribution, we simulate the full conditional distribution of each parameter given all of the other parameters. This procedure requires us to select initial values for each parameter and to simulate the parameter values in a predetermined cycle for a specified number of iterations. We next illustrate such a procedure.

Suppose we are given a joint density function of three unknown parameters (U, V, and W) that we consider to be random variables. We denote the joint density of U, V, and W by $[U,V,W]$. We suppose that we are interested in obtaining the marginal density of U, denoted by $[U]$, and calculated analytically as $\int\int [U,V,W]\, dv\, dw$. This marginal density is often difficult to calculate directly. We denote the full conditionals by $[U\,|\,V,W]$, $[V\,|\,U,W]$, and $[W\,|\,U,V]$. These full conditionals allow us to generate a sample from the marginal distribution of U without resorting to integration. We now sketch the procedure we use to do this.

In order to simulate the first value, $U^{(1)}$, of U, we start with initial values $V^{(0)}$ and $W^{(0)}$, of V and W, respectively. Then, using $U^{(1)}$, and $W^{(0)}$, we simulate $V^{(1)}$. Finally, we use $U^{(1)}$ and $V^{(1)}$ to simulate $W^{(1)}$. The triplet, $(U^{(1)}, V^{(1)}, W^{(1)})$ forms the first draw from the joint distribution of $[U,V,W]$. Under mild regularity conditions, the distribution of U^j converges to the distribution of U as j gets large. For large m, the observation $U^{(m)}$ can be treated as a realization of the random variable U. In practice, one simulates a sequence with a large m and discards the first k values to eliminate the dependency of the sequence on the initial values. The remaining $m - k$ values constitute the estimated distribution of U.

CHAPTER 14

A CASE STUDY:
THE MISCODED MORTGAGE RECORDS

14.1 INTRODUCTION

In this chapter we describe an analysis of data anomalies in computer records on 246 federally-insured mortgages. Twenty-three of the corresponding mortgages were sampled and all were found to have identical amortization plans and to have been insured under the same insurance fund. The question posed, in probabilistic terms, is the following: how many of the remaining 223 mortgages are identical in these two aspects to the 23 sampled mortgages? We conclude this chapter with a related example that may be of interest to state insurance departments.

14.1.1 BACKGROUND

The Federal Housing Administration (FHA) provides insurance on mortgages. The risk insured against is the inability of the borrower to make timely payments of principal and interest. The FHA consists of four insurance funds, (i) the Mutual Mortgage Insurance Fund (MMIF), (ii) the General Insurance Fund (GIF), (iii) the Special Risk Insurance Fund (SRIF), and (iv) the Cooperative Management Housing Insurance Fund (CMHIF). All of the insurance programs of these funds operate under the provisions of the National Housing Act of 1934 and subsequent statutes enacted by the Congress of the United States.

The Mutual Mortgage Insurance Fund consists of insurance on single-family home mortgages under the provisions of Section 203(b) of the National Housing Act. In addition, single-family graduated payment mortgages may be insured under the provisions of both Section 203(b) and Section 245(a). We denoted the last by Section 203(b)/245(a).

Since September 1, 1983, almost all of the mortgages insured under the Mutual Mortgage Insurance Fund have been subject to either a "one-time premium" charge or an "upfront premium" charge payable at the origination of the mortgage. At the time this analysis was conducted, single-family mortgages insured under the General Insurance Fund and the Special Risk Insurance Fund were not subject to a large initial premium payment but instead were required to pay annual insurance premiums over the life of the mortgage.

Each FHA-insured single-family mortgage is supposed to be represented by a single case record on FHA's single-family insurance database. This database includes a field called the ADP Section-of-the-Act Code which indicates the exact program under which each mortgage is insured. Another field in the database indicates whether the mortgage's borrower paid a one-time premium at the origination of the mortgage.

14.1.2 Statement of the Problem

In the course of some work on FHA's single-family coinsurance mortgage program, 1191 mortgage records were discovered to have ADP Section-of-the-Act Code 245, 545, 294, or 594, none of which have the required statutory authority. In particular, ADP Section-of-the-Act code 245 does **not** correspond to Section 245(a) of the National Housing Act. So a seemingly natural mistake is to use ADP Section-of-the-ACT code 245 for FHA single-family mortgages insured under Section 245(a) of the National Housing Act. Of these 1191 mortgage records, 249 were recorded in FHA's single-family insurance data system as having a one-time premium amount.

A sample of casebinders on 26 of these 249 mortgages was examined (23 whose ADP Section-of-the-Act Code was 245 and all three whose ADP Section-of-the-Act Code was either 294 or 594). All 23 of the mortgages recorded under ADP Section-of-the-Act Code 245 should have been recorded under Section 203(b)/245(a) of the National Housing Act. This is the section that specifies graduated payment mortgages. Of the other three mortgages whose casebinders were examined, two were under Section 203(b)/245(a) and one was intended to be under a combination of Section 234(c) and Section 244. This indicates that the mortgage was for a condominium unit that was insured through the FHA single-family coinsurance program – a combination that FHA has never allowed, for which there is no statutory authority. There are 223 other cases recorded on FHA's single-family insurance data system with ADP Section-of-the-

Act Code 245 and a one-time premium amount. The question is as follows: Is it necessary to examine the other 223 casebinders, or could FHA just assume that all of the mortgages in question were insured under Section 203(b)/245(a)?[1]

The above question can be restated as a probabilistic question so that it can be answered in mathematical terms. A description of the methodological approach employed is given in the following section.

14.1.3 OVERVIEW OF THE METHODOLOGICAL APPROACH

We know of no frequentist/classical statistical approach that will lead us to an answer, so our only choice is to use Bayesian methods. We assume that the data are from a sequence of independent Bernoulli trials with probability of "success" equal to Θ. Thus we assume that we have statistical independence in the sense that the results of one case record do not influence those of any other case record. The likelihood function can be considered to be the binomial. We compute our results under the assumption that the prior density function of Θ is a beta density function $f(\theta \mid a,b)$. The beta is used for computational convenience because it is the conjugate prior density of the binomial density. We used four pairs of parameters for the beta density in order to test the sensitivity of results to the choice of parameters. We describe the results below.

14.2 BETA PRIOR DENSITIES
AND CONDITIONAL PROBABILITIES

The prior density function, $f(\theta \mid a,b)$, of Θ is

$$f(\theta \mid a,b) = \begin{cases} \dfrac{\Gamma(a+b)}{\Gamma(a)\cdot\Gamma(b)}\cdot\theta^{a-1}\cdot(1-\theta)^{b-1} & 0<\theta<1 \\ 0 & \text{elsewhere} \end{cases}.$$

---

[1] Since FHA began insuring graduated payment single-family mortgages in 1977, it has insured more than 300,000 such mortgages under Section 203(b)/245(a). It is amazing that so few FHA single-family mortgage insurance records ended up under ADP Section-of-the-Act Code 245 because that would have been a natural error to make. Hopefully this scarcity of errors is an indication of the high degree of accuracy of this data element on other records in FHA's single-family insurance system.

The corresponding mean is $\frac{a}{a+b}$.

For $i = 1, 2, ..., m+n$, with n and m positive integers, let X_i denote the result of the ith trial where 1 denotes a "success" and 0 denotes a "failure." As shown in Section 8.2.1, if (1) the likelihood of the data is binomial with r successes in n trials and (2) the prior density function of the parameter Θ is $f(\theta \mid a, b)$, then the posterior density function of Θ is $f(\theta \mid a+r, b+n-r)$. (The mean of the posterior density of Θ is $\frac{a+r}{a+b+n}$.)

For $x = 0, 1, ..., m$, we obtain

$$P\left[\sum_{i=n+1}^{m+n} X_i = x \middle| \sum_{i=1}^{n} X_i = r\right]$$

$$= \int_0^1 P\left[\sum_{i=n+1}^{m+n} X_i = x \mid \Theta = \theta\right] \cdot f(\theta \mid a+r, b+n-r)\, d\theta$$

$$= \int_0^1 \binom{m}{x} \cdot \theta^x (1-\theta)^{m-x} \cdot \frac{\Gamma(a+b+n)}{\Gamma(a+r) \cdot \Gamma(b+n-r)} \cdot \theta^{a+r-1}(1-\theta)^{b+n-r-1}\, d\theta$$

$$= \binom{m}{x} \cdot \frac{\Gamma(a+b+n)}{\Gamma(a+r) \cdot \Gamma(b+n-r)} \cdot \int_0^1 \theta^{a+r+x-1}(1-\theta)^{b+n-r+m-x-1}\, d\theta$$

$$= \binom{m}{x} \cdot \frac{\Gamma(a+b+n)}{\Gamma(a+r) \cdot \Gamma(b+n-r)} \cdot \frac{\Gamma(a+r+x) \cdot \Gamma(b+n-r+m-x)}{\Gamma(a+b+n+m)}$$

$$= \binom{m}{x} \cdot \frac{(a+b+n-1)\binom{a+b+n-2}{a+r-1}}{1} \cdot \frac{1}{(a+b+n+m-1)\binom{a+b+m-2}{a+r+x-1}}$$

$$= \binom{m}{x} \cdot \frac{(a+b+n-1)}{(a+b+n+m-1)} \cdot \frac{\binom{a+b+n-2}{a+r-1}}{\binom{a+b+n+m-2}{a+r+x-1}}. \tag{14.1}$$

Assuming that a and b are both positive integers, we can rewrite the last expression as

$$\binom{m}{x} \cdot \frac{\Gamma(a+b+n)}{\Gamma(a+r) \cdot \Gamma(b+n-r)} \cdot \frac{\Gamma(a+r+x) \cdot \Gamma(b+n-r+m-x)}{\Gamma(a+b+n+m)}$$

$$= \binom{m}{x} \cdot \frac{(a+b+n-1)}{(a+b+n+m-1)} \cdot \frac{\binom{a+b+n-1}{a+r-1}}{\binom{a+b+n+m-2}{a+r+x-1}}.$$

In the last derivation, we twice employ the result

$$\frac{\Gamma(\alpha+\beta)}{\Gamma(\alpha) \cdot \Gamma(\beta)} = (\alpha+\beta-1)\binom{\alpha+\beta-2}{\alpha-1}$$

which is valid whenever α and β are positive integers.

The results for the special case at hand are summarized in Table 14.1. Here we have $n = 23$, $r = 23$, and $m = 223$, so the posterior estimate of the mean of Θ is $\frac{a+r}{a+b+n} = \frac{a+23}{a+b+23}$ since the number of successes is $r = 23$ and the number of initial trials is $n = 23$. In order to assess the sensitivity of the results to different values of the parameters a and b, we employ four pairs of values of a and b.

Using Equation (14.1), we compute each of the following:

(1) The probability of 223 successes (or, equivalently, no failures) in 223 independent Bernoulli trials.

(2) The probability of at least 219 successes (or, equivalently, no more than 4 failures) in 223 independent Bernoulli trials.

(3) The probability of at least 214 successes (or, equivalently, no more than 9 failures) in 223 independent Bernoulli trials.

TABLE 14.1

Parameter Values		Prior Estimate of Mean of Θ	Posterior Estimate of Mean of Θ	Probability of all Successes	Probability of no more than 4 failures	Probability of no more than 9 failures
a	b	$\frac{a}{a+b}$	$\frac{a+23}{a+b+23}$			
1	1	.50	.960	.071	.403	.647
9	1	.90	.970	.125	.491	.745
22	1	.96	.978	.168	.604	.846
99	1	.99	.992	.354	.889	.988

14.3 THE UNIFORM DENSITY FUNCTION

We note that when $a=1$ and $b=1$, $f(\theta \mid a,b)$ becomes the uniform density function over the interval [0,1], given by

$$f(\theta \mid a,b) = \begin{cases} 1 & 0 \le \theta \le 1 \\ 0 & \text{elsewhere} \end{cases}.$$

In this case, for $x = 0, 1, \ldots, 23$, we obtain the initial probabilities

$$P\left[\sum_{i=1}^{23} X_i = x\right] = \int_0^1 P\left[\sum_{i=1}^{23} X_i = x \mid \Theta = \theta\right] \cdot f(\theta) \, d\theta$$

$$= \int_0^1 \binom{23}{x} \theta^x (1-\theta)^{23-x} \cdot 1 \, d\theta$$

$$= \binom{23}{x} \cdot \int_0^1 \theta^{x+1-1} (1-\theta)^{24-x-1} \, d\theta$$

$$= \left\{\frac{23!}{x! \cdot (23-x)!}\right\} \cdot \frac{\Gamma(x+1) \cdot \Gamma(24-x)}{\Gamma(25)}$$

$$= \left\{\frac{23!}{x! \cdot (23-x)!}\right\} \cdot \left\{\frac{x! \cdot (23-x)!}{24!}\right\}$$

$$= \frac{1}{24} = .04167,$$

because the last integral is that of a constant times a beta density function. Thus we find that the initial probabilities $P\left[\sum_{i=1}^{23} X_i = x\right]$ do not depend on the value of x. In other words, if the prior density function of Θ is the uniform density function over $[0,1]$, then the initial probabilities are equidistributed over the range of values $x = 0, 1, ..., 23$.

14.4 CONCLUDING REMARKS ON CASE STUDY

Based on our assumptions and the ensuing results of Table 14.1, the probability that all 223 case records represent Section 203(b)/245(a) mortgages ranges from .071 to .354. Restated, the probability ranges from .646 (which is 1−.354) to .929 (which is 1−.071) that at least one of the 223 case records represents a loan not insured under Section 203(b)/245(a), but most likely under a combination of Section 234(c) and Section 244. This would represent a condominium unit having FHA mortgage insurance under FHA's single-family coinsurance program. This is a combination that, as we noted earlier, FHA has never allowed. The probability ranges from 1−.988 = .012 to 1−.647 = .353 that at least ten of the 223 case records represent loans *not* insured under Section 203(b)/245(a).

14.5 A SIMILAR APPLICATION – LOSS RATIOS

State insurance departments often observe that the ratio of actual losses to expected losses for particular insurance companies exceeds 100% for a number of consecutive years. They then ask if this trend is likely to continue into the future. With little or no additional effort, the methodology presented earlier in this chapter can be successfully applied to such problems. In order to be specific, we first introduce some notation.

14.5.1 NOTATION

For $i = 2005, 2006, ..., 2009$, let X_i denote the random variable representing the ratio of actual losses to expected losses for the ABC Insurance Company during calendar year i. We seek

$$P\left[1.2 \le X_{2009} \le 1.3 \mid 1.2 \le X_i \le 1.3, \text{ for } i = 2005, ... 2008\right]. \quad (14.2)$$

In other words, we seek the probability that the ratio of actual losses to expected losses during 2009 for the ABC Insurance Company is between 120% and 130%, given that it is in that range for each of the years 2005-2008.

14.5.2 ASSUMPTIONS

We make the following assumptions:

1. We assume that the X_i's are independent, identically distributed random variables so that there is a random variable for which

$$\Theta = P[1.2 \le X_i \le 1.3, \text{ for } i = 2005, ..., 2009].$$

2. We assume that Θ has the Beta distribution, $\beta(a,b)$, with fixed parameters a and b.

14.5.3 POSTERIOR PROBABILITY

It turns out that the derivation of the posterior probability

$$P[1.2 \le X_{2009} \le 1.3 \mid 1.2 \le X_i \le 1.3, \text{ for } i = 2005, ..., 2008]$$

is identical to that of Section 14.2 with $m = 1$ and $x = 1$. Making the appropriate substitutions into Equation (14.1), the desired posterior probability is

$$\left(\frac{a+b+3}{a+b+4} \right) \frac{\binom{a+b+2}{a+3}}{\binom{a+b+3}{a+4}}.$$

In the particular case that the prior distribution is the uniform distribution (the special case, $\beta(1,1)$, of the beta distribution with $a = 1$ and $b = 1$), then the posterior probability is $\frac{5}{6}$. Thus, we have gone here from a prior probability of $\frac{1}{2}$ to a revised probability of $\frac{5}{6}$ based on the results of our four years of observations.

If, instead, the prior distribution is the beta distribution, $\beta(2,2)$, with parameters $a = 2$ and $b = 2$, then the posterior probability decreases to $\frac{3}{4}$. The reason for this decrease is that when $a = 2$ and $b = 2$, the prior mean of $\frac{1}{2}$ is given more weight than when $a = 1$ and $b = 1$.

14.5.4 FREQUENTIST APPROACH TO THIS PROBLEM

If we use the maximum likelihood procedure, then our estimate of Θ is 0/4 or 0. Because we desire a value of Θ satisfying $0 < \Theta < 1$, this is an unacceptable result. Thus, in this case, we feel that the Bayesian paradigm gives a reasonable result while the frequentist paradigm does not.

Of course, if we had instead sought the probability of $1.2 \leq X_{2009} \leq 1.3$ given that only three of $X_{2005}, X_{2006}, X_{2007}, X_{2008}$ were observed to fall in the interval $[1.2, 1.3]$, then the maximum likelihood estimate of Θ would have been $\frac{1}{4}$ – a more reasonable result.

14.5.5 ALTERNATIVE PRIOR DISTRIBUTION

Next, suppose that instead of employing a member of the beta family of distributions as a prior distribution, we use the density function

$$f(\theta) = \begin{cases} 4\theta & 0 \leq \theta \leq .5 \\ 4(1-\theta) & .5 \leq \theta \leq 1 \\ 0 & \text{otherwise} \end{cases}.$$

As above, our goal is to calculate the probability of Equation (14.2). Because $f(\theta)$ is not a conjugate prior in this situation, we have to do more work here.

We first determine the constant of proportionality, the reciprocal of the integral of the product of (1) the prior density function of Θ, $f(\theta)$, and (2) the likelihood of Θ on $X_{2005}, ..., X_{2008}$, obtaining

$$\left(\frac{1}{\int_0^1 f(\theta)\theta^4 \, d\theta} \right) = \frac{240}{31},$$

since the likelihood here is θ^4. We obtain

$$P\left[1.2 \leq X_{2009} \leq 1.3 \,|\, 1.2 \leq X_i \leq 1.3, \text{ for } i = 2005,\ldots,2008\right]$$

$$= \int_0^1 P\left[1.2 \leq X_{2009} \leq 1.3 \,|\, \theta\right]$$

$$\times f\left(\theta \,|\, 1.2 \leq X_i \leq 1.3, \text{ for } i = 2005,\ldots,2008\right) d\theta$$

$$\propto \int_0^1 \theta \cdot f(\theta)\theta^4 \, d\theta = \frac{3}{32}.$$

Because the constant of proportionality is $\frac{240}{31}$, the desired conditional probability is

$$\left(\frac{3}{32}\right)\left(\frac{240}{31}\right) = \frac{45}{62}.$$

Similarly, we can show that

$$P\left[X_{2009} > 1.3 \text{ or } X_{2009} < 1.2 \,|\, 1.2 \leq X_i \leq 1.3, \text{ for } i = 2005,\ldots,2008\right]$$

$$= \left(\frac{17}{480}\right)\left(\frac{240}{31}\right) = \frac{17}{62}.$$

'We can show that the unconditional probabilities $P[1.2 \leq X_{2009} \leq 1.3]$ and $P[X_{2009} > 1.3 \text{ or } X_{2009} < 1.2]$ are both equal to .50, as follows:

(1) $P[1.2 \leq X_{2009} \leq 1.3] = \int_0^1 \theta \cdot f(\theta) \, d\theta = E[\Theta] = .50$, since $f(\theta)$ is symmetric about .50; and

(2) $P[X_{2009} > 1.3 \text{ or } X_{2009} < 1.2] = \int_0^1 (1-\theta) \cdot f(\theta) \, d\theta$

$$= E[1-\Theta]$$

$$= 1 - E[\Theta] = 1 - .50 = .50.$$

It is instructive to compare the two conditional probabilities above to their corresponding unconditional probabilities of .50 and to observe the effects of the four years of experience data.

14.6 EXERCISES

14.1 Introduction
14.2 Beta Prior Densities and Conditional Probabilities

14-1 Suppose that the prior probability of "success," Θ, is uniformly distributed over the interval [0,1]. During the first 50 independent Bernoulli trials of an experiment, 50 successes were observed. What is the probability of observing 25 successes in the next 25 independent Bernoulli trials?

14-2 Suppose that the prior probability of "success," Θ, is uniformly distributed over the interval [0,1]. During the first 50 independent Bernoulli trials of an experiment, 45 successes were observed. What is the probability of observing 15 successes in the next 25 independent Bernoulli trials?

14-3 Suppose that the prior probability of "success," Θ, is uniformly distributed over the interval [0,1]. During the first 50 independent Bernoulli trials of an experiment, 45 successes were observed. What is the probability of observing 25 successes in the next 25 independent Bernoulli trials?

14-4 Suppose that the prior probability of "success," Θ, has a beta distribution with parameters $a = 2$ and $b = 5$. During the first 100 independent Bernoulli trials of an experiment, 95 successes were observed. What is the probability of observing 15 successes in the next 25 independent Bernoulli trials?

14.3 The Uniform Density Function

14-5 Suppose that the prior probability of "success," Θ, is uniformly distributed over the interval [0,1]. What is the probability of observing x successes in the first n independent Bernoulli trials, for $x = 0,1,...,n$?

14-6 Suppose that the prior probability of "success," Θ, is uniformly distributed over the interval $[0,1]$. What is the probability of observing 20 successes in the first 24 independent Bernoulli trials?

14.4 Concluding Remarks on Case Study
14.5 A Similar Application

14-7 Using the notation of Section 14.5.1, assumption 1 of Section 14.5.2, and the prior density function of Section 14.5.5, calculate

$$P\left[1.2 \leq X_{2009} \leq 1.3 \mid 1.2 \leq X_i \leq 1.3, \text{ for } i = 2007, 2008\right].$$

14-8 Using the assumptions of Section 14.5.2 with $a = 4$ and $b = 5$, calculate

$$P\left[1.2 \leq X_{2009} \leq 1.3 \mid 1.2 \leq X_i \leq 1.3, \text{ for } i = 2005, ..., 2008\right].$$

CHAPTER 15

MORRIS-VAN SLYKE ESTIMATION

15.1   INTRODUCTION

In this chapter we discuss a procedure originally developed by Morris and van Slyke [1979] to price classes of automobile insurance. This procedure can, of course, be applied to other types of insurance problems as well. The Morris - van Slyke procedure is (1) an application of empirical Bayesian procedures (as mentioned in Section 6.6), (2) similar to the Bühlmann-Straub model of Chapter 7, and (3) a generalization of a well-known statistical procedure formulated by Charles Stein and described in James and Stein [1961]. The generalization arises because the James-Stein procedure requires an equal number of exposure units in each rating class (as does the Bühlmann model), whereas the Morris - van Slyke procedure can handle unequal numbers of exposure units across rating classes (as can the Bühlmann-Straub model). In this chapter, we begin with the development of the more general Morris - van Slyke model, and merely note in passing the special case of the James-Stein model.

In order to motivate the discussion, we consider the following example, the solution of which is deferred to Section 15.3.

EXAMPLE 15.1

Let an insurer's automobile business in an individual Canadian province be partitioned into ten territories or classes for insurance rating purposes. The experience data for calendar years 1985-1987 are summarized in Table 15.1. The idea is to use these data to estimate the relative risks of the drivers across the ten territories of the province. Because the overall level of automobile accident claims may vary from one year to the next due to weather or economic conditions, we consider the problem of estimating the difference between the observed claim rate for each individual territory and the observed claim rate over all ten territories. We refer to such differences as **claim rate differentials**. In particular, we use the data on the 1985 and

1986 claim rate differentials to predict the 1987 claim rate differentials for each of the ten territories. Because we have the results for 1987, this allows us to test the accuracy of our approach.

TABLE 15.1

1985-87 Automobile Experience by Territory								
	Calendar Year							
	1985			1986			1987		
Territory	No. of Policies	Claim Rate	Differ-ential	No. of Policies	Claim Rate	Differ-ential	No. of Policies	Claim Rate	Differ-ential
1	1,240	3.95%	–1.18%	764	4.45%	–0.27%	970	2.27%	–2.14%
2	7,002	8.83	3.70	6,494	7.91	3.19	6,774	6.95	2.54
3	8,733	4.59	–0.54	7,000	6.37	1.65	8,942	5.51	0.11
4	36,831	8.44	3.31	43,108	7.44	2.72	57,639	5.53	1.12
5	26,643	8.12	2.99	25,958	8.05	3.33	29,011	8.82	4.41
6	29,972	5.89	0.76	35,807	5.93	1.21	38,383	5.81	1.40
7	5,078	6.77	1.64	5,144	6.07	1.35	5,757	5.21	0.80
8	9,559	0.95	–4.18	12,483	1.22	–3.50	18,537	2.62	–1.79
9	54,088	1.85	–3.28	61,155	1.25	–3.47	66,869	1.04	–3.37
10	9,448	1.35	–3.78	9,301	1.45	–3.27	9,753	2.61	–1.80
Overall	188,594	5.13%		207,214	4.72%		242,605	4.41%	

Note that the entries in Table 15.1 might not add exactly due to rounding.

15.2   THE MORRIS - VAN SLYKE MODEL

Let Y_{it} denote the (random) claim rate of the ith territory during calendar year t, where $i = 1, 2, ..., k$ and $t = 1, 2, ..., r+1$. Let E_{it} denote the number of individual drivers insured in the ith territory during calendar year t, where again $i = 1, 2, ..., k$ and $t = 1, 2, ..., r+1$. (In Example 15.1, $k = 10$ because there are 10 territories and $r = 2$ because we use two calendar years of experience data to predict the results of the final calendar year.) Assuming that the proportion of insured drivers among the k territories is nearly constant from one calendar year to the next, we define the weights for the k territories to be

$$w_i = \frac{\sum\limits_{t=1}^{r} E_{it}}{\sum\limits_{i=1}^{k} \sum\limits_{t=1}^{r} E_{it}}. \tag{15.1}$$

for $i = 1, 2, ..., k$. The numerator in Equation (15.1) is the sum of the exposure units in territory i during the first r calendar years and the denominator is the total number of exposure units over all territories during the first r calendar years. Clearly, the sum of the weights is 1. The exposure measures, E_{ij}, of this chapter are similar to the exposure measures, m_{ij}, of Chapter 7 on the Bühlmann-Straub approach.

We assume that the random variables Y_{it} are mutually independent, and further assume that

$$E[Y_{it}] = \mu_0 + \alpha_i + \beta_t \qquad (15.2)$$

and

$$Var(Y_{it}) = \frac{\sigma^2}{w_i}, \qquad (15.3)$$

for $i = 1, 2, ..., k$ and $t = 1, 2, ..., r+1$.

There are three types of unknown parameters in Equation (15.2):

(1) μ_0 represents the grand mean.

(2) α_i represents the ith territorial effect.

(3) β_t represents the tth calendar year effect.

These parameters are subject to the constraints

$$\sum_{i=1}^{k} w_i \cdot \alpha_i = 0 \qquad (15.4)$$

and

$$\sum_{t=1}^{r} \beta_t = 0. \qquad (15.5)$$

Equation (15.4) states that the weighted sum of the territorial effects is zero, and Equation (15.5) states that the sum of the calendar year effects is zero.

We set the claim rate differentials for the tth calendar year to be

$$X_{it} = Y_{it} - Y_{\cdot t}, \qquad (15.6)$$

for the territory $i = 1, 2, ..., k$, where $\bar{Y}_{.t} = \sum\limits_{i=1}^{k} w_i \cdot Y_{it}$. Because the Y_{it}'s are mutually independent, so are the X_{it}'s. The idea is that X_{it} is Y_{it} with the calendar year effect removed. So, as shown in Exercise 15-1, X_{it} is an unbiased estimator of the territorial effect α_i.

As shown in Exercise 15-2, an unbiased estimator of σ^2 is

$$\hat{\sigma}^2 = \frac{1}{k}\sum_{i=1}^{k}\frac{w_i}{1-w_i}\cdot\frac{SSW_i}{r-1}, \tag{15.7}$$

where

$$SSW_i = \sum_{t=1}^{r}(X_{it}-\bar{X}_{i\cdot})^2 \tag{15.8}$$

and

$$\bar{X}_{i\cdot} = \frac{1}{r}\sum_{t=1}^{r}X_{it}. \tag{15.9}$$

We can now restate the problem to be one of estimating the k parameters $\alpha_1, \alpha_2, ..., \alpha_k$. To do this we make two additional assumptions. For $i = 1, 2, ..., k$, we assume that given the α_i's, the random variables $\bar{X}_i$ are mutually conditionally independent, with

$$E[\bar{X}_{i\cdot}|\alpha_i] = \alpha_i \tag{15.10}$$

and

$$Var(\bar{X}_{i\cdot}|\alpha_i) = V_i = \frac{\sigma^2}{r}\cdot\frac{1-w_i}{w_i}. \tag{15.11}$$

We also assume that for $i = 1, 2, ..., k$, the territorial effects, α_i, are sampled from a normal probability distribution with mean, μ, and variance, τ^2. Using Bayes' theorem, it can be shown (see Exercise 15-3) that

$$E[\alpha_i | \bar{X}_{i\cdot}] = \zeta_i \cdot \bar{X}_{i\cdot} + (1-\zeta_i) + \mu \tag{15.12}$$

and

$$Var(\alpha_i | \bar{X}_{i\cdot}) = \zeta_i \cdot V_i, \tag{15.13}$$

where

$$\zeta_i = \frac{\tau^2}{\tau^2 + V_i}. \tag{15.14}$$

The ζ_i values are the "true credibilities," but are unknown. We use the conditional expectation given by Equation (15.12) as the estimator of α_i. In order to compute realizations of this estimator, we need to estimate the values of μ and τ^2 (since, given τ^2, we can use Equation (15.14) to obtain estimates of ζ_i).

To obtain maximum likelihood estimators of μ and τ^2, we proceed as follows. We first note that, as shown in Exercise 15-4,

$$E[\overline{X}_i.] = \mu \tag{15.15}$$

and

$$Var(\overline{X}_i.) = V_i + \tau^2, \tag{15.16}$$

for $i = 1,2,...,k$. Maximum likelihood estimators of μ and τ^2 can be constructed based on Equations (15.15) and (15.16), respectively, by assuming that each $\overline{X}_i.$ is normally distributed and that the random variables $\overline{X}_1.,\overline{X}_2.,...,\overline{X}_k.$ are mutually independent. Because the variances, V_i, may be unequal, realizations of the maximum likelihood estimators of μ and τ^2 must be obtained by an iterative procedure.

Finally, for $i = 1,2,...,k$, we will use

$$\hat{V}_i = \frac{\hat{\sigma}^2}{r} \cdot \frac{1 - w_i}{w_i} \tag{15.17}$$

as our estimator of V_i.

15.2.1 ITERATIVE PROCEDURE

The justification for the following iterative procedure is found in Efron and Morris [1973, 1975, and 1977].

Step 1:   Select an initial estimate, $\hat{\tau}^2$, of τ^2. (Because Equations (15.17) and (15.14), with τ^2 replaced by $\hat{\tau}^2$ and V_i replaced by $\hat{V}_i$, imply that

$$\hat{\tau}^2 \;=\; \frac{\frac{\hat{\sigma}^2}{r} \cdot \frac{1-w_i}{w_i}}{1-\zeta_i}, \tag{15.18}$$

then one possible initial estimate of $\hat{\tau}^2$ could be the value of Equation (15.18) with $w_i = \frac{1}{k}$ and $\zeta_i = .50$.)

Step 2:   Using the value of $\hat{\tau}^2$ from Step 1, compute initial estimates of $\zeta_i = \frac{\hat{\tau}^2}{\hat{V}_i + \hat{\tau}^2}$, for $i = 1, 2, ..., k$.

Step 3:   Using the values of ζ_i obtained in Step 2, compute the realization of the minimum variance unbiased estimator of μ, given by

$$\hat{\mu} \;=\; \frac{\sum\limits_{i=1}^{k} \zeta_i \cdot \overline{x}_i.}{\sum\limits_{i=1}^{k} \zeta_i}. \tag{15.19}$$

Step 4:   Compute the maximum likelihood estimate of τ^2, using the results of Steps 2 and 3, as

$$\hat{\tau}^2 \;=\; \frac{\sum\limits_{i=1}^{k} \zeta_i^2 \left[(\overline{x}_i. - \hat{\mu})^2 - \hat{V}_i \right]}{\sum\limits_{i=1}^{k} \zeta_i^2}. \tag{15.20}$$

Step 5:   Use the estimate of $\hat{\tau}^2$ computed in Step 4 as the new initial estimate of $\hat{\tau}^2$, and then recompute Steps 2, 3, and 4. This produces revised estimates of ζ_i, $\hat{\mu}$, and $\hat{\tau}^2$.

Stopping Rule: The iterative procedure terminates when successive estimates of $\hat{\tau}^2$ change little. This usually takes three or four iterations. As demonstrated in Exercise 15-5, the procedure converges in one step if $w_i = \frac{1}{k}$ for all i so that all of the V_i are equal as well.

If the $\overline{X}_i.$ are not normally distributed, then the ζ_i do not provide the best weights for computing estimates of μ and τ^2; however, the weights are still reasonable since they are based on convex combinations of nearly unbiased estimates.

15.2.2 FINAL ESTIMATORS OF THE CREDIBILITY FACTORS

Instead of using $\dfrac{\hat{\tau}^2}{\hat{V}_i+\hat{\tau}^2} = 1-\dfrac{\hat{v}_i}{\hat{v}_i+\hat{\tau}^2}$ as the final estimator of the ith credibility factor, Z_i, we use

$$\hat{Z}_i = 1-\frac{k-3}{k}\cdot\frac{\hat{V}_i}{\hat{V}_i+\hat{\tau}^2}. \tag{15.21}$$

The factor of $\frac{k-3}{k}$ corrects for the following two phenomena:[1]

(1) $\hat{\mu}$ is estimated, not known, in the computation of $\hat{\tau}^2$ in Step 4; this costs one degree of freedom.

(2) As shown in Exercise 15-6, the concavity of $\zeta_i = \dfrac{\tau^2}{V_i+\tau^2}$ as a function of τ^2 causes $\dfrac{\hat{\tau}^2}{\hat{V}_i+\hat{\tau}^2}=1-\dfrac{\hat{V}_i}{V_i+\hat{\tau}^2}$ to underestimate ζ_i, on the average.

15.2.3 FINAL ESTIMATORS OF THE α_i's

The final estimator of α_i, is

$$\hat{\alpha}_i = Z_i\overline{X}_i.+(1-Z_i)\hat{\mu}, \tag{15.22}$$

---

[1] Therefore, in order to obtain a non-trivial result, we must have $k \geq 4$ distinct territories.

for $i = 1, 2, ..., k$. Equation (15.22) provides the James-Stein estimator of α_i when all of the weights are equal, i.e., $w_i = \frac{1}{k}$ for all i. In other words, Equation (15.22) provides the James-Stein estimator of α_i when each rating class has an equal number of exposure units. In this case the credibility factor does not vary with i, so that $\hat{Z}_i = \hat{Z}$.

15.2.4 MEASURES OF FIT

As a measure of the closeness of the estimates, $\hat{\alpha}_i$, to the observed values $\alpha_{i,r+1}$, for the last calendar year $(r+1)$, we use

$$\sum_{i=1}^{k} w_{i,r+1}(\hat{\alpha}_i - \alpha_{i,r+1})^2, \qquad (15.23)$$

where

$$w_{i,r+1} = \frac{E_{i,r+1}}{\sum_{i=1}^{k} E_{i,r+1}}.$$

Thus the measure of closeness is a weighted average of the sum of the squares of the differences between the observed and predicted values.

15.3 WORKED SOLUTION OF AUTOMOBILE RATING CLASS EXAMPLE

We now apply the method described in Section 15.2 to the data displayed in Table 15.1. Since we have 10 territories, $k = 10$. Because we are using two years of experience data (1985 and 1986) to predict the experience for 1987, we have $r = 2$. As per the discussion above and Exercise 15-7, we select .1869 as our initial estimate of $\hat{\tau}^2$ The results of four iterations of the ensuing iterative process are summarized in Table 15.2. For reasons of space, we display only the values of ζ_1 in Table 15.2.

TABLE 15.2

Results of the Iterative Process			
Iteration Number	Step 2 $\zeta_1 = \dfrac{\hat{\tau}^2}{\hat{V}_1 + \hat{\tau}^2}$	Step 3 $\hat{\mu}$	Step 4 $\hat{\tau}^2$
1	.0839	.1928	8.269
2	.8021	.1408	7.303
3	.7816	.1427	7.334
4	.7823	.1427	7.333

The reader can see from Table 15.2 that the estimates of τ^2 have converged to 7.33 in four iterations.

TABLE 15.3

Measure of Closeness of Alternative Estimators	
Estimator	Measure of Closeness
$\overline{X}_{i.}$ (Mean of the Observations in the ith Territory) Credibility = 1	1.56
Morris - van Slyke Estimator $\hat{\alpha}_i = \hat{Z}_i \overline{X}_{i.} + (1 - \hat{Z}_i)\hat{\mu}$	1.52
$\hat{\mu}$ (Overall [weighted] Mean of the Observations) Credibility = 0	6.72

Thus, according to our measure-of-closeness criterion, the Morris - van Slyke model has performed the best, with the full credibility model a close second, and the zero credibility model a distant third.

15.4 SUMMARY OF THE MORRIS - VAN SLYKE MODEL

Goal: To obtain reasonable estimates of the claim rate differentials for the next calendar year.

Step 1:   Determine k, the number of territories.

(Note that we must have $k \geq 4$.)

Step 2:   Compute the weights, w_i, using Equation (15.1).

Step 3:   Compute the average claim rates, $\overline{Y}_{.t}$.

Step 4:   Compute the claim rate differentials, X_{it}, using Equation (15.6).

Step 5:   Compute the average claim rate differentials, $\overline{X}_{i.}$, using Equation (15.9).

Step 6:   Compute the sum of the squared differences, SSW_i, using Equation (15.8).

Step 7:   Compute the estimated variance, $\hat{\sigma}^2$, using Equation (15.7).

Step 8:   Compute the estimated conditional variance of $\overline{X}_{i.}, \hat{V}_i$, using Equation (15.17).

Step 9:   Carry out the iterative procedure of Section 15.2.1 to obtain estimates of $\zeta_i, \hat{\mu}_i$, and $\hat{\tau}_i$.

Step 10:   Compute the credibility factors, $\hat{Z}_i$, using Equation (15.21).

Step 11:   Compute the final estimates of the claim rate differentials, $\hat{\alpha}_i$, using Equation (15.22).

Step 12:   In order to evaluate the fit of the model to the data, compute the measure of fit given by Expression (15.23).

15.5 FURTHER REMARKS

The contrast between the approaches employed to solve the problems of Chapters 14 and 15 is striking. The approach of Chapter 14 was a straightforward application of the Bayesian paradigm. The empirical Bayesian approach of Chapter 15, on the other hand, was anything but straightforward, requiring a wide variety of sophisticated mathematical tools and assumptions to arrive at the final solution. For example, in Equation (15.4) it is necessary to adopt the frequentist perspective that α_i is a fixed, but unknown, parameter. Later, in Equation (15.12), it is necessary to view α_i as a random variable so as to compute its conditional expectation. A Bayesian might argue that this is typical of applications of the frequentist paradigm.

15.6 EXERCISES

15.1 Introduction
15.2 The Morris - van Slyke Model

15-1 Show that X_{it} is an unbiased estimator of α_i, for $i = 1, 2, ..., k$ and $t = 1, 2, ..., r$.

15-2 (a) For $i = 1, 2, ..., k$ and $t = 1, 2, ..., r$. show that

$$Var(X_{it}) = \left(\frac{1 - w_i}{w_i} \right) \sigma^2.$$

(b) Use the result of part (a) to show that Equation (15.7) is an unbiased estimator of σ^2.

15-3 Derive Equation (15.12).

15-4 (a) Derive Equation (15.15).
(b) Derive Equation (15.16).

15-5 Let $w_i = \frac{1}{k}$ for $i = 1, 2, ..., k$, so that

$$\hat{V}_i = \frac{\sigma^2}{r} \cdot \frac{1 - w_i}{w_i} = -\frac{\hat{\sigma}^2}{r} \cdot \frac{1 - k}{k} = c$$

does not vary with i.. Then show each of the following:

(a) $\hat{\mu} = \dfrac{\sum\limits_{i=1}^{k} \overline{x}_{i\cdot}}{k}$ (b) $\hat{\tau}^2 = \dfrac{\sum\limits_{i=1}^{k} \left\{ (\overline{x}_{i\cdot} - \hat{\mu})^2 - c \right\}}{k}$

(In this case the iterative process of Section 15.2.1 converges in a single iteration and does not require an initial estimate of τ^2.)

15-6 (a) Show that $\zeta_i = f(\tau^2) = \dfrac{\tau^2}{\hat{V}_i + \tau^2}$ is a concave function of τ^2.

(b) Use Jensen's inequality and the result of part (a) to show that the quantity $f(\hat{\tau}^2)$ underestimates ζ_i on the average.[2]

15-7 Derive the initial estimate of $\hat{\tau}^2 = .1869$ employed in the solution of the automobile rating class example in Section 15.3.

15.3 Worked Solution of Automobile Rating Class Example
15.4 Summary of the Morris - van Slyke Model
15.5 Further Remarks

15-8 Which of the following statements are true?

I.   The use of a conjugate prior density function simplifies the computational process and usually produces the optimal result as well.

II. The frequentist approach sometimes requires a wide variety of mathematical tools to produce a final solution.

---

[2] This is a fairly difficult problem.

15-9 Let an insurer's automobile business in a certain Canadian province be partitioned into four territories for insurance rating purposes. The experience data for calendar years 2004-2006 are summarized in the following tables.

TABLE 15.4

Number of Exposure Units by Territory			
	Calendar Year of Exposure		
Territory	2004	2005	2006
1	28,611	25,385	17,847
2	99,321	86,018	58,208
3	138,136	134,503	99,562
4	35,780	35,157	27,529
Total	301,848	281,063	203,146

TABLE 15.5

Reported Accident Rates by Territory			
	Calendar Year of Accident		
Territory	2004	2005	2006
1	6.23%	7.14%	9.84%
2	4.55	4.98	6.69
3	6.13	5.38	6.19
4	7.91	6.67	6.59

(a) Use the Morris - van Slyke model, together with the 2004 and 1995 experience data, to estimate the claim rate differentials for calendar year 2006.

(b) Calculate the measure of fit described in Section 15.2.4 for the results of part (a).

APPENDIX A
PREDICTIVE MODELING OF COSTS FOR A CHRONIC DISEASE WITH ACUTE HIGH-COST EPISODES[1]

Marjorie A. Rosenberg and Philip M. Farrell[2]

ABSTRACT

Chronic diseases account for 75% of U.S. national health care expenditures as estimated by the Centers for Disease Control. Many chronic diseases are punctuated by acute episodes of illnesses that occur randomly and create cost spikes in utilization from one year to the next. Modeling to account for these random events provides better estimates of (1) future costs and (2) their variability.

A Bayesian statistical model is used to predict the incidence and cost of hospitalizations for one chronic disease. A two-part statistical model is described that separately models the utilization and cost of hospitalization. Individual demographic characteristics are included as well as a simple biological classification system to adjust for the severity of disease among individuals.

Results by child, as well as by calendar year, are presented. Using a simple approach to incorporate severity, the model produces reasonable estimates of the number of hospitalizations and cost of hospitalization for the group in total, as well as for a separate group of High Utilizers.

The study reflects real-world experiences of persons entering and leaving a group. Modeling at an individual level provides a way to adjust for individual-level severity. The ability to model uneven and unpredictable occurrence of utilization, and potential cost, would be beneficial in the design of insurance programs or for disease management programs.

---

[2] Marjorie A. Rosenberg, PhD, FSA, is Associate Professor in the Wisconsin School of Business and the School of Medicine and Public Health at the University of Wisconsin–Madison. mrosenberg@bus.wisc.edu.

Phillip M. Farrell, MD, PhD, is Professor in the School of Medicine and Public Health at the University of Wisconsin–Madison. pmfarrell@wisc.edu.

A.1 INTRODUCTION

The most prevalent chronic diseases in the United States are heart disease, cancer, and diabetes mellitus (Centers for Disease Control and Prevention 2004). The predicted aging of the U.S. population will contribute to a rise in the incidence of chronic diseases (Bonow et al., 2002). Approximately 34% of the U.S. population (70,000,000 people) have one or more types of cardiovascular disease, which constitute 38% of all deaths (American Heart Association 2005). Many chronic diseases are associated with acute episodes of illnesses that require extensive therapeutic interventions. Thus, although a stable pattern of the incidence of costs over time may appear for a large population in the aggregate, closer analysis of the costs at the individual level may reveal a different pattern. For instance, there could be some level of baseline costs incurred, with frequent occurrence of acute care episodes. The ability to forecast these potentially uneven and random occurrences of utilization, and their cost, would be beneficial in the design of insurance programs or for disease management programs.

The purpose of this article is to demonstrate the usefulness of a predictive model that estimates the incidence and costs of hospitalization over time for a heterogeneous group of individuals with a chronic disease. Predictive modeling involves the use of data to forecast future events (Rosenberg et al. 2007). Application areas of predictive modeling in health care include underwriting and pricing of groups, stratifying risks for clinical management, and program evaluation of clinical and financial outcomes (Rosenberg and Johnson 2007).

The number of hospitalizations vary by individual by year, where the observed number of hospitalizations are random variables from an underlying probability distribution. Similarly the cost per hospitalization is also a random variable from some underlying probability distribution. Both the number and cost random variables have probability distributions that are long-tailed, with large values having a positive, although small, probability of occurring. To model these quantities for individuals with chronic diseases requires a way to include the individual-level severity of the disease, as well as other individual-level covariates such as age and sex. Using individual-level data allows the model to reflect differences in numbers of hospitalizations and cost per hospitalization by individuals.

Actuaries generally model health care costs using trend factors. The advantage of using trend factors is the simplicity of their application to predict the next year's aggregate claims. The disadvantage of this method is that it does not incorporate the movement of individuals in and out of a group; depending on their level of utilization this movement would impact the projections.

A Bayesian two-part model is used to predict the frequency of hospitalization by year of age in the first part, and conditional on usage, the cost per hospitalization in the second part. Two-part models are useful for health care data that often feature a large proportion of zeros as well as incorporate long-tailed distributions in both the first and second parts. Actuaries commonly use two-part models as in Bowers et al., (1997, Chap. 2, p. 28).

The next section provides a short description of the data and the model, and demonstrates how the predictions are calculated. The results depict the viability of the statistical model, and the article concludes with a discussion of the findings and other application areas.

A.2   METHODS

A.2.1   DATA

The study uses hospital utilization and cost data for children with cystic fibrosis (CF), a genetically inherited disease that affects the pulmonary and gastrointestinal systems and nutritional status of the patient. Individuals with CF have potential compromises in their digestive, respiratory, and endocrine systems (Marshall 2004; Fitzsimmons 1995). Because of the variability of symptoms among patients, the disease can be difficult to diagnose, and treatment is often delayed unless newborn screening programs exist (Fost and Farrell 1989; Farrell and Mischler 1992; Farrell et al. 2000). Hospitalizations are a major cost factor for children with CF. Silber, Gleeson, and Zhao (1999) showed that children with major organ disease (like CF) showed a 54% increase in length of hospital stays and 79% increase in hospital charges as compared with children without chronic disease.

The data were collected from a randomized clinical trial in Wisconsin. The overall purpose of the trial was to address the hypothesis that early diagnosis of cystic fibrosis through neonatal screening would be medically beneficial without major risks (Farrell and Mischler 1992). Wisconsin babies with CF born from April 1985 to June 1994 were screened for CF at birth and then randomized to either a control group or a screened group. Newborns with CF in the control group were diagnosed through traditional means, such as signs and symptoms, family history, or when the results from the newborn screening were disclosed after the child reached four years of age in accordance with an ethically sound design and avoidance of selection bias (Fost and Farrell 1989).

Electronic data for 77 children were available from July 1989 to June 2003 leading to both truncated and censored observations. Truncated observations arose as the data collection period began after the birth of some children who may have incurred costs before the data were available. Censored observations occurred when the data collection phase ended and children were still alive and at risk or when children discontinued participation in the study.

Table A.1 summarizes the data for 1990–2002, those calendar years with a full year of data.[3] The number of children, exposure, number of hospitalizations, and cost of hospitalizations are shown for each calendar year. In 1990 there were 45.5 children-years of exposure, growing to a maximum of 67.6 in 1994. Exposure declined in 1995–2002 from 62.8 to 53.0. Table 1 reflects a total of 244 hospitalizations over the 13 years. A subset of eight children, labeled "High Utilizers," had a higher number of hospitalizations during the study period with a total of 144 hospitalizations, or 59% of the hospitalizations overall. One child had 38 hospitalizations. The rate of hospitalization per year was consistently higher for the High Utilizers as compared to the remainder of the children.

Figure A.1 shows the distribution of the rate of hospitalization per year per child, which is adjusted for the exposure of each child in the study. The y-axis shows the number of children, and the x-axis shows the rate per year. The right-skewed distribution shows a point mass at zero reflecting the 30 children who had no hospitalizations during the study period. The dark shaded boxes are the High Utilizers, who are generally shown at the high end of the utilization.

---

[3] All years given are calendar years unless otherwise noted.

TABLE A.1

Number of Children, Exposure, Number of Hospitalizations, and Facility Cost for 1990-2002 in Total, High Utilizers, and Remainder of Children							
	1990	1991	1992	1993	1994	1995	1996
# of Children							
All	46	48	57	66	69	65	61
High Utilizers	8	8	8	8	8	7	7
Remainder	38	40	49	58	61	58	54
Exposures							
All	45.5	47.1	56.6	65.3	67.6	62.8	60.0
High Utilizers	8.0	8.0	8.0	8.0	7.5	7.0	7.0
Remainder	37.5	39.1	48.6	57.3	60.1	55.8	53.0
# of Hospitalizations							
All	37	40	22	19	21	14	23
High Utilizers	26	31	12	11	10	4	9
Remainder	11	9	10	8	11	10	14
Cost of Hospitalizations							
All	$572,107	$443,747	$209,944	$178,336	$209,029	$74,975	$233,279
High Utilizers	406,171	371,737	88,720	82,136	130,592	21,382	77,277
Remainder	165,936	72,010	121,224	96,200	78,437	53,593	156,002
	1997	1998	1999	2000	2001	2002	
# of Children							
All	59	59	57	55	55	53	
High Utilizers	7	7	7	6	6	5	
Remainder	52	52	50	49	49	48	
Exposures							
All	59.0	57.9	56.3	55.0	54.4	53.0	
High Utilizers	7.0	7.0	06.5	6.0	5.8	5.0	
Remainder	52.0	50.9	49.8	49.0	48.6	48.0	
# of Hospitalizations							
All	145	15	11	6	9	12	
High Utilizers	7	10	9	4	4	7	
Remainder	8	5	2	2	5	5	
Cost of Hospitalizations							
All	$129,896	$182,461	$133,178	$84,254	$164,587	$203,930	
High Utilizers	77,880	147,077	125,561	70,287	75,510	87,930	
Remainder	52,016	35,384	7,617	13,967	89,077	143,305	

All costs were adjusted to 2001 dollars by adjusting costs on a monthly basis using the medical care component of the Consumer Price Index (http://data.bls.gov). For this study we used cost related to the care inside

the hospital such as nursing, pharmacy, and laboratory, which was collected from a detailed cost-accounting process at the University of Wisconsin–Madison Hospitals and Clinics. Table A.1 shows the cost of the
hospitalizations for 1990–2002 for the group, High Utilizers, and the
Remainder. Similar to the numbers of hospitalization, the High Utilizers
had 61% of the total cost.

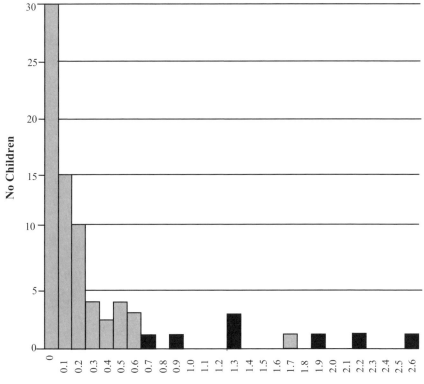

**Distribution of Number of Hospitalizations per Year
by Child Adjusted for Exposure with
High Utilizers Shown as Dark-Shaded Cells**

Average Number of Hospitalizations

FIGURE A.1

Figure A.2 illustrates the wide variation of the cost per hospitalization by
child for those with at least one hospitalization. The *y*-axis shows the
proportion of children in each category adjusted for the length of the
amount interval so that the area of each bar equals the proportion of the

total cost that is attributed to that interval. The x-axis is the average cost per hospitalization per child. Forty-seven children had at least one hospitalization; the cost per hospitalization per child ranged from $1,000 to $47,100, with the majority of the costs between $5,000 and $20,000 per visit. The distribution of the cost per hospitalization is also right-skewed. The eight High Utilizers are shown above the bars, indicating that they are dispersed in this distribution and not all to the right.

Distribution of Cost per Hospitalization by Child

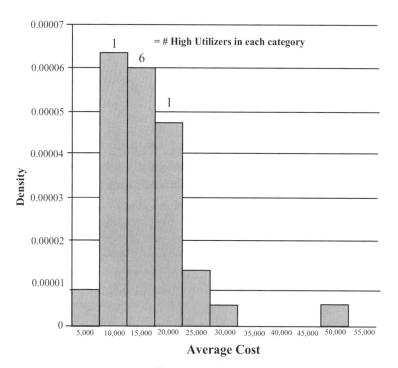

FIGURE A.2

A.2.2 MODEL

Details of the Bayesian two-part model and inference of the parameters are found in Rosenberg and Farrell (2007). We modeled by year of age to allow for the left-truncation and right-censoring of the data (Lin et al., 1997). We used WinBUGS version 1.4 for this analysis, which is a specialized software program designed to implement Bayesian models. For a tutorial on WinBUGS see Scollnik (2001) or Fryback, Stout, and Rosenberg (2001), or for further reading on understanding Bayesian models see Gelman et al. (2004) and Gilks, Richardson, and Spiegelhalter (1996).

The Markov Chain Monte Carlo (MCMC) technique was used to estimate the parameters.

MCMC is a simulation technique (the Monte Carlo part) and combined with Markov chain concepts creates simulated draws from the posterior distribution of the parameters. The set of all draws form the joint posterior distribution of the parameters. A description of MCMC is provided in the Appendix.

Although a majority of children had no hospitalizations, some children had multiple hospitalizations within a year of age. We modeled the number of hospitalizations for a child i at a particular age j as a Poisson distribution with parameter $e_{ij} \cdot \mu_{ij}$, where e_{ij} represents the exposure for the child within the year of age, and μ_{ij} represents the average number of hospitalizations within the year of age for the child. The logarithm of the mean number of hospitalizations at each year of age for each child, $\log(\mu_{i,j})$, was modeled as a linear combination of unknown parameters and explanatory variables, plus a random effects term that incorporated variation at the child level.[4] The logarithm was used to ensure that the estimate of the mean was greater than zero. We assumed noninformative priors for the unknown parameters that were normally distributed with a zero mean and very large variance. The priors for the individual random effects terms were assumed to have a normal distribution with mean of zero and a common variance across children. The prior for the common variance term was assumed to have a noninformative Inverse Gamma distribution.

The second part modeled costs for the jth hospitalization for the ith child as Gamma random variables. Gamma random variables have two parameters, α and θ, where α is the shape parameter and θ is the scale parameter. The parameterization as defined by Klugman, Panjer, and Willmot (2004) was used, where the mean was equal to $\alpha \cdot \theta$, so that

---

[4] In Klugman, Panjer, and Willmot (2008) the Negative Binomial distribution was motivated using a Poisson distribution with the mean having a Gamma distribution. Here we are using a Poisson distribution, with an assumption that the mean has a Lognormal distribution.

an increasing scale parameter increased average costs. The Gamma distribution was chosen based on the shape of the data in Figure A.2. We allowed the shape and scale parameter to vary by individual. The shape parameter was assumed to be distributed as a Gamma random variable, with the prior parameters set at (5.0, 2.0) so that it was a proper distribution but with wide variance. Sensitivity analyses were completed using other prior distributions, and the final choice of the parameters of the prior distribution did not impact the ultimate results. The scale parameter for the ith child was a function of the demographic and severity information. As in the first part of the model, noninformative priors were assumed for the regression parameters.

The following explanatory variables were included in both parts of the model. A simple biological severity system was defined that grouped children with meconium ileus, an obstruction of the intestine (ileus), in one category (21% of children), children with a severe form of the disease (as measured by genotype) in a second category (51% of the children), and the remainder in a third category (28% of the children). Other explanatory variables included an indicator of female gender, age at hospitalization, indicator of being assigned to the screened group, and age at diagnosis. The first part also included attained age as an explanatory variable.

The Bayesian MCMC process was verified for convergence. Alternative statistical models were explored, varying the assumed distributions and the priors, as well as ways to include the explanatory variables. The statistical importance of the explanatory variables, as well as the fit of the posterior expected number and costs of hospitalizations by year of age by child, was summarized in Rosenberg and Farrell (2007).

A.2.3 PREDICTION

Parameters were estimated for both parts of the model that covered ages 0–18. In this article, we focused on the posterior distribution of numbers of hospitalizations and costs of hospitalization in a year of age for two particular children and for the entire group of active children for a particular calendar year. The posterior distribution of the parameters by child were used as inputs to a simulation of the numbers of hospitalization by year of age and the cost per hospitalization by child to determine the aggregate costs by child and by calendar year. Estimates of total costs for 77 children in a particular calendar year were based on age and exposure of children in that calendar year.

To simulate the frequency of hospitalizations, we used the draws for $\mu_{i,j}$ from the MCMC simulation, as this parameter represented the expected number of hospitalizations by year of age for child i. Poisson random variables were simulated for each child with an adjustment of the known exposure made for comparisons to the observed numbers.

For each of the predicted hospitalizations, we simulated the cost per hospitalization. Different methods of prediction were required for those children who had incurred at least one hospitalization during the study period as well as for those children who had no hospitalizations. For children without observed costs, the simulation may have generated some hospitalizations; therefore some method of generating costs was needed.

For those 47 children with cost data we used the simulated values for (α_i, θ_i) for each child as generated by our model, and simulated a Gamma random variable with those parameters for the number of hospitalizations required.

For each of the 30 children without cost data we needed (α_i, θ_i) to simulate costs. A simulated value of $\log(\theta_i)$ was found based on individual characteristics and posterior distributions of cost regression parameters. For these children their α_i is a random variable from the posterior distribution based on the values of all α_i from all children with costs. Once the (α_i, θ_i) were simulated, then the costs were simulated as for those children who had hospitalizations.

Bayesian models assume that parameters are random variables and not point estimates. Using the parameters generated by the MCMC process produces a distribution of either the number of hospitalizations or cost per hospitalization. For example, each $\mu_{i,j}$ was used to simulate the number of hospitalizations for child i at age j, and for each hospitalization each (α_i, θ_i) was used to simulate the cost per hospitalization. The mean, variance, percentiles, or other function is found by using the simulated sample.

Ignoring the randomness of the parameter estimates underestimates the variance of any predictions that were calculated. For example, let $S_{i,\text{Age}}$ be the random variable for the total costs, $N_{i,\text{Age}}$ be the random variable for the number of hospitalizations, and X_i be the random variable for the cost per hospitalization for child i at a particular age. Using conditional expectation, then $E[S_{i,Age}] = E[N_{i,Age}] \cdot E[X_i]$, $E[N_{i,Age}] = E[\mu_{i,Age}]$, and $E[X_i] = E[\alpha_i \cdot \theta_i]$. Note that the expectations of $\mu_{i,Age}$ and $\alpha_i \cdot \theta_i$, the mean of a Poisson and Gamma random variable, respectively, are over their posterior distribution. The variance of total costs per child per age was found by

$$Var[S_{i,Age}] = Var[N_{i,Age}] \cdot \left(E[X_i]\right)^2 + E[N_{i,Age}] \cdot Var[X_i],$$

where

$$Var[N_{i,Age}] = E[\mu_{i,Age}] + Var[\mu_{i,Age}]$$

and

$$Var[X_i] = E[\alpha_i \cdot \theta_i^2] + Var[\alpha_i \cdot \theta_i].$$

In non-Bayesian studies the variance of the number of hospitalizations by year of age would just be the first component; similarly for the variance of the cost per hospitalization. In the Bayesian analysis the variances of $N_{i,Age}$ and X_i each have an added component to the variance that adjusts for the extra variation for the parameters. Note also that using a point estimate for the mean in a Monte Carlo simulation will understate the variance regardless of the number of trials used for the simulation.

There are other ways of reflecting the variability of the parameter estimates without using a Bayesian model. However, the Bayesian model incorporates this variability more naturally.

A.3   RESULTS

The usefulness of the model is illustrated by showing the results for two children in the study. Child B is a high utilizer, while child A is not. We show results for four years – 1990, 1992, 1996, and 1999 – in aggregate, for the group of High Utilizers, and for the remainder.

Figures A.3 and A.4 show the posterior distributions of the *average number* of hospitalizations for child A and B for age 0. The graphs show that the average is not a fixed-point estimate, but rather a distribution of values. The overall average for the posterior distribution for the mean number of hospitalizations at age 0 for child A is 0.72, while the overall average for child B is 5.76. The distribution for the High Utilizer is shifted to the right of child A with a much higher variance.

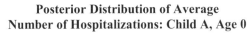

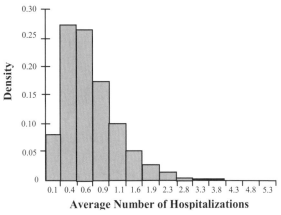

FIGURE A.3

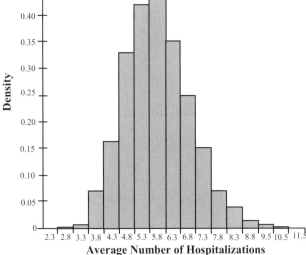

FIGURE A.4

Figures A.5 and A.6 show a similar pattern for the *average cost* per hospitalization for child A and child B, respectively. These are the posterior distributions of the averages, which are also both skewed to the right. The average cost per hospitalization is higher for this High Utilizer ($8,100 vs. $3,100), and the skewness is approximately 1.4.

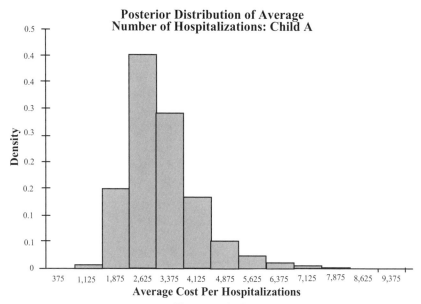

FIGURE A.5

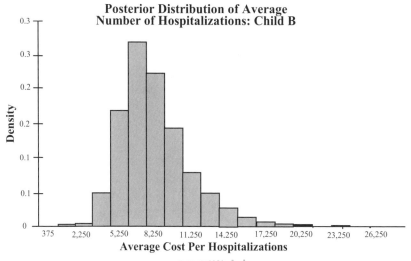

FIGURE A.6

Using the distributions for the average number of hospitalizations, we simulate the total number of hospitalizations for each child at age 0. These distributions are shown in Figures A.7 and A.8. The outcomes are integer-valued to depict the number of hospitalizations. Child A has a 53% probability of not having a hospitalization at age 0, while child B has a 1% chance of not being hospitalized. Not surprisingly, the overall average of the count distributions for each child is the same as the average of the averages discussed above. These distributions are what could be outcomes at each year of age. The figures show how widespread the data are; the summary statistics provide a more concise way of describing the data. Percentiles are easy statistics to calculate from the distribution and are informative about the spread of the data for long-tailed distributions, perhaps more so than the standard deviation.

Predictive Distribution of Number of Hospitalizations: Child A, Age 0

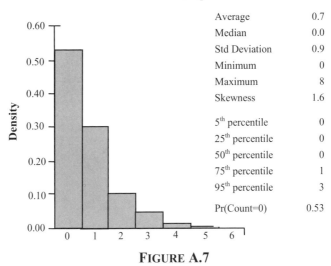

Average	0.7
Median	0.0
Std Deviation	0.9
Minimum	0
Maximum	8
Skewness	1.6
5th percentile	0
25th percentile	0
50th percentile	0
75th percentile	1
95th percentile	3
Pr(Count=0)	0.53

FIGURE A.7

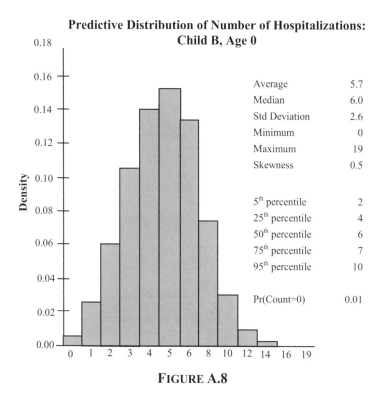

FIGURE A.8

Similarly Figures A.9 and A.10 show the predictive distributions of the aggregate costs for children A and B, respectively. This distribution is the combined result of the simulation of the numbers of hospitalizations and the cost per hospitalization. For child A the average is $2,218 with a standard deviation of $3,330; however, the simulation resulted in one outcome of $38,123. For child B the average cost is $46,404 with a standard deviation of $27,871. Here the 95th percentile is $98,460, but one trial of the simulation was $241,568. These results show the impact of the two long-tailed distributions used in the first and second parts of the model, where costs are widely spread.

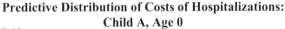

Predictive Distribution of Costs of Hospitalizations: Child A, Age 0

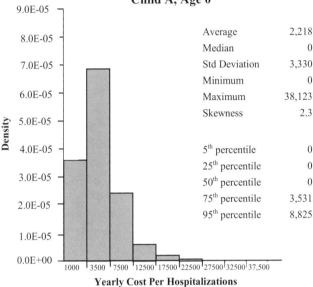

Average	2,218
Median	0
Std Deviation	3,330
Minimum	0
Maximum	38,123
Skewness	2.3
5th percentile	0
25th percentile	0
50th percentile	0
75th percentile	3,531
95th percentile	8,825

Yearly Cost Per Hospitalizations

FIGURE A.9

Predictive Distribution of Costs of Hospitalizations: Child B, Age 0

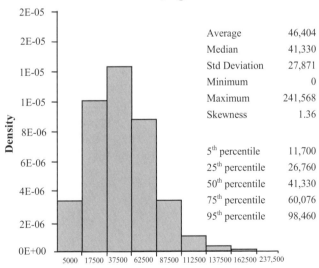

Average	46,404
Median	41,330
Std Deviation	27,871
Minimum	0
Maximum	241,568
Skewness	1.36
5th percentile	11,700
25th percentile	26,760
50th percentile	41,330
75th percentile	60,076
95th percentile	98,460

Yearly Cost of Hospitalizations

FIGURE A.10

Figures A.11–A.14 show the predictive distributions of the number of hospitalizations, and Figures A.15–A.18 show the aggregate costs for the entire group of children for 1990, 1992, 1996, and 1999. The horizontal scales are identical for the four years so that changes from one year to the next are more readily apparent. Also included on the graphs are the exposure, the actual number or cost of hospitalizations for the calendar year, and some summary statistics detailing the simulated average, standard deviation, and 5th through 95th percentiles.

For these four years the observed number of hospitalizations is within one standard deviation of the expected. Although the exposure increases until 1996, the number and cost of hospitalizations decrease over time. The observed values fall in different percentiles over time, from the 75th percentile in 1990, 5th percentile in 1992, 83rd percentile in 1996, and 50th percentile in 1999. The costs generally followed the same percentile, except in 1996, where costs were in the 59th percentile. These figures show the long-tailed nature of the data and that an observed value in the tail of the distribution does not necessarily make it wrong but does indicate it is rare.

Predictive Distribution of Number of Hospitalizations in 1990

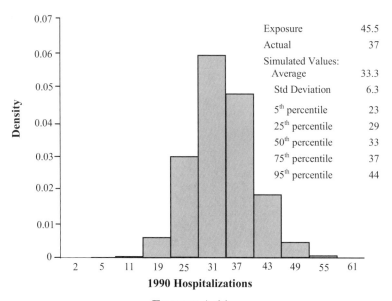

FIGURE A.11

Predictive Distribution of Number of Hospitalizations in 1992

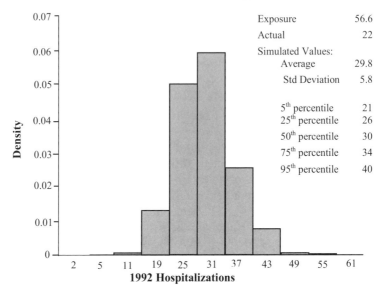

FIGURE A.12

Predictive Distribution of Number of Hospitalizations in 1996

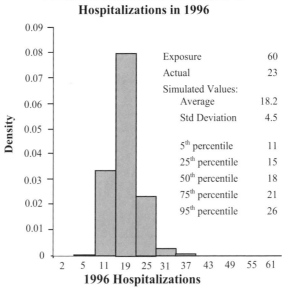

FIGURE A.13

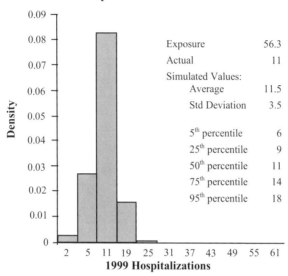

FIGURE A.14

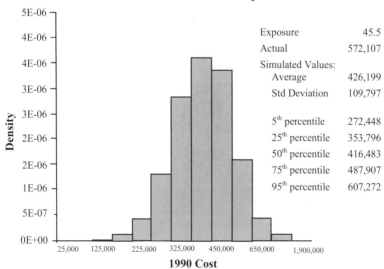

FIGURE A.15

Predictive Distribution of Cost of Hospitalizations in 1992

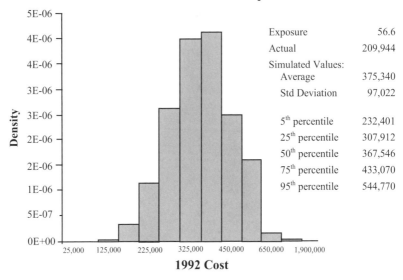

FIGURE A.16

Predictive Distribution of Cost of Hospitalizations in 1996

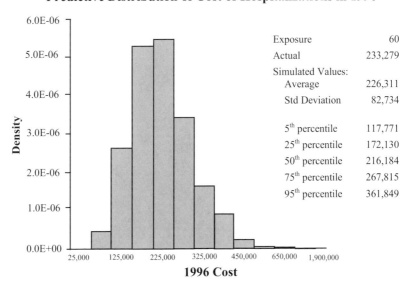

FIGURE A.17

Predictive Distribution of Cost of Hospitalizations in 1999

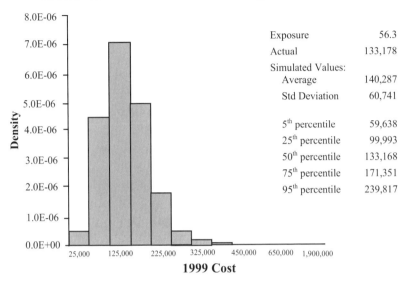

Exposure	56.3
Actual	133,178
Simulated Values:	
Average	140,287
Std Deviation	60,741
5th percentile	59,638
25th percentile	99,993
50th percentile	133,168
75th percentile	171,351
95th percentile	239,817

FIGURE A.18

Figures A.19, A.20, and A.21 illustrate the posterior distributions of the number of hospitalizations in aggregate, for the High Utilizers, and for other than these High Utilizers in 1996. In aggregate the exposure was 60, and the exposure for the High Utilizers was 7. Interestingly, the distribution of counts in 1996 for the High Utilizer is very similar to the rest of the group, even though there was a vast difference in exposure. Figures A.22, A.23, and A.24 show the predictive distributions for the cost in aggregate, for the High Utilizers, and for other than these High Utilizers. Here the distribution for cost shows a longer tail for other than High Utilizers.

All of these statistics, and others such as the coefficient of variation, skewness, minimum, and maximum, are shown in Tables 2 – 5 by calendar year, separately for the entire group, High Utilizers, and all other.

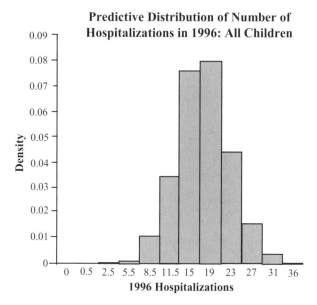

FIGURE A.19

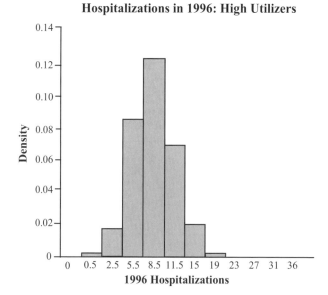

FIGURE A.20

**Predictive Distribution of Number of
Hospitalizations in 1996: Other than High Utilizers**

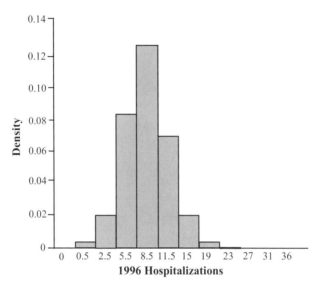

FIGURE A.21

**Predictive Distribution of Cost of
Hospitalizations in 1996: All Children**

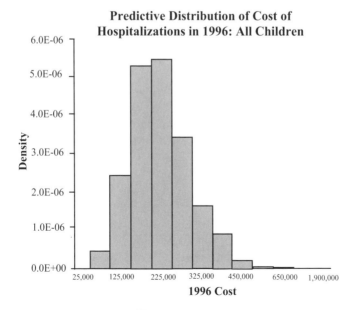

FIGURE A.22

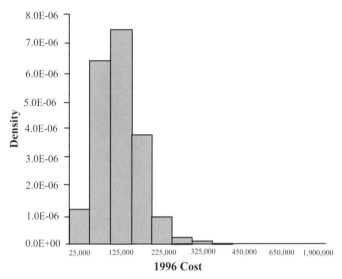

**Predictive Distribution of Cost of
Hospitalizations in 1996: High Utilizers**

FIGURE A.23

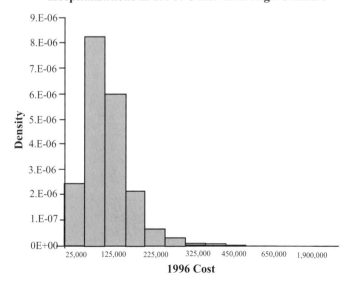

**Predictive Distribution of Cost of Cost of
Hospitalizations in 1996: Other than High Utilizers**

FIGURE A.24

TABLE A.2

1990 Hospitalization Summary for Entire Group, High Utilizers, and Remainder

Statistic	Number			Cost		
	Entire Group	High Utilizers Only	Remainder	Entire Group	High Utilizers Only	Remainder
Actual	37	26	11	572,107	406,171	165,936
Simulated values						
Average	33.3	22.9	10.3	426,199	290,403	135,796
Median	33.0	23.0	10.0	416,483	285,029	125,412
Standard Deviation	6.3	5.1	3.5	109,797	78,656	76,300
Coefficient of Variation	0.2	0.2	0.3	0.3	0.3	0.6
Minimum	13.0	6.0	0.0	114,517	73,449	0
Maximum	61.0	45.0	26.0	3,462,740	693,371	3,290,141
Skewness	0.2	0.2	0.3	2.6	0.4	7.8
Percentiles						
5th percentile	23	15	5	272,448	171,392	48,779
25th percentile	29	19	8	353,796	234,214	90,273
50th percentile	33	23	10	416,483	285,029	125,412
75th percentile	37	26	13	487,907	339,964	168,098
95th percentile	44	32	16	607,272	428,470	250,155
Pr(Simulated Total < Actual)	70%	70%	54%	92%	92%	74%

TABLE A.3

1992 Hospitalization Summary for Entire Group, High Utilizers, and Remainder

Statistic	Number			Cost		
	Entire Group	High Utilizers Only	Remainder	Entire Group	High Utilizers Only	Remainder
Actual	22	12	10	209,944	88,720	121,224
Simulated values						
Average	29.8	18.3	11.5	375,340	232,796	142,543
Median	30.0	18.0	11.0	367,546	227,169	133,268
Standard Deviation	5.8	4.5	3.7	97,022	70,104	66,864
Coefficient of Variation	0.2	0.2	0.3	0.3	0.3	0.5
Minimum	11.0	3.0	1.0	118,167	40,467	785
Maximum	55.0	39.0	28.0	1,107,436	594,231	912,354
Skewness	0.2	0.2	0.4	0.7	0.4	1.7
Percentiles						
5th percentile	21	11	6	232,401	126,890	55,959
25th percentile	26	15	9	307,912	183,353	97,306
50th percentile	30	18	11	367,546	227,169	133,268
75th percentile	34	21	14	433,070	276,921	175,698
95th percentile	40	26	18	544,770	356,824	257,764
Pr(Simulated Total < Actual)	7%	6%	21%	2%	1%	42%

TABLE A.4

1996 Hospitalization Summary for Entire Group, High Utilizers, and Remainder					
	Number			Cost		
Statistic	Entire Group	High Utilizers Only	Remainder	Entire Group	High Utilizers Only	Remainder
Actual	23	9	14	233,279	77,277	156,002
Simulated values						
Average	18.2	9.1	9.1	226,311	118,526	107,785
Median	18.0	9.0	9.0	216,184	112,964	96,492
Standard Deviation	4.5	3.1	3.1	82,734	49,613	65,924
Coefficient of Variation	0.2	0.3	0.3	0.4	0.4	0.6
Minimum	4.0	0.0	0.0	32,773	0	0
Maximum	39.0	23.0	26.0	1,763,026	384,669	1,670,289
Skewness	0.3	0.4	0.4	2.1	0.6	3.9
Percentiles						
5th percentile	11	4	4	117,771	46,682	35,507
25th percentile	15	7	7	172,130	82,415	67,686
50th percentile	18	9	9	216,184	112,964	96,492
75th percentile	21	11	11	267,815	148,263	132,601
95th percentile	26	15	14	361,849	208,612	210,295
Pr(Simulated Total < Actual)	83%	45%	91%	59%	21%	85%

TABLE A.5

1999 Hospitalization Summary for Entire Group, High Utilizers, and Remainder					
	Number			Cost		
Statistic	Entire Group	High Utilizers Only	Remainder	Entire Group	High Utilizers Only	Remainder
Actual	11	9	2	133,178	125,561	7,617
Simulated values						
Average	11.5	5.6	5.9	140,287	72,075	68,212
Median	11.0	5.0	6.0	133,168	67,338	60,067
Standard Deviation	3.5	2.5	2.5	60,741	37,829	47,387
Coefficient of Variation	0.3	0.4	0.4	0.4	0.5	0.7
Minimum	1.0	0.0	0.0	1,175	0	0
Maximum	27.0	18.0	21.0	1,228,494	271,518	1,179,855
Skewness	0.3	0.5	0.5	2.3	0.8	4.5
Percentiles						
5th percentile	6	2	2	59,638	18,998	15,891
25th percentile	9	4	4	99,993	44,347	38,598
50th percentile	11	5	6	133,168	67,338	60,067
75th percentile	14	7	7	171,351	94,022	87,304
95th percentile	18	10	10	239,817	141,780	143,725
Pr(Simulated Total < Actual)	40%	87%	2%	50%	91%	2%

A.4 CONCLUSION

This Bayesian model provides an approach to predict hospitalizations and costs based on long-tailed, complex data. The model was able to consider whether data were censored or truncated and to distinguish by child. The Bayesian model produced posterior distributions of the parameters that enabled predictions of costs for a child, as well as in the aggregate. While averages and standard deviations are useful, the entire distribution shows a range of possible values that is helpful when the distribution is skewed. For long-tailed distributions like utilization and cost, outliers are not necessarily true outliers, but rather can be samples in the right tail of a distribution with a fat tail. These observations should not necessarily be trimmed or thrown out, especially for small groups. The predictive distribution allows one to compute the probability of having a cost as high as the one that was incurred. The built-in severity component enabled costs and utilization to be automatically adjusted for any individual movement in or out of the group. The model, while not designed for calendar time, adapted to changes in utilization over time through changes in exposure and the ages of the exposed children.

As a simple comparison, we used a sample from the 2003 Healthcare Cost and Utilization Project (HCUP) Nationwide Inpatient Sample sponsored by the Agency for Healthcare Research and Quality. The HCUP data are a nationwide representative sample of hospital discharges. We sampled 1,938 discharges where the records contained an ICD9 code of cystic fibrosis (277.00, 277.01, 277.02, 277.03, 277.09) in any of the diagnosis fields on the record. The All Patient Refined Diagnosis Related Group (APR-DRG) is a system of classifying discharges based on more clinically meaningful groups and includes another code for disease severity. Of these 1,938 discharges, 95 were missing the APR-DRG code and severity. Of the remaining 1,843 discharges, 1,270 had an APR-DRG of cystic fibrosis, and the remaining 573 (31%) had an APR-DRG of something other than cystic fibrosis. In fact, there were 106 APR-DRGs for these 573 discharges. Sixteen hundred fifty-nine of the 1,938 (85%) were from one of three Major Diagnostic Groups (MDGs) (respiratory system, digestive system, or endocrine, nutritional, and metabolic system). The other 15% of discharges were from 16 other MDGs. Seventy-four percent were either level 2 or 3 for severity (moderate or major loss of functioning) and 64% for level 1 mortality (minor likelihood of dying). Although the data are discharge-based and not by person, the data showed the heterogeneity of CF hospitalization data with the variety of diagnostic groups represented. The Bayesian model designed for this study was simple from a variable inclusion perspective, but accurate in predicting costs and hospitalizations by calendar year.

While the prevalence of cystic fibrosis in the population is low as compared to the prevalence of heart disease, cancer, and other leading chronic diseases, analysis of utilization of health care services for children with CF provides a useful approach to modeling costs from these other diseases. Extending the lifetime of those with CF will increase the prevalence of those with the disease and increase the overall costs of the disease over time. For instance, those living longer with CF can live long enough to develop chronic lung disease or diabetes mellitus. Children with chronic disease with increased life expectancy grow to be adults with chronic disease. Smoking status, weight, and age are examples of risk factors that can be included in individual-level modeling for heart disease or cancer. Prediction of cost outcomes for use in disease management programs is easily completed for comparing one subgroup with another as shown with the comparison of some High Utilizers with the rest of children.

Actuaries are often involved in the design and analysis of disease management and case management programs. In case management programs, health care professionals coordinate the care (Dove and Duncan 2004). For instance, Kretz and Pantos (1996) analyzed data for one female CF patient with a severe form of the disease, where case management decreased the cost of care by 33% through a reduction of hospitalizations by aggressively trying to improve lung function, having nursing care in a home setting, and improving the nutritional status of the patient. Disease management programs coordinate health care interventions (www.dmaa.org). These programs require some analysis to gauge their success. Models, such as the one presented in this article, would provide information to help measure the success of a program or provide input to pricing of insurance programs.

A.5 ACKNOWLEDGMENTS

We would like to thank Anita Laxova, University of Wisconsin School of Medicine and Public Health, Mary Sue Nevel, University of Wisconsin Hospital and Clinics, and Danielle Rhiner, University of Wisconsin Medical Foundation, for their assistance in the data collection process. This work was supported by grants from the National Institutes of Health (DK 34108 and M01 RR03 186 from the National Center for Research Resources to the University of Wisconsin Medical School) and the Cystic Fibrosis Foundation (A001-5-01).

APPENDIX

MARKOV CHAIN MONTE CARLO TECHNIQUE

In the early 1990s the Markov Chain Monte Carlo (MCMC) approach to conducting Bayesian analyses was introduced (Gelfand et al., 1990). The technique revolutionized the use of Bayesian models, as it was a simulation-based method that could generate posterior distributions of unknown parameters and functions of the parameters. With the increasing power of computers, today Bayesian models are increasingly seen in published papers. Using key words ''Bayesian health care'' in a Google search produced a listing of over 24,000 papers. Makov (2001), along with the accompanying discussion, summarized the use of Bayesian models in actuarial-related areas.

The original MCMC methods were the Metropolis-Hastings algorithm, with a special case called the Gibbs Sampler (Metropolis et al. 1953; Hastings 1970). The Gibbs Sampler is described here. The interested reader is referred to textbooks such as Gelman et al., (2004) and Gilks, Richardson, and Spiegelhalter (1996).

The key idea involves generating a sample from a distribution that cannot be simulated from directly. Using ideas from Markov chain theory, an equilibrium distribution is found from which simulated draws are taken. The equilibrium distribution in this case is the posterior distribution. Simulated values of the Markov chain are used to summarize the posterior distribution. The mean of the simulated values is an estimate of the mean of the posterior distribution, and similarly the variance of the simulated values is an estimate of the variance of the posterior distribution. A graph of all of the simulated values is a graphical estimate of the posterior density (Smith and Roberts 1993).

To create the posterior distribution, the full conditional of each unknown parameter, given all the other parameters, is determined. These full conditionals are distributions that can be simulated. Initial values for each parameter are determined, and the full conditionals are sampled in a predetermined cycle for a specified number of iterations.

The following details are modified from Rosenberg and Young (1999). Suppose we are given a joint density of three unknown parameters, considered as random variables. Let the joint density of U, V, and W be denoted by $[U, V, W]$, and suppose we are interested in obtaining the marginal density of U, denoted by $[U]$, and calculated analytically as $[U] = \iint [U \mid V, W] \, dv \, dw$. This marginal distribution is generally difficult to calculate directly. The full conditionals are defined as $[U \mid V, W]$, $[V \mid U, W]$, and $[W \mid V, U]$ and provide a way to generate a sample from the marginal of U without calculating $[U]$ via integration.

We start with initial values of V and W, $V^{(0)}$ and $W^{(0)}$ to simulate $U^{(1)}$. Then using $U^{(1)}$ and $W^{(0)}$ we simulate a $V^{(1)}$. Finally, $U^{(1)}$ and $V^{(1)}$ are used to simulate $W^{(1)}$. The triplet $(U^{(1)}, V^{(1)}, W^{(1)})$ form one draw from the joint density of $[U, V, W]$. Under mild regularity conditions the distribution of $U^{(j)}$ converges to the marginal distribution of U as j gets large. For large m the observation $U^{(m)}$ can be treated as a realization of the random variable U. In practice one simulates a sequence with m large, and discards the first k values, called a burn-in, to eliminate the dependency of the sequence on the initial values. The remaining $m - k$ values are then used to estimate the density of U or other functions of U.

In this article, we use the joint draws from the posterior distributions of the parameters to simulate the number of hospitalizations per child for each year of age. For each hospitalization we simulate a cost per hospitalization. The predictive distributions of the total number of hospitalizations, and their respective costs, for each calendar year are sums of the number and costs of hospitalizations for the children in the study. Thus, here these predictive distributions are a function of the regression parameters used to simulate the number and cost of hospitalizations for each child.

REFERENCES

American Heart Association. 2005. *Heart Disease and Stroke Statistics.* 2005 Update. Dallas: American Heart Association.

Bonow, R.O., L.A. Smaha, S.C. Smith, G.A. Mensah, and C. Lenfant. 2002. The International Burden of Cardiovascular Disease: Responding to the Emerging Global Epidemic. *Circulation* 106: 1602–5.

Bowers, Newton L., JR., Hans U. Gerber, James C. Hickman, Donald A. Jones, and Cecil J. Nesbitt. 1997. *Actuarial Mathematics. 2nd* edition. Schaumburg, IL: Society of Actuaries.

Centers For Disease Control and Prevention. 2004. The Burden of Chronic Diseases and Their Risk Factors: National and State Perspectives 2004. www.cdc.gov/nccdphp/burdenbook 2004.

Farrell, P.M., and D.E. H. Mischler. 1992. Newborn Screening for Cystic Fibrosis. *Advances in Pediatrics* 39: 35–70.

Farrell, P.M., and Wisconsin Cystic Fibrosis Neonatal Screening Study Group. 2000. Improving the Health of Patients with Cystic Fibrosis through Newborn Screening. *Advances in Pediatrics* 47: 79–115.

Fitzsimmons, S. 1995. Cystic Fibrosis: What's New. *Journal of Insurance Medicine* 27(2): 124–30.

Fost, N.C., and P.M. Farrell. 1989. A Prospective Randomized Trial of Early Diagnosis and Treatment of Cystic Fibrosis: A Unique Ethical Dilemma. *Clinical Research* 37: 495–500.

Fryback, D., N. Stout, and M. Rosenberg. 2001. An Elementary Introduction to Bayesian Computing Using WinBUGS. *International Journal of Technology Assessment in Health Care* 77(1): 98–113.

Gelfand, A., S. Hills, A. Racine-Poon, and A. Smith. 1990. Illustration of Bayesian Inference in Normal Data Models Using Gibbs Sampling. *Journal of the American Statistical Association* 85: 972–85.

Gelman, Andrew, John B. Carlin, Hal S. Stern, and Donald B. Rubin. 2004. *Bayesian Data Analysis. 2nd* edition. London: Chapman and Hall.

Gilks, W., S. Richardson, and David Spiegel Halter. 1996. *Markov Chain Monte Carlo in Practice.* London: Chapman and Hall.

Hastings, W. K. 1970. Monte Carlo Sampling Methods Using Markov Chains and Their Applications. *Biometrika* 57: 97–109.

Klugman, Stuart A., Harry H. Panjer, and Gordon E. Willmot. 2004. *Loss Models: From Data to Decisions.* 2nd ed. New York: John Wiley and Sons.

Lin, D.Y., E.J. Feuer, R. Etzioni, and Y. Wax. 1997. Estimating Medical Costs with Incomplete Followup Data. *Biometrics* 53: 419–34.

Makov, Udi E. 2001. Principal Applications of Bayesian Methods in Actuarial Science: A Perspective. *North American Actuarial Journal* 5(4): 53–73.

Marshall, B.C. 2004. Pulmonary Exacerbations in Cystic Fibrosis: It's Time to Be Explicit. *American Journal of Respiratory and Critical Care Medicine* 169: 781–82.

Metropolis, N., A. Rosenbluth, A. Teller, and E. Teller. 1953. Equation of State Calculations by Fast Computing Machines. *Journal of Chemical Physics* 21: 1087–92.

Rosenberg, Marjorie A., and Philip M. Farrell. 2007. Impact of a Newborn Screening Program on Inpatient Utilization for Children with Cystic Fibrosis. Working paper. http://research3.bus.wisc.edu/mrosenberg.

Rosenberg, Marjorie A., Edward W. Frees, Jiafeng Sun, Paul H. Johnson Jr., and James M. Robinson. 2007. Predictive Modeling with Longitudinal Data: A Case Study of Wisconsin Nursing Homes. *North American Actuarial Journal* 11(3): 54–69.

Rosenberg, Marjorie A., and Paul H. Johnson Jr. 2007. Health Care Predictive Modeling Tools. *Health Watch* 54: 24–27.

Rosenberg, Marjorie A., and Virginia R. Young. 1999. A Bayesian Approach to Understanding Time Series Data. *North American Actuarial Journal* 3(2): 130–43.

Scollnik, D.P.M. 2001. Actuarial Modeling with MCMC and BUGS. *North American Actuarial Journal* 5(2): 96–124.

Silber, J.H., S.P. Gleeson, and H.M. Zhao. 1999. The Influence of Chronic Disease on Resource Utilization in Common Acute Pediatric Conditions: Financial Concerns for Children's Hospitals. *Archives of Pediatric and Adolescent Medicine* 153(2): 169–79.

Smith, A.F.M., and G.O. Roberts. 1993. Bayesian Computation via the Gibbs Sampler and Related Markov Chain Monte Carlo Methods. *Journal of Royal Statistical Society, Series B* 55: 3–23.

APPENDIX B

COMPARING CREDIBILITY ESTIMATES OF HEALTH INSURANCE CLAIMS COSTS[1]

Gilbert W. Fellingham, H. Dennis Tolley, Thomas N. Herzog [2]

ABSTRACT

We fit a linear mixed model and a Bayesian hierarchical model to data provided by an insurance company located in the Midwest. We used models fit to the 1994 data to predict health insurance claims costs for 1995. We implemented the linear mixed model in SAS and used two different prediction methods to predict 1995 costs. In the linear mixed model we assumed a normal likelihood. In the hierarchical Bayes model, we used Markov chain Monte Carlo methods to obtain posterior distributions of the parameters, as well as predictive distributions of the next year's costs. We assumed the likelihood for this model to be a mixture of a gamma distribution for the nonzero costs, with a point mass for the zero costs. All prediction methods use credibility-type estimators that use relevant information from related experience. The linear mixed model was heavily influenced by the skewed nature of the data. The assumed gamma likelihood of the full Bayesian analysis appeared to underestimate the tails of the distributions. All prediction models underestimated costs for 1995.

[2] Gilbert W. Fellingham, PhD, Professor, Dept. of Statistics, Brigham Young University
Contact: 212 TMCB, Provo, UT 84602, USA
Phone:(801)422-2806,
email:gwf@byu.edu

H. Dennis Tolley, ASA, PhD, Professor, Dept. of Statistics, Brigham Young University, Probo, UT e-mail: tolley@byu.edu.

Thomas N. Herzog, ASA, PhD, Distinguished Scholar in Insurance Regulation at the National Association of Insurance Commissioners.

293

B.1 BACKGROUND

One of the goals of the Society of Actuaries' Credibility for Health Coverages Task Force organized several years ago was to investigate the utility of credibility theory as a practical method of estimating and updating premium calculations for health insurance products. In connection with the work of this task force, a major health insurance provider provided a database summarizing recent claims experience for select health insurance coverages in Illinois and Wisconsin. These data were made available to the authors to illustrate the calculations and utility of credibility methods.

Credibility methods are actuarial techniques of using data from insurance claims (experience) to estimate claims in the future. Some of these methods are ad hoc, while others are founded on statistical principles. Both empirical Bayes and full Bayesian methods would be identified by the practicing actuary under the rubric of "credibility" methods. Though credibility methods have been used for years in the casualty insurance area, only recently have these methods been applied to health insurance data. This new application also brings with it a more complex problem in two ways. First the assumptions associated with the analysis may be more complicated than those of the linear mixed model, which assumes normal data and normal random effects. Second, health measures, risk factors, and type of care show a high level of variety, eventually mandating that credibility be viewed with models containing many covariates and possibly multivariate response profiles. This paper illustrates the use of currently available statistical techniques to initiate solutions to this more difficult application of credibility methods.

B.2 INTRODUCTION

The purpose of this paper is to use both a linear mixed model (LMM) as implemented in SAS (Littell, et al., 1996) and a Bayesian hierarchical model (BHM) to estimate health care costs with an eye to predicting expected costs for the coming year. These models could be used in premium calculations for small groups, and in premium calculations for blocks of business in new areas, as well as to calculate experience-based refunds. As methods for health finance improve, the need for a full Bayesian treatment of the problems faced by the industry is expected to grow.

One of the underlying principles of these methods is improvement of the process of estimating, say, the pure premium for a block of business, by "borrowing strength" from related experience. For example, if the exposure for a block is small enough, the experience for the previous years may be limited. In this case, estimates of future costs may be based on a combination of previous experience with other, related experience in an effort to mitigate the effects of random variation on the estimation process. Also, the thoughtful use of expert opinion along with current experience in other market areas could be used to improve prediction of expected experience in new markets.

Various paradigms for estimating expected experience have been presented in detail by several authors (see e.g., Herzog (1999), and Klugman (1992). Though these presentations provide the essentials for involved problems, even in these simpler paradigms the examples are restricted to smaller, textbook type problems. Several authors (Morris and Van Slyke (1978), Venter (1990), Tolley, Nielsen, and Bachelor, (1999) have provided computational shortcuts for more involved models.

Two key papers that synthesize several credibility models are Frees, et al. (1999) and Frees, et al. (2001). In these papers, the authors make explicit the relationship between credibility procedures and the parametric statistical methods used for longitudinal and panel data analysis.

An implementation of a full Bayesian approach had been possible only for a limited class of models until the advent of MCMC numerical methods. Scollnik (2001) shows how to implement Bayesian methods in actuarial models using currently available software. The data set we use for illustration is fairly large, and requires estimation of nearly 3600 parameters. The size of the data set mitigates the necessity of eliciting precise prior information. However, the methods would clearly generalize to smaller problems, where more precise prior information would be useful.

B.3 THE DATA

The data set is from a major medical plan, covering a block of medium-sized groups in Illinois and Wisconsin for 1994 and 1995. Each policy-holder was part of a group plan. The groups consisted of from 1 to 280 employees with a median size of 24 and an average size of 35.2 in 1994. We have claims information on 40,631 policyholders from 1,177 groups. Policies were of three basic types: (1) employee only (employee), (2) employee plus one individual (spouse), and (3) employee plus multiple individuals (family). Table B.1 gives the number of employees and summary information about costs per day for the different policy types. Though the data are dated from a business perspective, they provide the ability to examine a full Bayesian analysis without divulging proprietary information. Only data from 1994 are used for building the model. 46,691 observations from 1995 are used to validate model predictions.

TABLE B.1

Policy Type	n	Mean	Std. Dev.	Median	Maximum	Proportion Zero Claims
Employee	22,618	2.77	12.74	0	823.45	0.574
Spouse	8,921	6.79	21.01	1.11	643.02	0.315
Family	9,092	7.97	14.81	2.44	277.64	0.211

Data consist of claims costs by policyholder. While age and gender of policyholder were known, age and gender of the claimant were only known when the claimant was the policyholder.

Costs were assigned to each policyholder on a yearly basis and not assigned by episode of care or by medical incident. The costs were total costs, with deductible and copayments added back in. The total yearly costs were then divided by the number of days of exposure. As per the policy of the company providing the data, all policies with annual claims costs exceeding $25,000 were excluded from all analyses, including the 1995 prediction set. Large daily costs are still possible if the number of days of exposure were small enough that total costs did not exceed $25,000.

B.4 THE MODELS

B.4.1 THE LINEAR MIXED MODEL

The data set did contain some covariate information about the insureds on which to base premium estimates, however these data are limited. For example, although we knew both the policy type and group for each policy, we did not know the individual identification of any claimant from the policy. Thus, we did not have access to information on gender or age of claimant, or if multiple claims were made on the policy by the same individual or different individuals covered by the policy during the year. Whether or not the policy covered the same people from year to year was not known. Consequently, we will use only policy type and group as predictors of cost to illustrate and compare the mixed model methods with the Bayesian methods if estimating future costs. Knowledge and use of additional policy and claimant specific data would improve prediction. However, such information would also make the presentation more difficult to follow with the additional detail. We use the data available to present an expository illustration. The methods are readily extended to more involved data sets.

In the classical terminology associated with mixed models (see e.g., Littell, et al. (1996)), parameters associated with policy type would be considered "fixed." This means that our predictions are to be based on the same set of three policy types considered here. On the other hand, groups are "random," meaning that predictions of costs will not be restricted to only a fixed set of insured groups. In essence, we consider the risk characteristics of a group of policies to be a random draw from a pool of risks. This draw is a one-time event, meaning that whatever risk characteristics were drawn from the pool for a specific group remain the same over time. Thus, experience gained on a specific group in one year can be used to predict outcomes in future years.

The general form of the linear mixed model (see Frees, et al. (1999), or Frees, et al. (2001)) is as follows:

$$\mathbf{Y} = \mathbf{X}\boldsymbol{\beta} + \mathbf{Z}\mathbf{u} + \mathbf{e} \qquad (B.1)$$

where $\mathbf{Y}$ is an $n \times 1$ vector representing the observed data (in this example n is 40,631), $\mathbf{X}$ is an $n \times p$ design matrix of known constants (p is the number of fixed effects, in this case 3 policy types), $\boldsymbol{\beta}$ is a $p \times 1$ vector representing the fixed effects of the policy types, $\mathbf{Z}$ is an $n \times q$ design matrix of known constants (q is the number of random effects, in this cases 1,177 groups), $\mathbf{u}$ is a $q \times 1$ vector representing random effects of the groups, and $\mathbf{e}$ is an $n \times 1$ vector representing the errors. The distributional assumptions are that $\mathbf{u}$ and $\mathbf{e}$ are independent multivariate normal (MVN) random variables with $\mathbf{u} \sim MVN(\mathbf{0},\mathbf{G}), \mathbf{e} \sim MVN(\mathbf{0},\mathbf{R})$. The vector $\boldsymbol{\beta}$ is a vector of fixed regression parameters to be estimated.

Equation (B.1) provides the basis for predicting future costs. Heuristically we can envision the estimation process as follows. We assume values for $\mathbf{G}$ and $\mathbf{R}$, whether known or estimated, and estimates of the vector $\boldsymbol{\beta}$ obtained from previous data. For any policy type we will know the set of X values. The group to which the policy belongs will specify the Z values. We predict the costs of any such policy by plugging into Equation (B.1) the estimates of $\boldsymbol{\beta}$, the appropriate X and Z values, and then drawing a random vector of $\mathbf{u}$ values, and solving. Any temporal effects on costs, such as medical inflation costs, changes in utilization patterns, etc., would be included in the X values to have an estimate adjustment in the vector $\boldsymbol{\beta}$. In this paper, we made no such temporal judgment, and therefore expect a downward bias in our predictions due to medical inflation.

Concerning the draw of the random vector $\mathbf{u}$, one of two conditions obtain. In the first case, the group is the same group on which experience already exists (the classical credibility problem). In this case, a new draw of risk characteristics is unnecessary since risk characteristics have already been "drawn" and the effect of these characteristics for the group can be estimated from this experience. In the second case, the group is a new group for which no previous experience is available. In this case we simulate the costs by repeatedly drawing realizations of u and plugging them into Equation (B.1). The resulting set of costs will be an estimate of the distribution of costs one might expect for this group. In actuality, of course, we need not formally make all the draws, but rather substitute for u its expected value and calculate the predicted costs directly. In either case, the estimate of future costs is a linear equation in the $\boldsymbol{\beta}$ and $\mathbf{u}$ parameters. Equations for making these estimates are given below.

It follows from the distributional assumptions that $\mathbf{Y} \sim MVN(\mathbf{X}\boldsymbol{\beta},\mathbf{V})$ where $\mathbf{V} = \mathbf{Z}\mathbf{G}\mathbf{Z}' + \mathbf{R}$. If $\mathbf{V}$ were known, the best linear unbiased estimate (the maximum likelihood estimate) of $\boldsymbol{\beta}$ would be the generalized least squares estimate given as:

$$\hat{\boldsymbol{\beta}} = (\mathbf{X}'\mathbf{V}^{-1}\mathbf{X})^{-1}\mathbf{X}'\mathbf{V}^{-1}\mathbf{Y}. \tag{B.2}$$

When $\mathbf{V}$ is unknown, $\mathbf{G}$ and $\mathbf{R}$ are usually estimated using either the full likelihood (ML) or a restricted form of the likelihood (REML) and then $\boldsymbol{\beta}$ is estimated using generalized least squares with $\mathbf{V}$ replaced by $\hat{\mathbf{V}}$. Since this approximation procedure is well-established and programmed in some statistical packages, we will use the notation and representation of estimates common in statistical literature. Note that using the generalized least squares approach assumes that we can get consistent estimates of $\mathbf{G}$ and $\mathbf{R}$ and then use these to form estimates of $\boldsymbol{\beta}$ and $\mathbf{u}$. The assumption of normality in $\mathbf{u}$ and $\mathbf{e}$ is used to form an estimation procedure. One might generalize this to an *m*-estimate in future work. Here we proceed without concern about this assumption. One might try to appeal to the Central Limit Theorem to reduce the effect of many zero values in the data. However, even with this fairly large data set, the sample sizes within groups are limited. Alternatively, one might try a conditional analysis conditioned on a positive claim amount. In summary, there is need for caution in forming estimates of $\mathbf{G}$ and $\mathbf{R}$ using likelihood methods where many responses are zero.

Using the mixed model shown in Equation (B.1), a linear combination $\mathbf{L}$ of the parameters (e.g. for estimates of future costs) is estimated as:

$$\mathbf{L}\begin{pmatrix} \hat{\boldsymbol{\beta}} \\ \hat{\mathbf{u}} \end{pmatrix}, \tag{B.3}$$

where $\hat{\mathbf{u}} = \hat{\mathbf{G}}\mathbf{Z}'\hat{\mathbf{V}}^{-1}(\mathbf{Y}-\mathbf{X}\hat{\boldsymbol{\beta}})$ and where $\hat{\boldsymbol{\beta}}$ is as in Equation (B.2) with $\mathbf{V}$ replaced by its estimate $\hat{\mathbf{V}}$. Standard errors of these estimates are computed as:

$$\sqrt{\mathbf{L}\hat{\mathbf{C}}\mathbf{L}'}, \tag{B.4}$$

where

$$\hat{\mathbf{C}} = \begin{pmatrix} (\mathbf{X}'\hat{\mathbf{V}}^{-1}\mathbf{X})^{-1} & -(\mathbf{X}'\hat{\mathbf{V}}^{-1}\mathbf{X})^{-1}\mathbf{X}'\hat{\mathbf{V}}^{-1}\mathbf{Z}\hat{\mathbf{G}}' \\ -\hat{\mathbf{G}}\mathbf{Z}'\hat{\mathbf{V}}^{-1}\mathbf{X}(\mathbf{X}'\hat{\mathbf{V}}^{-1}\mathbf{X})^{-1} & (\mathbf{Z}'\hat{\mathbf{R}}^{-1}\mathbf{Z}+\hat{\mathbf{G}}^{-1})^{-1} \\ & +\hat{\mathbf{G}}\mathbf{Z}'\hat{\mathbf{V}}^{-1}\mathbf{X}(\mathbf{X}'\hat{\mathbf{V}}^{-1}\mathbf{X})^{-1}\mathbf{X}'\hat{\mathbf{V}}^{-1}\mathbf{Z}\hat{\mathbf{G}} \end{pmatrix}. \tag{B.5}$$

See McLean and Sanders (1988) for more details.

To make predictions of future cost, we must specify the $\mathbf{X}$ values signifying the type of policy and an indicator $\mathbf{Z}$ for the group. These make up the $\mathbf{L}$ in Equation (B.3). Letting $\mathbf{X}_m$ denote the policy type, and $\mathbf{Z}_m$ the group, then Equation (B.3) reduces to:

$$\hat{\mathbf{Y}} = \mathbf{X}_m\,\hat{\boldsymbol{\beta}} + \hat{\mathbf{C}}_m\hat{\mathbf{V}}^{-1}(\mathbf{Y}-\mathbf{X}\hat{\boldsymbol{\beta}}) \qquad (B.6)$$

where $\hat{\mathbf{C}}_m = \mathbf{Z}_m\hat{\mathbf{G}}\mathbf{Z}'$.

Equation (B.6) resembles the classical credibility formula where the overall experience of the block, estimated by the first term on the right-hand side of Equation (B.6) is adjusted for the experience of the group, the second term on the right-hand side of Equation (B.6). In statistical terminology, the estimates produced by Equation (B.6) are called empirical best linear unbiased predictions (or EBLUPs) for costs. In case the policy of interest is from a new group, the indicator vector, $\mathbf{Z}_m$, will only contain zeros. In this case, $\mathbf{C}_m$ will be null and the second term will be zero. This indicates that there is no credibility adjustment for past experience as there is no past experience.

To quantify the improvement in estimation, we examine the variance of the estimate given by Equation (B.6). The variance of predicted costs given by Equation (B.6) is:

$$\hat{\mathbf{V}}_m - \hat{\mathbf{C}}_m\hat{\mathbf{V}}^{-1}\hat{\mathbf{C}}'_m + [\mathbf{X}_m - \hat{\mathbf{C}}_m\hat{\mathbf{V}}^{-1}\mathbf{X}]$$
$$\times (\mathbf{X}'\hat{\mathbf{V}}^{-1}\mathbf{X})^{-1}[\mathbf{X}_m - \hat{\mathbf{C}}_m\hat{\mathbf{V}}^{-1}\mathbf{X}]', \qquad (B.7)$$

where $\hat{\mathbf{V}}_m$ is the model-based variance matrix of $\mathbf{Y}$.

We note here that the value of $\hat{\mathbf{V}}_m$ depends on the general sampling model. In the case we consider, $\hat{\mathbf{V}}_m = \hat{\sigma}^2_{error} + \hat{\sigma}^2_{group}$. The two improvements on using a mixed model credibility estimate are the adjustment for group specific experience in Equation (B.6) and the reduction of the variance of predicted costs as given by the second term in Equation (B.7).

SAS's approach in Proc Mixed is the one mentioned previously, where the variance components $\mathbf{G}$ and $\mathbf{R}$ are estimated using either the full likelihood (ML) or a restricted or residual form of the likelihood (REML) (Littell, et al, 1996). Using $\hat{\mathbf{V}}$ instead of $\mathbf{V}$ in Equation (B.2) gives estimated generalized least squares estimates of the $\boldsymbol{\beta}$'s. REML is the default method of Proc Mixed and is used in our analysis.

There are at least two different methods of calculating the predictions given by Equation (B-6) using SAS. SAS will automatically produce predicted values for any new group that has only the independent (or covariate) terms entered and no dependent variable. The first method is to use the *random* command. In this case, SAS will automatically determine the EBLUPs using Equation (B.6). However, the variance quoted by SAS is the variance of the estimate (the third term in Equation (B.7)). The $\hat{\mathbf{V}}_m$ term, $\hat{\sigma}^2_{error} + \hat{\sigma}^2_{group}$, must be added to this estimate, and the second term, $\hat{\sigma}^2_{group}$, subtracted.

The second SAS method is the *repeated* option. Since the covariance structure in the problem is compound symmetric ($\hat{\sigma}^2_{error} + \hat{\sigma}^2_{group}$ on the diagonal, σ^2_{group} off the diagonal of the covariance matrix), identical estimates of the variance components (and by extension of $\hat{\boldsymbol{\beta}}$) are available by using the *repeated* statement in SAS, where groups are treated as the factor of repetition. Using this approach, no random effects are estimated, but EBLUPs are still available.

Theoretically, the two procedures will yield identical values for the EBLUPs. However, the computational algorithms are not the same, and thus the estimates often do not agree in every decimal place. Also, the degree to which the variance terms are adjusted by SAS for $\hat{\mathbf{V}}_m$ as noted above is different, although the variance of the estimates will be the same once the adjustment is made. We note here that the *repeated* command in SAS appears to adjust out incorrectly σ^2_{group} (the second term in Equation (B.7)) when the policy predictions are for policies from a new group. In this case, $\hat{\mathbf{C}}_m \hat{\mathbf{V}}^{-1} \mathbf{C}'_m$ would be 0, not σ^2_{group}.

Estimates were computed using both formulations and compared to each observed data point in 1995. We will make reference to this model as LMM when the formulations yield identical results. However, when referring to predicted values, these two formulations will be called LMM(random) and LMM(repeated).

B.4.2 THE HIERARCHICAL BAYES MODEL

In the Bayesian framework, the model consists of the likelihood of the data given the parameters, multiplied by probability densities for each of the parameters. The densities on the parameters are called the "prior" probabilities as they are formulated prior to the collection of the data. Based on Bayes theorem, posterior densities for the parameters given the data are then available from the scaled product of the likelihood and the priors. (For a review of Bayesian methods in general see e.g., Gelman, et al. (1998), Klugman (1992), Scollnik (2001), or Makov (2001)). We call this model hierarchical since subjects are considered to be a random draw of all possible subjects within a group, and each group is considered to be a random draw from all possible groups. It is this sequential nesting that gives the model its hierarchical structure.

There are two things to consider when thinking about the form of the likelihood. Propensity, the probability a claim is made, differs from group to group, and in our data is around 0.60. Thus, about 40% of the data are zeros, representing no claims. We chose to deal with this by having a likelihood with a point mass at zero with probability π_{g_i} for group i. The parameter π_{g_i} depends on the group membership. It would also be reasonable to include a parameter for propensity based on the policy type, and such a parameterization should be pursued in future analyses. Severity, the cost of a claim given that a claim is paid, is positively skewed. We chose a gamma density for this portion of the likelihood with parameters r and θ. Since we desire to estimate both policy type and group effects for this portion of the likelihood, we write r as $r_{p_j} + r_{g_i}$ and θ as $\theta_{p_j} + \theta_{g_i}$. Thus we estimate a component of the r parameter for each group (r_{g_i}) and for each policy type (r_{p_j}) and a component of the θ parameter for each group (θ_{g_i}) and for each policy type (θ_{p_j}). Implicit in this formulation is the assumption that policy type and group effect parameters are additive. This is not the same as assuming additivity in an analysis of variance model, or in assuming the effect is the sum of random variables. Rather this additivity assumption is a simple method of generating a prior for r and θ by component realizations of hyperpriors. Though the components have gamma distributions, their sums, in general, will not. Although other formulations are clearly possible, this likelihood seems to us to be reasonable. The likelihood follows using a compound distribution argument:

$$\prod_{i=1}^{1,117} \prod_{j=1}^{3} \prod_{k=1}^{j(i)} \left[\pi_{g_i[y_{ijk}=0]} + (1-\pi_{g_i}) \right.$$

$$\times \left(\frac{1}{(\theta_{p_j} + \theta_{g_i})^{(r_{p_j}+r_{g_i})} \Gamma(r_{p_j} + r_{g_i})} \right.$$

$$\left. \left. \times y_{ijk}^{r_{p_j}+r_{g_i}-1} e^{\left[y_{ijk}/(\theta_{p_j}+\theta_{g_i})\right]} \right)_{[y_{ijk}>0]} \right], \qquad (B.8)$$

where

i	indexes the group number,
j	indexes the policy type,
k	indexes the observation within a specific group and policy type,
$j(i)$	is the number of observations of policy type j within group i,
π_{g_i}	is the propensity parameter for group i,
θ_{p_j} and r_{p_j}	are the severity parameters for policy type j,
θ_{g_i} and r_{g_i}	are the severity parameters for group i, and
y_{ijk}	is the cost per day of exposure for each policyholder.

Thus, we have a point mass probability for $y_{ijk} = 0$, and a gamma likelihood for $y_{ijk} > 0$.

The assignment of prior distributions could be a critical part of an analysis where data are limited. One of the strengths of the full Bayesian approach is the ability the analyst has to incorporate information from other sources. In this case we had 40,631 data points for 1,177 groups, so the likelihood will dominate the analysis whatever prior information is used. We chose priors that seemed to us to be reasonable, but knowing they have only modest influence on the result.

We assigned each parameter a prior distribution as follows:

$$\theta_{p_j} \sim Gamma(2,2)$$

$$r_{p_j} \sim Gamma(2,2)$$

$$\pi_{g_i} \sim Beta(c_g, d_g)$$

$$\theta_{g_i} \sim Gamma(a_g, b_g)$$

$$r_{g_i} \sim Gamma(e_g, f_g).$$

The parameters associated with each group, in classical parlance the random factors, have another set of parameters in their prior distributions. In the BHM, it is the depth of the hierarchical structure that is used to distinguish between what are known as fixed and random factors in the LMM (see e.g., Brophy and Joseph, (2000), or Stangl and Berry(2000)). These parameters, known has hyperparameters, also need a prior structure. These priors are called hyperpriors. Since, as we have already noted, the prior distributions will have minimal impact on the posteriors in this case (and by extension of that argument, the hyperpriors will have an even smaller effect), we assigned the same hyperprior to each of the parameters $a_g, b_g, c_g, d_g, e_g,$ and f_g. We assumed each was distributed as an *Exponential*(1). We note that while the choice of hyperparamters should not materially affect posterior distributions, choices for hyperparameters can dramatically affect convergence in a model of this size if the hyperprior distributions are too steep. We ran the same model with hyperprior distributions of *Exponential*(0.1) with no change in posteriors. However, steeper hyperprior distributions led to MCMC runs that clearly had not converged, even after runs on the order of 80,000 iterations.

This formulation yields a full posterior proportional to:

$$e^{-a_g}e^{-b_g}e^{-c_g}e^{-d_g}e^{-e_g}e^{-f_g}\left[\prod_{i=1}^{3}\theta_{p_j}e^{(-\theta_{p_j}/2)}r_{p_j}e^{(-r_{p_j}/2)}\right]$$

$$\times\left[\prod_{i=1}^{1,117}\frac{b_g^{-a_g}}{\Gamma(a_g)}\theta_{g_i}^{a_g-1}e^{(-\theta_{g_i}/b_g)}\frac{\Gamma(c_g+d_g)}{\Gamma(c_g)+\Gamma(d_g)}\pi_{g_i}^{c_g-1}\right.$$

$$\left.\times(1-\pi_{g_i})^{d_g-1}\frac{f_g^{-e_g}}{\Gamma(e_g)}r_{g_i}^{e_g-1}e^{(-r_{g_i}/f_g)}\right]$$

$$\times\left[\prod_{i=1}^{1,117}\prod_{j=1}^{3}\prod_{k=1}^{j(i)}\left\{\pi_{g_{i[y_{ijk}=0]}}+(1-\pi_{g_i})\right.\right.$$

$$\times\left(\frac{1}{(\theta_{p_j}+\theta_{g_i})^{(r_{p_j}+r_{g_i})}\Gamma(r_{p_j}+r_{g_i})}\right.$$

$$\left.\left.\left.\times y_{ijk}^{r_{p_j}+r_{g_i}-1}e^{(-y_{ijk}/\theta_{p_j}+\theta_{g_i})}\right)_{[y_{ijk}>0]}\right\}\right].\qquad\text{(B.9)}$$

Posterior distributions for such a complicated model are not available in closed form. Current methods to analyze such a model include implementation of Markov chain Monte Carlo (MCMC) to produce samples from the posterior distributions which can then be evaluated (Gilks, et al (1995)). MCMC is essentially Monte Carlo integration using Markov chains. Monte Carlo integration draws samples from the required distribution, and then forms sample averages to approximate expectations. MCMC draws these samples by running a cleverly constructed Markov chain for a long time. There are many ways of constructing these chains, but all of them are special cases of the general framework of Metropolis, et al. (1953) and Hastings (1970). Loosely speaking, the MCMC process draws samples from the posterior distributions by sampling throughout the appropriate support in the correct proportions. This is done using a Markov chain with the posterior as its stationary distribution.

More precisely, we first formulated the posterior distribution of each parameter, conditional on the other parameters and assigned an initial value to each parameter. Then a new value is drawn from a "proposal" distribution. The ratio of the values of the complete conditionals computed using the proposed value and the old value of the parameters is computed and compared to a random uniform variate. If the ratio exceeds the random uniform, the proposed value is kept, otherwise the old value is kept. Using this method on each parameter, and cycling through the parameters, yields a distribution that converges to the appropriate posterior for each parameter. For a more complete exposition of this methodology, the interested reader should refer to Scollnik (2001).

B.5 RESULTS

B.5.1 THE GROUPS

Besides predicting outcomes for all individuals in 1995, we also chose three groups to model in more detail. We selected group 115 primarily because it contained the largest data point, $823.45 per day, although in other respects it was quite similar to the other groups. Group 980 was included because of high propensity, and because it was a small group. Group 1,034 was chosen primarily because the severity data were heavily right skewed, especially in the spouse policy type, and also because it was one of the larger groups. In Table B.2 we show summary statistics for the raw data in these three groups in 1994.

TABLE B.2

1994 Raw Data Summary Information for Three Selected Groups, 115, 980, and 1,034						
Group	Policy Type	N	Mean	Std. Dev.	Minimum	Maximum
	Individual	26	35.81	161.04	0.00	823.45
115	Spouse	2	29.75	18.20	16.89	42.62
	Family	4	11.84	13.31	2.43	21.25
	Individual	4	7.19	12.72	0.08	26.23
980	Spouse	2	33.77	41.82	4.20	63.34
	Family	6	9.68	8.88	2.31	25.33
	Individual	41	14.56	42.46	0.00	193.58
1,034	Spouse	85	56.92	115.01	0.00	556.41
	Family	13	2.31	3.29	0.00	12.32

B.5.2 THE CHAIN

The MCMC procedures of the BHM involve sampling from the posterior distributions of the parameters of interest, as well as from the predictive distributions. Although we know that our methodology guarantees convergence to the appropriate distributions, we do not know with certainty that any particular chain of sampled values has converged to the appropriate place. With a model of this many parameters, convergence may not happen quickly. In order to maximize the probability of the chains converging, we proceeded as follows.

We ran 70,000 burn-in iterations followed by 10,000 iterations sampled every second one for 5,000 samples from the posterior distributions of the parameters. We saved all 5,000 samples for the policy type severity parameters, but only computed means and standard deviations for the 1,177 group severity and propensity parameters. We also took 5,000 draws from the predictive distributions for groups 115, 980, and 1,034, as well as 5,000 draws from a predictive distribution for a new group.

We used the *gibbsit* program described by Raftery and Lewis (1995) and the *Bayesian Output Analysis Program* (Smith (2001)) to check for sequence convergence. All diagnostic procedures were indicative of convergent chains.

B.5.3 THE PARAMETERS

The LMM estimates for the variance components were $\hat{\mathbf{G}} = 5.44\mathbf{I}_{1177}$ and $\hat{\mathbf{R}} = 230.0\mathbf{I}_{40631}$. Group variability is quite small relative to residual variance. Estimates for the fixed effects in this model are expected mean costs for a subject averaged across groups. Estimates $\pm$ estimated standard errors were: \$2.82 per day $\pm$ \$0.13 for employee only, \$6.76 per day $\pm$ \$0.18 for spouse, and \$8.04 per day $\pm$ \$0.18 for family. The LMM(random) model estimates of the random effects for groups 115, 980, and 1,034 are shown in Table B.3.

TABLE B.3

Estimates of Random Effects (û) and Their Standard Errors for Groups 115, 980, and 1,034 for 1994 Using LMM (random)		
Group	Random Effect	Standard Error
115	12.64	1.79
980	1.50	2.06
1,034	25.79	1.13

These random effects are reflective of the large claim costs in groups 115 and 1,034. Many of the groups had random effects more like that of group 980, showing little need to take the group effect into account in predicting next year's values. The large random effects of groups 115 and 1,034 are reflected in the predicted values we see for these groups (see Section B.5.4).

In Table B.4 we display some summary information for the six policy parameters from the BHM. These parameters describe the underlying likelihoods for the non-zero costs for the three policy types. It is interesting to note that the expected values for these distributions (equal to $r_{p_j}\theta_{p_j}$, ignoring group effects) increase as policy types change from employee only to employee plus spouse to employee plus family as we would expect. However, the variances of the distributions (equal to $r_{p_j}\theta_{p_j}^2$, ignoring group effects) are largest for employee plus spouse.

TABLE B.4

Means, Standard Deviations, and Selected Quantiles of Posterior Distributions from the BHM of Policy Parameters θ_{p_j} and r_{p_j}					
Parameter	Mean	Std. Dev.	0.025	0.500	0.975
Employee θ_{p_1}	13.30	0.260	12.80	13.30	13.80
Employee r_{p_1}	0.49	0.006	0.47	0.49	0.50
Spouse θ_{p_1}	18.40	0.450	17.50	18.40	19.20
Spouse r_{p_1}	0.53	0.009	0.52	0.53	0.55
Family θ_{p_1}	15.30	0.340	14.70	15.30	16.00
Family r_{p_1}	0.65	0.010	0.63	0.65	0.67

In Table B.5 we show some information on the group parameters for the three groups (115, 980, and 1,034) that we chose to examine in more detail.

TABLE B.5

Means and Standard Deviations for Posterior Distributions from the BHM of Severity Parameters (θ_{g_i} and r_{g_i}) and Propensity Parameter (π_{g_i}) for Three Selected Groups						
Group	Mean (θ_{g_i})	SD(θ_{g_i})	Mean (r_{g_i})	SD(r_{g_i})	Mean (π_{g_i})	SD(π_{g_i})
115	0.102	0.019	0.00009	0.00008	0.49	0.06
980	0.101	0.018	0.00009	0.00008	0.15	0.08
1,034	0.104	0.019	0.00009	0.00008	0.50	0.05

Bayesian estimators borrow strength from all the data (Gelman, et al. (1998)). This can perhaps most easily be seen in the mean value of the posterior of $\pi_{g_{980}}$, which is 0.15 despite the fact that there are no zero values in this group, which would mean the maximum likelihood estimator for these data would be zero. Thus, the Bayesian estimate has borrowed strength from the other data in producing the posterior that is not centered over zero. It certainly appears from Table B.5 that the inclusion of group parameters r_{g_i} and θ_{g_i} was an unnecessary addition to the likelihood. These parameters converged to virtually the same (small) values in each group. Estimating the propensity parameters (π_{g_i}) for each group, however, appears to be of reasonable importance in describing the data.

B.5.4 PREDICTED VALUES

Generating predicted values using the LMM (either random or repeated) can be done automatically using SAS. Proc Mixed will produce a predicted value for any data point with covariate information but no value for the dependent variable.

Generating predicted values for future observations is quite straightforward using the BHM paradigm. At each iteration, take the current draws of the parameters for each group and policy type and use these to make a draw from the likelihood (these draws will include both zero and non-zero values). Using this procedure, 5,000 predicted observations were made for all three policy types in groups 115, 980, and 1,034. To get predicted observations for groups not found in 1994, draw group parameters from the distributions defined for the current draws of the hyperparameters, and use these parameters in the likelihood to draw observations. This technique was used to produce 5,000 draws for each policy type in a "new" group. This method essentially integrates over all sources of uncertainty to produce predicted values that display appropriate levels of variability.

In Table B.6 we show the actual mean costs and standard deviations using the 1995 data for the three selected groups and for a "new" group. The "new" group consists of all groups that were represented in the data in 1995 that were not represented in 1994. There are actually 85 groups represented in the "new" group. In Table B.7 we show model predicted mean costs and estimated standard deviations of the predicted values for both the LMM (random) and the LMM (repeated). Also in Table B.7 we display the actual predicted density mean and standard deviation for the BHM for the three selected groups as well as the "new" group.

Again, the point estimates for LMM (random) and LMM (repeated) are theoretically equivalent, yet will sometimes differ only because of computational issues. However, the standard deviations are computed differently. As described in Section B.4.1, the variance terms for the LMM (random) does not include the first two terms in Equation (B.7). The first term in Equation (B.7) is $\hat{\sigma}^2_{error}+\hat{\sigma}^2_{group} = 230.0+5.44$. The second term for all groups seen in 1994 is $\hat{\sigma}^2_{group} = 5.44$. For a group not seen in 1994, the second term is 0. Hence, the standard deviation for LMM (repeated) for groups seen in 1994 is obtained by squaring the entry in column 4 of Table B.7 (the standard deviation for LMM (random)), and adding $230 + 5.44 - 5.44$ and then taking the square root. The answer corresponds to than given in column 6. So for group 115, the LMM (repeated) standard deviation is $\sqrt{1.79^2+230.0+5.44-5.44} = 15.27$. For a new group, SAS computes the standard deviation of LMM (repeated) as $\sqrt{2.34^2+230.0+5.44-5.44} = 15.34$. This is incorrect. The appropriate standard deviation should be $\sqrt{2.43^2+230.0+5.44-0.00} = 15.52$.

It is obvious that both the LMM methods are quite sensitive to the outliers. The predicted values for groups 115 and 1,034 are quite large, and some of the data for these two groups are extreme (from Table B.2 the largest value in group 115 is 4.89 standard deviations larger than the mean, and the largest value in group 1,034 is 4.34 standard deviations larger than the mean). These large estimates are reflective of the large random effects for these groups we noted in Table B.3. In group 980, the group without many extreme values, the standard deviations of LMM (random) reflect the actual data reasonably well.

The LMM predicted values for the "new" group are functions of the fixed effects only. There is no random effect from the previous years (or shrinkage based on the other estimated groups) to move the predicted values higher. Again, the standard deviations of LMM (random) are too small, while those for LMM (repeated) are closer to the actual data.

While the LMM estimates for the groups with highly skewed data are in general too large, the BHM estimates for these same groups tend to be too small. This is reflective of the convergence of the group severity parameters to essentially zero. Thus, the BHM is not effectively using the previous year's data for the estimation of the predicted values in the groups with highly skewed data. The BHM does estimate different propensity parameters for the groups. This is shown in the larger estimates for costs in group 980, a group with high propensity to have claims. The BHM point estimates for the "new" group also seem to be very reasonable. However, the BHM predictive density standard deviations are consistently too small relative to the actual variability in the data.

TABLE B.6

1995 Raw Data Summary Information for Three Selected Groups, 115, 980, and 1,034, and a "New Group"				
Group	Policy Type	N	Data Mean	Data Std. Dev.
115	Individual	27	6.21	12.54
	Spouse	3	12.51	10.96
	Family	2	15.62	18.34
980	Individual	4	0.63	0.74
	Spouse	2	6.99	0.70
	Family	4	10.08	6.21
1,034	Individual	57	4.16	12.03
	Spouse	91	7.69	12.98
	Family	10	15.50	21.49
New	Individual	1,318	2.68	12.48
	Spouse	428	6.15	16.54
	Family	592	8.03	18.48

Note: Raw data for the "new" group include all groups that existed in 1995 that did not exist in 1994.

TABLE B.7

		1995 Predicted Values and Standard Deviation from LLM (random), LLM (repeated), and Predicted Density Summary Information from the BMM for Three Selected Groups, 115, 980, and 1,034, and a "New Group"					
Group	Policy Type	LMM (random) Predicted Value	LMM (random) Predicted Std. Dev.	LMM (repeated) Predicted Value	LMM (repeated) Predicted Std. Dev.	LMM Predicted Density Mean	LMM Predicted Density Std. Dev.
115	Individual	15.46	1.79	15.44	15.27	3.49	7.61
	Spouse	19.40	1.79	19.38	15.27	4.92	10.53
	Family	20.68	1.79	20.66	15.27	5.26	10.41
980	Individual	4.33	2.06	4.33	15.30	5.60	8.95
	Spouse	8.26	2.07	8.26	15.30	8.26	12.92
	Family	9.54	2.07	9.54	15.30	8.40	11.88
1,034	Individual	28.61	1.13	28.59	15.21	3.16	7.23
	Spouse	32.55	1.13	32.53	15.21	4.98	10.79
	Family	33.83	1.14	33.81	15.21	5.05	10.20
New	Individual	2.82	2.34	2.82	15.34	4.12	8.02
	Spouse	6.76	2.34	6.76	15.34	6.98	11.81
	Family	8.04	2.34	8.04	15.34	7.78	11.77

Since we computed a predicted value for all the 46,691 observations in 1995, we also computed both total error (computed as actual minus predicted), and total error as a percentage of total daily costs for the year. These results are shown in Table B.8. Both formulations of the LMM, and the BHM, underestimate actual costs accrued in 1995, although the LMM outperforms the BHM.

TABLE B.8

Total Error and Percentage Error of Actual Cost Minus Model Predicted Cost for 46,691 Observations in 1995 Using LMM (random), LMM (repeated), and the BHM		
Model	Total Error	Percentage Error
LMM (random)	14,029.48	5.9%
LMM (repeated)	14,023.37	5.9
BHM	26,589.38	11.2

B.6 DISCUSSION

We believe these methods offer the actuary effective tools to predict costs when covariate data are limited. All the models have "credibility" type estimators. While the LMM may be derived in a classical framework (see e.g., Harville (1977)), Laird and Ware (1982) show how the LMM (random) estimators may also be thought of as empirical Bayes. The LMM (repeated) estimators are also shrinkage-type estimators. The BHM is a full Bayesian approach.

It appears that the normal likelihood assumption of the LMM may be too sensitive to the outliers often seen in health care insurance costs. The predictive estimates for groups with outliers tend to be too large. Since group variability is small relative to residual error, the estimates are not "shrunk" back to the mean at the level which appears to be necessary. On the other hand, estimators from groups with small group effects tend to underestimate costs.

The BHM, while computationally more intense, gives the actuary the ability to specify a likelihood structure that may be more realistic for this type of data. However, appropriate determination of the likelihood seems to us to be key. In our example, we believe that the gamma likelihood for the severity data is not rich enough to capture the extreme variability present in this type of data. We are currently exploring the generalized beta (McDonald and Xu (1995)) density as a possibility. While this five parameter density may be too rich, leading to difficulties with convergence, it is likely that stepping back from this general form will lead to a more appropriate choice. Also, based on our experience, the inclusion of group parameters in the severity portion of the likelihood seems to unduly complicate the model, and is not necessary for the likelihood we used. However, use of group severity parameters might be necessary when the likelihood is more appropriately specified. Inclusion of group parameters for propensity seems to be appropriate.

The Bayesian hierarchical model, used with MCMC technology, allows for the fitting of the kinds of general models necessary to predict costs in the highly volatile health insurance industry. We believe this general framework has great potential for wide applicability in insurance.

ACKNOWLEDGMENTS

The authors wish to express their appreciation to the anonymous referees and the editor whose comments greatly improved the manuscript.

REFERENCES

Brophy, J., and L. Joseph (2000). "A Bayesian meta-analysis of randomized mega-trials for the choice of thrombolytic agents in acute myocardial infarction." In *Meta-Analysis in Medicine and Health Policy*, edited by D. Stangl and D. Berry, 83-104. New York: Marcel Dekker.

Frees, E.W., V.R. Young, and Y. Luo (1999). "A longitudinal data analysis interpretation of credibility models." *Insurance: Mathematics and Economics* 24: 229-248.

_____, (2001). "Case studies using panel data models." *North American Actuarial Journal*, 5(4): 24-43.

Gelman, A., J. B. Carlin, H.S. Stern, and D.B. Rubin (1998). *Bayesian Data Analysis*. London: Chapman & Hall.

Gilks, W.R. (1995). "Full conditional distributions." In *Markov Chain Monte Carlo in Practice*, edited by W.R. Gilks, S. Richardson, and D.J. Spiegelhalter, 75-88. London: Chapman & Hall.

Gilks, W.R., Richardson, and D.J. Spiegelhalter, eds. (1995). *Markov Chain Monte Carlo in Practice*. London: Chapman & Hall.

Harville, D.A. (1977). "Maximum likelihood aproaches to variance component estimation and to related problems." *Journal of the American Statistical Association*, 72: 320-338.

_____, (1990). "BLUP (Best Linear Unbiased Prediction), and Beyond," in *Advances in Statistical Methods for Genetic Improvement of Livestock*, 239-276. New York: Springer.

Hastings, W.K. (1970). "Monte Carlo sampling methods using Markov chains and their applications." *Biometrika*, 57: 97-109.

Henderson, C.R. (1984) *Applications of Linear Models in Animal Breeding*. University of Guelph.

Herzog, T.N. (1999). *Introduction to Credibility Theory*. Winsted, CT: ACTEX.

Klugman, S. (1992). *Bayesian Statistics in Actuarial Science with Emphasis on Credibility*. Boston: Kluwer.

Laird, N.M. and Ware, J.H. (1982). "Random-effects models for longitudinal data." *Biometrics*, 38: 963-974.

Littell, R.C., G.A. Milliken, W.W. Stroup, and R.D. Wolfinger (1996). *SAS® System for Mixed Models*, Cary, NC: SAS Institute Inc.

Makov, U.E. (2001). "Principal applications of Bayesian methods in actuarial science." *North American Actuarial Journal*, 5(4): 53-73.

McDonald, J.B. and Y.J. Xu. (1995). "A generalization of the beta distribution with applications." *Journal of Econometrics*, 66: 133-152.

Mclean, R.A., and W.L. Sanders (1988). "Approximating degrees of freedom for standard errors in mixed linear models." *Proceedings of the Statistical Computing Section*, American Statistical Association Annual Meetings, New Orleans, 50-59.

Metropolis, N., A.W. Rosenbluth, M.N. Rosenbluth, A.H. Teller, and E. Teller (1953). "Equation of state calculations by fast computing machine." *Journal of Chemical Physics*, 21: 1087-1091.

Morris, C. and L. Van Slyke (1978). "Empirical Bayes methods for pricing insurance classes." *Proceedings of the Business and Economics Statistics Section*, American Statistical Association Annual Meetings, San Diego, 579-582.

Raftery, A.E. and S.M. Lewis (1995). "Implementing MCMC." In *Markov Chain Monte Carlo in Practice*, edited by W.R. Gilks, S. Richardson, and D.J. Spiegelhalter), 115-130. London: Chapman & Hall.

Scollnik, D. (2001). "Actuarial modeling with MCMC and BUGS." *North American Actuarial Journal*, 5(2): 96-124.

Smith, B.J. (2001). *Bayesian Output Analysis Program (BOA) Version 1.0.0 User's Manual*. www.public-health.uiowa.edu/boa/.

Stangl, D. and D. Berry (2000). "Meta-analysis: Past and present challenges." In *Meta-Analysis in Medicine and Health Policy*, Edited by D. Stangl and D. Berry, 1-28. New York: Marcel Dekker.

Tolley, H.D., M.D. Nielsen, and R. Bachler (1999). "Credibility calculations using analysis of variance computer routines." *Journal of Actuarial Practice*, 7: 223-228.

Venter, G.G. (1996). "Credibility." In Foundations of Casualty Actuarial Science. Arlington, VA, Casualty Actuarial Society: 375-483.

ANSWERS TO THE EXERCISES

Chapter 1

1-1   The concept of credibility

1-2   Frequentist (or classical);   Bayesian

1-3   7

1-4   160

1-5   Limited fluctuation; Greatest accuracy (or Bühlmann);
      Bayesian

Chapter 2

2-1 $\dfrac{3}{8}$

2-2 $\dfrac{25}{34}$

2-3 $\dfrac{25}{34}$

2-4   .75

2-5 $\dfrac{5.90}{5.95}$

2-6   .80

2-7 .261

2-8 $\left(\begin{array}{c}(r+x)+(y-x)-1\\y-x\end{array}\right)[(1-d)(1-p)]^{y-x}\left[1-(1-d)(1-p)\right]^{x+r}$,

  for $x = 0,1,\ldots,$ and $y = x, x+1, \ldots$.

2-9

Value of x	$P[Y = y \mid X = x]$				
	Value of y				
	2	3	4	5	6
0	16/31	8/31	4/31	2/31	1/31
1	32/88	24/88	16/88	10/88	6/88
2	16/99	24/99	24/99	20/99	15/99
3		8/64	16/64	20/64	20/64
4			4/29	10/29	15/29
5				1/4	3/4
6					1

2-10 $r_1^2 + 2$

2-11 15

2-12 (a) $\frac{4}{7}$ (b) $\frac{3}{4}$

2-13 (a) $4y^3$ (b) $\frac{3}{2}xy^{-2} + \frac{3}{4}x^2y^{-3}$ (c) $\frac{11y}{16}$

2-14 (a) $\frac{77}{16}$ (b) $\frac{29}{16}$

2-16 .70

2-17 (b) .55

2-18 1.50

Chapter 3

3-2   .20

3-3   17.64

3-4   7

3-5   0

3-6 $\dfrac{65}{18}$

3-7 $2\left[1 - 70p^4(1-p)^4\right]$

3-8 $\dfrac{23}{6}$

3-9   .035

3-10   The $\dfrac{100a}{a+b}$ percentile of the posterior distribution of Θ

3-12   I only

Chapter 4

4-3 $\dfrac{25}{34}$

4-4   .50

4-5 $\dfrac{25}{68}$

4-8 $\dfrac{26}{17}$

4-9 $\dfrac{56}{3}$

4-10 16.77; 19.75; 26.49

4-12 (a) $\dfrac{2^{n+1}+1}{2^{n+1}+2}$ (b) 1 (c) $\dfrac{2^{n+1}+1}{(2^{n+1}+2)^2}$ (d) 0

4-13 (a) Predictive distribution (b) Posterior distribution

4-14 (a) As having a fixed, but unknown, value
(b) As a random variable having an entire probability distribution

Chapter 5

5-1 40; 880

5-2 5

5-6 1082

5-7 5410

5-8 6675

5-9 4

5-10 III only

5-12 (b) 3360

5-14 Both

5-15 II only

Chapter 6

6-1 $\dfrac{2}{3}$

6-2 $\dfrac{49}{32}$; $\dfrac{57}{32}$; $\dfrac{105}{32}$

6-3   (a) .64   (b) 1.00   (c) $\dfrac{1.00}{.64}$ (d) .39   (e) 1.756

6-4   (a) 196   (b) 6440   (c) $\dfrac{230}{7}$ (d) $\dfrac{7}{237}$

6-5   5.14

6-6   0

6-7 $\dfrac{3}{7}$

6-8   .60

6-9   (a) increasing   (d) decreasing
       (b) 1   (e) increasing
       (c) decreasing

6-10 $\dfrac{1}{2}$

6-11 $\dfrac{13}{7}$

6-12   (a) .03   (b) 11.97   (c) 399   (d) $\dfrac{1}{400}$

6-13 $\dfrac{2}{3}$

6-14   10.70

6-15 5

6-16 I and II

6-17 (a) .618   (b) .618   (c) .088   (d) 7.02   (e) .125   (f) .791

6-18 (a) .50   (b) .50   (c) .038   (d) 13.20   (e) .07   (f) .465

6-20 $\dfrac{515}{72}$; $\dfrac{925}{72}$

6-21 (a) 1.193

6-22 1.756

6-23 (a) $\dfrac{1127}{274}$; (b) $\dfrac{1}{8}$, for $i=1,2,...,8$; (c) 4.5; (d) 4.5; (e) $5\frac{2}{3}$; 6; (f) 8

Chapter 7

7-1 I

7-2 Both

7-3 (a) = (b) = (d);   (c) = (e)
The relationship between (d) and (e) depends on the result of the first trial (i.e., the realization of X_1).

7-4 4.47825

7-5 3.30862

7-6 15,220.50;   18,060.45;   12,838.80

7-7 Both

7-8 .442;   .735;   1.028;   1.321

7-9 .11

Chapter 8

8-1 The prior probability of H, $P[H]$, and the likelihood of H on B, $P[B \mid H]$

8-3 3; 7

8-4 $108t^2 e^{-6t}$

8-5 $60\theta^2 (1-\theta)^3$

8-6 $4\theta^2 e^{-2\theta}$

8-7 .159

8-9 .195

8-10 .0028

8-11 .196

8-12 (a) Beta (b) Normal (c) Gamma

8-13 All

8-14 (a) $P[H = .25 \mid D_1 = 1] = \frac{2}{3}$; $P[H = .50 \mid D_1 = 1] = \frac{1}{3}$

(b) $P[D_2 = 0 \mid D_1 = 1] = \frac{2}{3}$; $P[D_2 = 1 \mid D_1 = 1] = \frac{1}{3}$

8-15 (a) .125 (b) $4(d+1)(d+2) \cdot 3^{-(d+3)}$ (c) N_1 and N_2

8-16 II only

8-17 (a) $\frac{46}{21}$ (b) $\frac{5}{21}$ (c) $N\left(\frac{46}{21}, \frac{5}{21}\right)$

8-18 5

8-19 $\dfrac{1}{2}$

8-20 1.50

Chapter 9

9-1 (a) $\dfrac{s^{n-1}}{\Gamma(n-1)}$

9-2 $\displaystyle\sum_{n=0}^{5}\binom{a+15+n-1}{n}\left(\dfrac{1}{\beta+4}\right)^{n}\left(\dfrac{\beta+3}{\beta+4}\right)^{\alpha+15}$

9-4 I only

9-6 20

9-7 .0384

9-8 $\left(1+\dfrac{300,000}{2,000,000+y'}\right)^{-m'-8}$

9-9 II and III

9-10 (a) .163   (b) 1.017

9-11 3593

9-12 44.83

9-13 I, II, VIII

9-14 III, IV, VII

9-15 (a) Bernoulli   (b) Negative Binomial   (c) Pareto

Chapter 10

10-2 $\dfrac{22}{12}$; $\dfrac{1}{12}$

10-3 $-\dfrac{10}{3}$; 4

10-4 2.50; 4.00; 8.50

10-5 10.60

10-6 True

Chapter 11

11-1 4.2

11-2 1

11-6 .02

Chapter 12

12-2 $a_1 = -.060$, $a_2 = .041$, $a_3 = .184$, $a_4 = .512$

12-3 11.608

12-4 .521

12-5 .833

12-6 2.833

12-7 2.5

12-8 (a) 4.5   (b) 6   (c) 7.5

Chapter 14

14-1 $\dfrac{51}{76}$

14-2 $\dbinom{25}{15} \cdot \dfrac{51}{76} \cdot \dfrac{\dbinom{50}{45}}{\dbinom{75}{40}}$

14-3 $1 \cdot \dfrac{51}{75} \cdot \dfrac{\dbinom{50}{45}}{\dbinom{75}{40}}$

14-4 $\dbinom{25}{15} \cdot \dfrac{106}{131} \cdot \dfrac{\dbinom{105}{96}}{\dbinom{130}{111}}$

14-5 $\dfrac{1}{n+1}$

14-6 $\dfrac{1}{25}$

14-7 $\dfrac{9}{14}$

14-8 $\dfrac{8}{13}$

Chapter 15

15-8 II only

15-9 (a) .00839;   .00880;   .00045;   .01367   (b) .00457

REFERENCES

1. Albert, J., "Teaching Inference about Proportions Using Bayes Rule and Discrete Models," *Journal of Statistics Education*, 3, 1995. Available at:
    http://www.amstat.org/publications/jse/v3n3/albert.html

2. Bailey, A.L., "Credibility Procedures – La Place's Generalization of Bayes' Rule and the Combination of Collateral Knowledge with Observed Data," PCAS, 37 (1950), 7-23, 94-115.

3. ____, "Sampling Theory in Casualty Insurance," PCAS, 29 (1942), 50ff: PCAS, 30 (1943), 13ff.

4. ____, "A Generalized Theory of Credibility," PCAS, 32 (1945), 13-20.

5. Berger, J., S*tatistical Decision Theory and Bayesian Analysis* (Second Edition). New York: Springer (1985).

6. Berry, D.A., "Comment: Ethics and ECMO", *Statistical Science*, 4, pages 306-310 (1989).

7. Bluhm, W.F., ed., *Group Insurance*, (Fifth Edition). Winsted: ACTEX Publications (2007).

8. Bowers,N., H.Gerber, J.Hickman, D.Jones, and C.Nesbitt, *Actuarial Mathematics (*Second Edition). Chicago: Society of Actuaries (1997).

9. Brosius, E., "Loss Development Using Credibility" (Part 7 Study Note). Arlington: Casualty Actuarial Society (1993).

10. Brown, R.L., *Introduction to Ratemaking and Loss Reserving for Property and Casualty Insurance* (Third Edition). Winsted: ACTEX Publications (2007).

11. Bühlmann, H., "Experience Rating and Credibility," ASTIN Bulletin, 4 (1967), 119-207.

12. ____, *Mathematical Methods in Risk Theory*. New York: Springer, 1970.

13. Bühlmann, H. and A. Gisler, "Credibility in the Regression Case Revisited," ASTIN Bulletin, 27 (1997), 83-98.

14. Bühlmann, H. and E. Straub, "Credibility for Loss Ratios" (Translated by C.E. Brooks), ARCH, 1972.2 (1972).

15. DiVenti, T.R. and T.N. Herzog, "Modeling Home Equity Conversion Mortgages," TSA, XLIII (1991), 261-275.

16. Draper, N. and H. Smith, *Applied Regression Analysis* (Third Edition). New York: John Wiley and Sons (1998).

17. Edwards, W., H. Lindman, and L.J. Savage, "Bayesian Statistical Inference for Psychological Research," 70 Psychological Review 193 (1963).

18. Efron, B. and C. Morris, "Stein's Estimation Rule and Its Competitors – An Empirical Bayes Approach," JASA, 68, No. 341 (1973), 117-130.

19. ____, "Data Analysis Using Stein's Estimator and Its Generalizations," JASA, 70, No. 350 (1975), 311-319.

20. ____, "Stein's Paradox in Statistics," *Scientific American*, 236, No. 5 (1977), 119-127.

21. Ericson, W.A., "On the Posterior Mean and Variance of a Population Mean," JASA, 65, No. 330 (1970), 649-52.

22. Fellingham, G.W., H.D. Tolley, and T.N. Herzog, "Comparing Credibility Estimates of Health Insurance Claim s Costs," North American Actuarial Journal, Vol. 9, No. 1 (2008).

23. Frees, E.W., V.R. Young, and Y. Luo (1999). "A longitudinal data analysis interpretation of credibility models." *Insurance: Mathematics and Economics* 24: 229-248.

24. _____, (2001). "Case studies using panel data models." *North American Actuarial Journal*, 5(4): 24-43.

25. Fuhrer, C., "Some Applications of Credibility Theory to Group Insurance," TSA, XL, Part 1 (1988), 387-404.

26. Gerber, H.U., *An Introduction to Mathematical Risk Theory* (S.S. Huebner Foundation Monograph Series No. 8). Homewood: Richard D. Irwin (1979).

27. _____, "A Teacher's Remark on Exact Credibility," ASTIN Bulletin, 25 (1995), 189-192.

28. Gilks, W., S. Richardson, and David Spiegel Halter. *Markov Chain Monte Carlo in Practice.* London: Chapman and Hall (1996).

29. Goovaerts, M.J. and W.J. Hoogstad, *Credibility Theory.* Rotterdam: Nationale-Nederlanden N.V. (1987).

30. Goulet, V., "Principles and Application of Credibility Theory," Journal of Actuarial Practice, 6 (1998), 5-62.

31. Hansen, M.D. and Y.R. Wang, Managing Data Quality: *A Critical Issue for the Decade to Come.* Cambridge: Sloan School of Management, Massachusetts Institute of Technology, 1991.

32. Heckman, P.E. and G.G. Meyers, "The Calculations of Aggregate Loss Distributions from Claim Severity and Claim Count Distributions," PCAS, 70 (1983), 22-74; PCAS, 71 (1984), 49-66.

33. Herzog, T.N., *An Introduction to Stochastic Simulation* (Exam 130 Study Note). Schaumburg. Society of Actuaries,1(983.)

34.   ____, "Bayesian Graduation of FHA/HUD Single-Family Home Mortgage Insurance Contracts – Section 203," Insurance: Mathematics and Economics, No. 2 (1983), 271-279.

35.   ____, "Credibility: The Bayesian Model Versus Bühlmann's Model," TSA, XLI (1989), 43-81.

36.   ____, Discussion of "AIDS: Exponential vs. Polynominal Growth Models," by H.H. Panjer, Insurance: Mathematics and Economics, 9 (1990), 291.

37.   Herzog, T.N. Introduction to Credibility Theory. Winsted, CT: ACTEX Publications, Inc. (1999).

38.   Herzog, T.N. and D.B. Rubin, "The Use of Multiple Imputations to Handle Nonresponse," Chapter 15 of Non-response in Sample Surveys: The Theory of Current Practice. New York: Academic Press (1983).

39.   Herzog, T.N., F.J. Scheuren, and W. E. Winkler, Data Quality and Record Linkages Techniques, Springer, New York (2007).

40.   Hewitt, C.C., Jr., "Credibility for Severity," PCAS, 57 (1970), 148-71; PCAS, 58 (1971), 25-31.

41.   ____, "Loss Ratio Distributions – A Model," PCAS, 54 (1967), 70-93.

42.   Hickman, J.C. and L. Heacox, "Credibility Theory: The Cornerstone of Actuarial Science," NAAJ, 3 (1999), 1-8.

43.   Hogg, R.V., A.T. Craig and J.W. Mckean, Introduction to Mathematical Statistics (Sixth Edition). Upper Saddle River: Pearson (2005).

44.   Hogg, R.V., and S.A. Klugman, Loss Distributions. New York: John Wiley and Sons (1984).

45.   Hossack, I.B., J.H. Pollard, and B. Zehnwirth, Introductory Statistics with Applications in General Insurance. New York: Cambridge University Press (1983).

46. James, W. and C. Stein, "Estimation with Quadratic Loss," Proceedings of the Fourth Berkeley Symposium on Mathematics, Statistics, and Probability, Vol. 1. Berkeley: University of California Press (1961), 361-379.

47. Jewell, W.S., "The Credible Distribution," ASTIN Bulletin, 7 (1974), 237-69.

48. ____, "Predicting IBNYR Events and Delays I: Continuous Time," ASTIN Bulletin, No. 19 (1989), 25-55.

49. ____, "Predicting IBNYR Events and Delays II: Discrete Time," ASTIN Bulletin, No. 20 (1990), 93-111.

50. ____, "A Survey of Credibility Theory," Operations Research Center, University of California, Berkeley (1976).

51. Kanellos, M., 18th-century theory is new force in computing, CNET News.com, February 18, 2003 (available at http://news.com /Old-school+theory+is+a+new+force/2009-1001_3-984695.html).

52. Kimeldorf, G.S. and D.A. Jones, "Bayesian Graduation," TSA XIX (1967), 66.

53. Klugman, S.A., "Credibility for Classification Ratemaking via the Hierarchical Normal Linear Model," PCAS, 74 (1987), 272-321.

54. ____, Bayesian Statistics in Actuarial Science. Boston: Kluwer Academic Publishers, (1992)

55. Klugman, S.A., H.H. Panjer, and G.E. Willmot, Loss Models: From Data to Decisions, (Third Edition) New York: John Wiley and Sons (2008).

56. Landsman, Z. and U. Makov, "Exponential Dispersion Models and Credibility," Scandinavian Actuarial Journal, 1 (1998a), 89-96.

57. ____, "On Stochastic Approximation and Credibility," Scandinavian Actuarial Journal, (1998b).

58. Laplace, P.S., *Philosophical Essay on Probabilities*, translated from the fifth French edition of 1825 by Andrew I. Dale. New York: Springer (1995)

59. London, D., *Graduation: The Revision of Estimates*. Winsted: ACTEX Publications (1985).

60. Longley-Cook, L.H., "An Introduction to Credibility Theory," PCAS, 49 (1962), 194-221.

61. Mayerson, A.L., "A Bayesian View of Credibility," PCAS, 51 (1964), 85-104; PCAS, 52 (1965), 121-127.

62. Mayerson, A.L., D.A. Jones, and N.L. Bowers, "The Credibility of the Pure Premium," PCAS, 55 (1968), 175-185.

63. Meinhold, Richard M, and Nozer D. Singpuruwalla, "Understanding the Kalman Filter," *The American Statistician*, Vol. 37, No. 2. (May, 1983), pp. 123-127.

64. Morgan, I.M., "Credibility Theory under the Collective Risk Model," Ph.D. dissertation. Madison: University of Wisconsin (1983).

65. Morris, C. and L. van Slyke, "Empirical Bayes Methods for Pricing Insurance Classes," *Proceedings of the American Statistical Association: 1978. Business and Economics Section,* (1979), 579-582.

66. Mosteller, F. and G.W. Tukey, *Data Analysis and Regression*. Reading: Addison-Wesley Publishing Company (1977).

67. Mowbray, A.H., "How Extensive a Payroll is Necessary to Give a Dependable Pure Premium?" PCAS, 1 (1914), 24-30.

68. Panjer, H.H. and G.E. Willmot, *Insurance Risk Models*. Schaumburg: Society of Actuaries (1992).

69. Perryman, F.S., "Some Notes on Credibility," PCAS,19 (1932), 65-84.

70. Philbrick, S., "An Examination of Credibility Concepts," PCAS, 48 (1981), 195-219.

71. Raiffa, H. and R. Schlaifer, *Applied Statistical Decision Theory.* Cambridge: Harvard University Press, 1961.

72. Rodermund, M., "Introduction," Chapter 1 of Foundations of Casualty Actuarial Science. New York: Casualty Actuarial Society (1989).

73. Rosenberg, Marjorie A., and Philip M. Farrell. "Impact of a Newborn Screening Program on Inpatient Utilization for Children with Cystic Fibrosis." (2007), Working paper. http://research3.bus.wisc.edu/mrosenberg.

74. _____, "Predictive Modeling of Costs for a Chronic Disease with Acute High-Cost Episodes," *North American Actuarial Journal*, Vol. 12, No. 1 (2008).

75. Rosenberg, Marjorie A., and Virginia R. Young. "A Bayesian Approach to Understanding Time Series Data." *North American Actuarial Journal* 3(2): 130–43.

76. Russo, G., "Continuous Time Models of the Reporting and Cost Process of Insurance Claims," Ph.D. dissertation. Berkeley: University of California, (1995).

77. Savage, L.J., *The Foundations of Statistics.* New York: John Wiley and Sons, (1954).

78. Scollnik, D.M., "Actuarial Modeling with MCMC and BUGS," *NAAJ*, Vol. 5, No. 2, 2001, pp. 96-125.

79. Stigler, S.M., *The History of Statistics; The Measurement of Uncertainty Before 1900.* Cambridge: Harvard University Press, (1986).

80. Sundt, B., "On Greatest Accuracy Credibility with Limited Fluctuation," *Scandinavian Actuarial Journal*, 2, 109-119 (1992).

81. Tukey, J.W., *Exploratory Data Analysis*. Reading: Addison-Wesley Publishing Company, (1977).

82. Velleman, P. and D. Hoaglin, Applications, Basics, and Computing of Exploratory Data Analysis. Boston: Duxbury Press, (1981).

83. Venter, G.G., "Credibility," Chapter 7 of Foundations of Casualty Actuarial Science. New York: Casualty Actuarial Society (1989).

84. Ware, J. H., "Investigating Therapies of Potentially Great Benefit: ECMO," *Statistical Science*, 4, pages 298-340 (including discussion), 1989. Available at http://projecteuclid.org/DPubS?service=UI&version=1.0&verb=Display&page=toc&handle=euclid.ss/1177012380

85. Waters, H.R., *Credibility Theory*. Edinburgh: Heriot-Watt University (1993).

86. Whitney, A., "The Theory of Experience Rating," PCAS, 4 (1918), 274-292.

87. Young, V.R., "Credibility Using a Loss Function from Spline Theory," *Scandinavian Actuarial. Journal*, 2 (1997), 160-185.

88. ____, "Credibility Using a Loss Function from Spline Theory: Parametric Models with a One-Dimensional Sufficient Statistic," *NAAJ*, 2, 1 (1998), 101-117.

89. Ziliak, S.T. and D.N. McCloskey, *The Cult of Statistical Significance*, The University of Michigan Press, Ann Arbor, (2008).

INDEX